W9-BQL-604

# INTRODUCTION TO PROBABILITY AND STATISTICS

A Series of Books in Mathematics

Editors: R. A. Rosenbaum
G. Philip Johnson

# Introduction to PROBABILITY AND STATISTICS

Fourth Edition

## HENRY L. ALDER
## EDWARD B. ROESSLER , 1902-

UNIVERSITY OF CALIFORNIA, DAVIS

BRIAR CLIFF COLLEGE
LIBRARY

SIOUX CITY, IOWA

W. H. FREEMAN AND COMPANY

San Francisco and London

QA
273
.A43
1968

Copyright © 1960, 1962, 1964, 1968 by W. H. Freeman and Company

No part of this book may be reproduced by any mechanical, photographic, or electronic process, or in the form of a phonographic recording, nor may it be stored in a retrieval system, transmitted, or otherwise copied for public or private use without written permission from the publisher.

Printed in the United States of America
Library of Congress Catalog Card Number: 68-14229

# Preface to the Fourth Edition

This book has been written to serve as a textbook for a one-semester introductory course in probability and statistics. It is also suitable for either a quarter course meeting four hours a week for ten weeks or a two-quarter course meeting three hours a week. The first edition of the text was a revision of the mimeographed and lithoprinted forms used for several years by instructors on the Davis campus of the University of California and at some other institutions. The many hundreds of students in these classes came from almost all fields of specialization in the natural and social sciences, and a few from the humanities.

In the typical American college or university, introductory statistics courses are offered in many different departments, are directed toward a great number of different specializations, and require widely differing levels of mathematical preparation. This phenomenon might lead to the mistaken impression that basic statistics is essentially different in the various fields of application. In this respect, instruction in statistics seems to occupy a unique position; in almost every other science there exists one introductory course with a fairly well-defined amount of subject material and anyone requiring some background in that science takes that course. Thus, almost every college or university offers an introductory chemistry course in which all students who need some knowledge of chemistry enroll. There seem to be no reasons except purely administrative or traditional ones why statistics should not be treated similarly. Indeed, much benefit could be derived from centralizing the teaching of basic statistics in one course in one department, which, in most schools, would be either the mathematics or the statistics department. If only one such course is offered, much needless duplication can be avoided and a single standard of achievement can be maintained. It is for such a course that this book is designed.

Mathematical knowledge equivalent to two years of high school algebra is all that is required as background for this textbook. At one point in Chapter 12 trigonometry is used, but readers without training in that subject may omit this passage without loss of continuity. The limited level of mathe-

53297

matical preparation required for this book makes it necessary to state some
theorems without proof. However, almost all theorems whose proofs depend
only on mathematics as commonly taught in two years of high school algebra
are proved. The reader may be surprised to find that the number of theorems
not proved here, because of the limited mathematical preparation assumed,
is relatively small, and he may find consolation in the fact that his understanding of the omitted proofs would not be increased appreciably even after
a course or two in beginning calculus. To avoid the mathematical difficulties
associated with limiting processes, with which the reader ordinarily will not
become acquainted until he studies calculus, discussions have been restricted,
wherever possible, to the finite case; in particular, all populations are assumed
to be finite.

The students who enroll in the statistics course at Davis come from all the
agricultural sciences, business administration, economics, home economics,
psychology, sociology, geology, and the medical sciences. To allow for these
differing fields of specialization, the examples and exercises have been chosen
from all of these subject areas.

Exercises are an integral part of the text. It has been our experience that
an introductory course in statistics is taught most effectively in the same
way as are other introductory courses in mathematics, a number of homework
problems being assigned after every lecture. Special care has been taken to
insure that exercises involve a minimum of computation, and that none
(except for a few in Chapter 15) requires machine calculation. This has often
necessitated the inclusion of fictitious data, although those in many exercises
represent the results of actual experiments.

Although most students taking the beginning course in statistics on the
Davis campus enroll in it during their second year in college, some are freshmen. To take this course as early as possible appears the best advice. There
seems no valid reason why it could not be taken in high school, since it is
certainly no more difficult than a course in trigonometry and, judging from
the reaction of many students, may even be simpler. An early course in
statistics enables the student to use his knowledge in the many courses in
which some form of statistics is presently applied. In addition to other
obvious benefits gained from an early exposure, a course in statistics is a
convenient and effective means of reviewing high school algebra before taking
other mathematics courses that demand a thorough knowledge of algebra.
Because of this, we have included exercises which involve almost all topics
ordinarily encountered in two years of high school algebra—students seem to
find solution of practical, interesting problems a much less painful way of
reviewing their algebra than traditional methods.

Chapters 1 through 13 constitute the basic core of information required in all fields where statistics is used. Chapters 14 and 15 are designed primarily for students in business administration and economics. Consequently it is recommended that instructors in general one-semester statistics courses, particularly those oriented towards the biological sciences, omit Chapters 14 and 15 and consider two possible alternatives: one, complete coverage of Chapters 1 through 13; the other, coverage of Chapters 1 through 10, 12, 13, 16, and 17. Instructors in one-semester courses oriented towards the social sciences—in particular, economics—may find it preferable to omit Chapters 16 and 17, but to include Chapters 11, 14, and 15. If the complete coverage of all chapters is desired, the text would be suitable for a one-semester course meeting four hours a week or a two-quarter course of ten weeks each meeting three hours a week.

With an increasing number of universities on the quarter system, more and more institutions now desire to cover the basic material of probability and statistics in a one-quarter course meeting four hours a week for ten weeks. Experience has shown that, for such a course, Chapters 1 through 13 of this text can be covered, with the following exclusions: Section 5-4; Chapter 11; Sections 12-6, 12-7, 12-8, 12-9; and Section 13-5. For such a course, it is recommended that Chapter 11 be given as a reading assignment after Chapter 10 has been covered.

The present Fourth Edition differs from the Third Edition not only in a large number of minor improvements but also in the following four major changes.

1. Since experience has indicated that many of our colleagues desire more detailed coverage of probability than that in previous editions of this text, we have expanded Chapter 5. We have given serious consideration to rewriting this chapter in such a way as to define probability by using set terminology. Because most students, however, are not yet familiar with the basic facts about sets, this would have required the addition of a chapter on sets, and the length of the text would thereby have been so increased that it would have become impossible to cover both probability and statistics in a one-semester or one-quarter course—which has been and remains the basic purpose of this text. Consequently, after consultation with many colleagues, we have rejected this idea.

Instead, we have expanded the chapter on probability slightly by adding a section on conditional probability and Bayes' Theorem, by adding a number of illustrative examples—in particular some which always seem to capture the students' interest, such as the hat-check and birthday problems—and by adding numerous exercises of various degrees of difficulty. The first 62 exercises are now arranged in the same order as the material covered in the sections of that chapter; miscellaneous exercises, arranged in increasing order of difficulty, begin with exercise 63. Section 5-4 on conditional probability and the exercises on this section (exercises 28 through 36) can be omitted without loss of continuity.

2. Recent work showing the excellent results obtained by use of certain nonparametric tests indicates that the skepticism with which these methods have long been regarded is unwarranted. There seems to be little doubt that the recently proved startling results that show the high efficiency of some of these tests will cause a much greater emphasis to be placed on nonparametric tests in elementary statistics courses. In addition, most of these tests make very modest demands in the way of mathematical background and certainly do not require knowledge of calculus, so that their inclusion seems particularly appropriate in a course requiring a background of only two years of high school algebra.

For this reason, Chapter 11, which had already been expanded in the Third Edition to include, in addition to the sign test, the Wilcoxon two-sample test for both small and large samples, has been further expanded to cover the situation in which there are ties in the ranks for both unpaired and paired comparisons.

3. Chapter 6 has been expanded to introduce the binomial distribution somewhat more leisurely.

4. About sixty-five new exercises of all grades of difficulty have been added to Chapters 5 through 13, a few have been dropped, others have been rearranged, and a few have been reworded to clarify their meaning.

We are indebted to Professor Sir Ronald A. Fisher, Cambridge, to Dr. Frank Yates, Rothamsted, and to Messrs. Oliver and Boyd Limited, Edinburgh, for permission to reprint in abridged form Tables II, III, and IV from their book *Statistical Tables for Biological, Agricultural, and Medical Research.*

We gratefully acknowledge the many valuable suggestions and comments made by Professors Hubert A. Arnold, George A. Baker, and Curtis M. Fulton in the course of their use of an early draft of this book in their classes. We are also indebted to Professor Jerry Foytik for his advice and helpful suggestions concerning the original draft and, in particular, for his comments on the material from economics covered in Chapter 15. Special thanks are due Mrs. Vi Raggi for her most careful and accurate typing of the original manuscript.

Henry L. Alder

*December, 1967*                                                Edward B. Roessler

# Contents

# 1 Introduction

Statistics is the science dealing with the *collection, organization, analysis,* and *interpretation* of numerical data.

"Collection of data" is the process of obtaining measurements or counts. Valid conclusions can result only from properly collected or from representative data. Although this is a very important part of statistical procedure, in the interest of conciseness we shall not discuss it but shall consider the treatment of data already available.

"Organization of data" is the task of presenting the collected measurements or counts in a form suitable for deriving logical conclusions. Representative methods of organizing and presenting data by means of tables and graphs are discussed in Chapter 2.

"Analysis of data" is the process of extracting from the given measurements or counts relevant information, from which a summarized and comprehensible numerical description can be formulated. The most important measures used for this purpose—the mean, the median, the range, the standard deviation, and others—are discussed in Chapter 4.

"Interpretation of data" is the task of drawing conclusions from the analysis of the data and usually involves the formulation of predictions concerning a large collection of objects from information available for a small collection of similar objects. The interpretation of data forms the main portion of the text.

Statistics, then, is a science which deals with problems capable of being answered to some degree by numerical information, that is, information obtained by counting or measuring. It matters little whether we are making insect counts for a biological study or surveying the number of workers or work-hours in an industrial plant. The duties of the statistician are first to select the kind of information needed, then to direct the proper and efficient collection and processing of that information, and, finally, to interpret the results. In interpreting results, especially where they are based on incomplete data, the statistician must apply principles and techniques which yield valid findings. He is often expected to make wise decisions in the face of uncertainty.

The word statistics has two greatly differing meanings. When used as a singular noun it has the meaning already described. It is a scientific procedure used in the study and evaluation of numerical data. When used in the plural it is synonymous with the term "numerical data." Thus if we say there are statistics in the *World Almanac* or in the *Statistical Abstract of the United States*, we mean there are numerical data in them. This is the older and more common meaning of the word. Originally, statistics were gathered for the purpose of providing governmental heads with data for managing the affairs of state. Such information expressed in numbers dates back to Aristotle and his treatises on the "matters of state." In fact, there is evidence that the words "statistics" and "state" are derived from the same root. From earliest times most civilized countries have compiled large scale "statistics" in order to ascertain, for military and fiscal reasons, the manpower and material strength of the nation. We read in the Bible of such censuses, and compilations for purposes of taxation were common practices in all parts of the Roman Empire.

In the sixteenth and seventeenth centuries, games of chance were especially popular with persons of wealth, and many questions involving probability were addressed to and answered by such well-known mathematicians as Cardano, Galileo, Pascal, Fermat, Leibnitz, and James Bernoulli.

During the same period, distinct advances were made in the development of statistics. In England, John Graunt made a semi-mathematical study of vital statistics, insurance, and economic statistics. His work was extended by Sir William Petty and Edmund Halley. The first extensive treatise on the theory as a whole was written by Jacob Bernoulli, who expounded the principle of the law of large numbers which was also treated in a paper by Poisson. In 1733 the normal distribution was first found by de Moivre and later rediscovered by Gauss and Laplace. Quetelet showed that biological and anthropological measurements conformed closely to the Gaussian law of error. In Germany, Knapp investigated extensively the statistics of mortality, and Lexis developed a procedure which, today, would be called one-way variance analysis. Other contributors to the theory were Stirling, Bayes, Daniel Bernoulli, Euler, Nicolas and John Bernoulli, Simpson, D'Alembert, Lagrange, Buffon, Montmort, Condorcet, and the great Laplace, who provided the most extensive treatment of probability in his monumental work, "Théorie Analytique des Probabilités."

During the last quarter of the nineteenth century, Sir Francis Galton, the founder of the School of Eugenics in England, and his great successor Karl Pearson, using problems from genetics, developed the ideas of regression and correlation. Later Pearson and Spearman extended this theory and applied it to studies in the social sciences. Pearson also studied extensively the effects of errors of sampling.

Early in the present century William S. Gosset, a statistician for Guinness, an Irish brewery, writing under the pseudonym of "Student," published many papers on statistical analysis, in particular on the interpretation of data obtained by sampling. He was the first to recognize the importance of developing methods of extracting reliable information from small samples. The methods developed by Gosset were later popularized in England by R. A. Fisher and his colleagues who greatly extended the theory and the fields of application, especially in agriculture.

Historically, statistical theory has had a long and slow development and is the result of the work of many people in many countries working in many different fields. Recently, great advances have been made in the development of mathematical statistics and its applications. Those who have made significant contributions are too numerous to mention.

Everyday life is influenced more and more by decisions based on quantitative information. The scientific sequence of hypothesis, experiment, and test of hypothesis is now a familiar approach to problems in every area of activity. Today, modern statistical methods, founded on probability theory, are proving indispensable as aids in the physical and biological sciences, in economics and sociology, in psychology and education, in medicine and agriculture, and in government and industry. The astronomer predicts future positions of heavenly bodies on the basis of statistical methods; conformity to genetic segregation is ascertained statistically; life insurance premiums and annuity payments are determined from mortality tables based on statistical records; power companies cannot supply electricity efficiently without statistical data of load requirements; research workers determine significance in agricultural field trials from statistical considerations; engineers find sampling theory invaluable in controlling quality of manufactured products; and business executives and governmental analysts use statistical procedures in decision-making. Although these are widely differing fields of application, most of the statistical methods employed are the same. One aspect of statistical analysis may be stressed more in one field of application than in another, but, in general, the same statistical procedures are used in all fields.

In approaching the study of statistics, a word of caution is in order. It is important to realize that no statistical procedure can, in itself, insure against mistakes, inaccuracies, faulty reasoning, or incorrect conclusions. The original data must be accurate; the methods must be properly applied; and the results must be interpreted by one who understands not only the methods themselves but also the field to which they are applied. The statistical methods discussed in this book are to be considered as tools which, in proper hands and applied to the situation for which they are designed, can produce useful results, but which, by themselves, have no power to work miracles.

# 2 Organization of Data

## 2.1. Introduction

Frequently, the collection of information leads to large masses of data which, if they are to be understood or to be presented effectively, must be in some manner summarized. Clear and forceful presentation is an important aid to the understanding and correct interpretation of such data. Two methods of presenting quantitative data are in common use. One method involves a summarized presentation of the numbers themselves, usually in tabular form; the other consists in presenting the quantitative data in pictorial form—graphs, diagrams, or other similar representations. Representation of a mass of data by either of these methods is the part of statistical analysis which should lead to a better over-all comprehension of the data.

## 2.2. Tabular and Graphical Methods of Presenting Data

In nearly all scientific and business publications, in government reports, in magazines and in newspapers, data of all sorts are presented by means of tables, diagrams, or pictures.

It is always possible to include quantitative data as a part of the textual material, but there are certain advantages in presenting them in tabular form. According to the report of the Federal Reserve System the total deposits of all banks in the continental United States in 1930 amounted to $58.1 billion; in 1935, $55.4 billion; in 1940, $76.0 billion; in 1945, $165.6 billion; in 1950, $175.3 billion; and in 1955, $220.4 billion. No doubt, this textual presentation is extremely uninteresting to the average reader, who may fail entirely to grasp the important aspects of the data. Certainly the presentation could be made more readable and effective by arranging the data in columnar form as a part of the text. The same information might be presented as follows: Total deposits, in billions of dollars, of all banks in the continental United States for five-year intervals from 1930 to 1955 were

| Year | Total Deposits |
|------|----------------|
| 1930 | 58.1 |
| 1935 | 55.4 |
| 1940 | 76.0 |
| 1945 | 165.6 |
| 1950 | 175.3 |
| 1955 | 220.4 |

This arrangement enables us to visualize much more easily the significant characteristics of the data. We see immediately that bank deposits have risen rapidly in the 25-year period and that they more than doubled between 1940 and 1945. Such features stand out much more clearly when the data are arranged in columnar form. However, to understand completely the meaning of the data in the right-hand column we must refer to the descriptive material in the text; this, then, must still be described as a textual presentation.

In tabular presentation the data are arranged in columns and rows, a form which retains the advantages of the columnar arrangement, and in addition includes all information necessary for a complete understanding of the table, thus eliminating reference to the text. The bank-deposit data are presented in tabular form in Table 2-1.

TABLE 2-1.   Total Deposits (in billions of dollars) of All Banks in the Continental United States from 1930 to 1955, in 5-Year Intervals

| Year | Total Deposits |
|------|----------------|
| 1930 | 58.1 |
| 1935 | 55.4 |
| 1940 | 76.0 |
| 1945 | 165.6 |
| 1950 | 175.3 |
| 1955 | 220.4 |

Source: Board of Governors of the Federal Reserve System.

Tables are usually numbered for rapid and positive identification, and any textual reference to the data can be made by citing specific table numbers.

**DEFINITION 2-1.**   A measurable characteristic is called a *variable*.

**DEFINITION 2-2.**   Individual measurements of a variable are called *variates*.

For the data of Table 2-1, the total bank deposit is a variable, and each deposit entry is a variate.

**DEFINITION 2-3.** Pictorial representations made for the purpose of studying changes in a single variable or comparing several similar or related variables are called *graphs*.

Although graphs do not supply any more information than can be obtained from numbers arranged in tabular form, they generally set forth the important facts more clearly and forcefully. To be effective a graph should be simple and should emphasize the significant aspects of the data.

There are many different types of pictorial representation used in delineating changes in a single variable or in comparing two or more variables. Some of the more common types will be discussed.

### 2.2.1. The Bar Graph

The bar graph makes comparisons by means of parallel bars placed either horizontally or vertically. From the standpoint of supplying identifying labels, horizontal bars are more convenient. Vertical bars are used chiefly for the presentation of data the magnitudes of which vary with time. Such data are known as time series, and they will be discussed in Chapter 15. In such diagrams the width and spacing of the bars are uniform, and their lengths are proportional to the variates represented. This type of graph is well adapted to the comparison of variables which are similar but which are

**Fig. 2-1. Total deposits of all banks in the Continental United States, 1930–1955.**

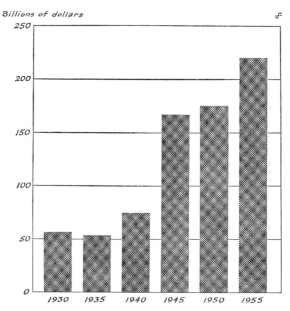

not necessarily related to one another. Usually a space of one-half the width
of the bar is left between adjacent bars in order to make easier identification
of the bar by its label. Typical uses of the bar graph are illustrated in the
following examples.

*Example 2-1.*   Construct a bar graph for the data of Table 2-1.
*Solution.*   See Figure 2-1.

*Example 2-2.*   Using the data of Table 2-2, construct a bar graph showing
the number of acres of Federally owned land in seven of the western states.

TABLE 2.2.   Total Land Acreage and Federally Owned Land Acreage (in millions
of acres) in Seven Western States, 1956

| State | Total Acreage | Acreage Federally Owned | Acreage Not Federally Owned |
|-------|---------------|-------------------------|-----------------------------|
| Arizona | 72.69 | 32.14 | 40.55 |
| California | 100.31 | 46.86 | 53.45 |
| Idaho | 52.97 | 34.59 | 18.38 |
| Montana | 93.36 | 28.07 | 65.29 |
| Nevada | 70.26 | 61.50 | 8.76 |
| Oregon | 61.64 | 31.64 | 30.00 |
| Washington | 42.74 | 12.70 | 30.04 |

*Solution.*

Fig. 2-2.   Federally owned land in seven western states, 1956.

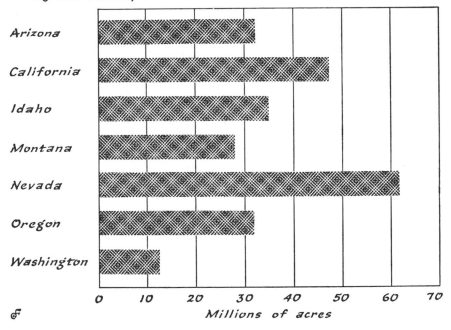

The bar graphs illustrated in Figures 2-1 and 2-2 are composed of individual, unsegmented bars, which are the types most commonly used. Two important adaptations, the component-part bar graph and the grouped bar graph, are shown in Figures 2-3 and 2-4, respectively. The data are those shown in Table 2-2.

Fig. 2-3. Federally and nonfederally owned land in seven western states, 1956.
Fig. 2-4. Federally and nonfederally owned land in seven western states, 1956.

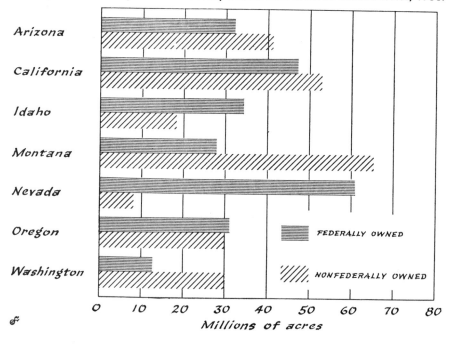

We see that the component-part bar graph furnishes a pictorial method for comparing changes in the whole quantity with changes in its component parts. If we wish to compare the component parts, not relating them to the whole, the grouped bar graph is the more effective device.

### 2.2.2.  The Broken-line Graph

The broken-line graph is particularly useful in representing the relation-ship between two different variables and is obtained by plotting as points pairs of corresponding values of the two variables and joining consecutive points by a series of straight lines. It is used in particular to emphasize changes in some variable occurring during an interval of time. For example, the data of Table 2-1 can be represented by a broken-line graph as well as by the bar graph shown in Figure 2-1. A broken-line graph can be obtained from a bar graph by joining with straight lines the midpoints of the tops of consecutive bars. A broken-line graph gives some indication of the change occurring during the interval of time represented by the width of each bar of a bar graph. In this case, therefore, a broken-line graph is more useful than a bar graph.

*Example 2-3.*  Draw the broken-line graph for the data of Table 2-1.
*Solution.*

**Fig. 2-5. Total deposits of all banks in the Continental United States, 1930–1955.**

### 2.2.3. The Curve-line Graph

The curve-line graph is a modification of the broken-line graph in which a smooth curve, instead of a series of straight lines, is drawn through the points. As the number of plotted points increases, the curve-line graph and the broken-line graph more nearly coincide. This type of graph is especially useful in showing variations in continuously changing variables such as temperature, rainfall, crop yields, bank deposits, commodity prices. Both types of graph are useful in estimating the value of one variable from a given value of the other within the plotted range of values. Estimating values outside the plotted range is frequently unreliable and should be avoided.

Although the curve-line graph may in some cases represent changes between the plotted points somewhat more realistically, there are those who prefer the broken-line graph because of its simplicity and the ease with which it can be drawn. Both are equally effective for the purpose of showing pictorially the general type of relationship existing between two variables.

*Example 2-4.* Draw a curve-line graph for the data of Table 2-1, and estimate the total amount of bank deposits in the continental United States in 1953.

*Solution.*

**Fig. 2-6. Total deposits of all banks in the Continental United States, 1930–1955.**

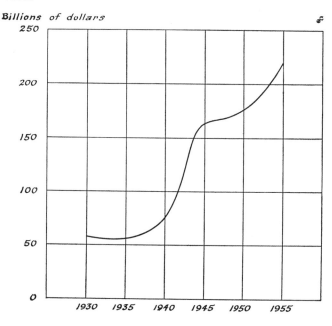

From the graph, an estimate of the total amount of bank deposits in the continental United States in 1953 appears to be close to $200 billion.

### 2.2.4.  The Circle Graph or Pie Diagram

This type of graph is useful in showing the apportionment of a total into its component parts. The components are expressed as per cents of the whole and are represented by segments of a circle whose central angles are the corresponding per cents of 360°. The pie diagram should not be subdivided into too many categories, and the labeling of the segments should be clear. Horizontal labels should be used except in the simplest cases where radial labels can be easily read.

*Example 2-5.* School enrollments in the United States in 1956, expressed to the nearest thousand students, were as follows: elementary, 27,927,000; secondary, 8,543,000; college and professional schools, 2,883,000. Represent by a circle graph the relation between enrollments in these three categories.

*Solution.* The per cent of the total school enrollment in the elementary grades is 71.0%, in the secondary grades 21.7%, and in collegiate institutions 7.3%. At the center of the circle the number of degrees representing the elementary school enrollment is 71.0% of 360°, or 255.6°, and so on. The resulting circle graph or pie diagram is shown in Figure 2-7.

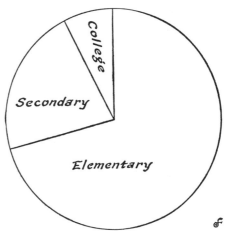

Fig. 2-7. School enrollment in the United States in 1956.

### 2.2.5.  The Ideograph or Pictorial Chart

Pictures are often used in the design of charts for popular presentation. This type of representation is common in government pamphlets and in advertisements. Such presentations register a meaningful impression in our mind almost before we think about them. They are useful in capturing the attention of persons who ordinarily would not look at a more formal chart or graph. They are most effective in displaying information which can be presented simply. The pictorial units used should be easily recognized, and

*Each symbol represents 50 billion dollars*

**Fig. 2-8. Total deposits of all banks in the Continental United States, 1930–1955.**

differences in magnitude should be indicated by differences in the number of units, not by differences in their size. Differences in size frequently lead to difficulties in interpretation because of the danger of optical illusion. Examples of this type of pictorial representation are shown in Figures 2-8 and 2-9.

**Fig. 2-9. Number of passenger cars and taxis registered in the United States at ten-year intervals, 1920–1950.**

*Each symbol represents 5 million passenger cars and taxis*

## 2.3. Frequency Distributions and Their Tabular and Graphical Representations

Statistical data usually consist of a set of measurements of a class of objects. Such a set of data, showing for a 90-year period the total seasonal rainfall (July 1–June 30) in Sacramento, California, is shown in Table 2-3.

TABLE 2-3. Seasonal Rainfall (in inches at Sacramento, California, for the 90-Year Period 1854–1944 (read horizontally)

| | | | | | | | | | |
|---|---|---|---|---|---|---|---|---|---|
| 18.6 | 13.8 | 10.4 | 15.0 | 16.0 | 22.1 | 16.2 | 36.1 | 11.6 | 7.8 |
| 22.6 | 17.9 | 25.3 | 32.8 | 16.6 | 13.6 | 8.5 | 23.7 | 14.2 | 22.9 |
| 17.7 | 26.3 | 9.2 | 24.9 | 17.9 | 26.5 | 26.6 | 16.5 | 18.1 | 24.8 |
| 16.6 | 32.3 | 14.0 | 11.6 | 20.0 | 33.8 | 15.8 | 15.2 | 24.0 | 16.4 |
| 24.1 | 23.2 | 17.3 | 10.5 | 15.0 | 20.2 | 20.2 | 17.3 | 16.6 | 16.9 |
| 22.0 | 23.9 | 24.0 | 12.2 | 21.8 | 12.2 | 22.0 | 9.6 | 8.0 | 20.4 |
| 17.2 | 18.3 | 13.0 | 10.6 | 17.2 | 8.9 | 16.8 | 14.2 | 15.7 | 8.0 |
| 17.7 | 16.1 | 17.8 | 11.6 | 10.4 | 13.6 | 8.4 | 12.6 | 8.1 | 11.6 |
| 21.1 | 20.5 | 19.8 | 24.8 | 9.7 | 25.1 | 31.8 | 24.9 | 20.0 | 17.6 |

DEFINITION 2-4. If a variable can assume only specific values (usually integers), it is called a *discrete* or *discontinuous* variable.

Examples of discrete variables are the number of children in a family, or the total value of all postage stamps used by a person on a given day.

DEFINITION 2-5. If a variable can assume any values whatsoever between certain limits, it is called a *continuous* variable.

Examples of continuous variables are the seasonal rainfall in Sacramento, and any variables representing length, weight, and time.

Since no measuring device is exact, the precision of measurements of a continuous variable is subject to the accuracy of the device and its operator. All measurements should therefore be recorded only to the appropriate number of decimal places (or significant figures). In Table 2-3 the rainfall figures are recorded to one-decimal accuracy; in recording a value of 18.6 inches we assume that the true value is more than 18.55 but less than or equal to 18.65, the usual rounding-off convention of leaving the final digit even in rounding off a number ending in a 5 having been adopted.

For large sets of data, as in Table 2-3, the variates must be presented in a summarized form in order for the mind to obtain any significant information from them. For concise description of the variates, some combination of them is imperative. This is achieved by constructing a frequency table which classifies the set of observations according to the number of variates falling within certain limits. A frequency table for the data of Table 2-3 is shown in Table 2-4.

TABLE 2-4. Frequency Table for Data of Table 2-3

| Class Boundaries (inches) | Class Midpoints (X) | Tallied Frequency | Frequency (f) | Cumulative Frequency |
|---|---|---|---|---|
| 7.5–10.5 | 9 | ┼┼┼┼ ┼┼┼┼ ‖ | 12 | 12 |
| 10.5–13.5 | 12 | ┼┼┼┼ ┼┼┼┼ | 10 | 22 |
| 13.5–16.5 | 15 | ┼┼┼┼ ┼┼┼┼ ┼┼┼┼ | 15 | 37 |
| 16.5–19.5 | 18 | ┼┼┼┼ ┼┼┼┼ ┼┼┼┼ ‖‖ | 19 | 56 |
| 19.5–22.5 | 21 | ┼┼┼┼ ┼┼┼┼ ‖ | 12 | 68 |
| 22.5–25.5 | 24 | ┼┼┼┼ ┼┼┼┼ ‖‖ | 14 | 82 |
| 25.5–28.5 | 27 | ‖‖ | 3 | 85 |
| 28.5–31.5 | 30 | | 0 | 85 |
| 31.5–34.5 | 33 | ‖‖‖ | 4 | 89 |
| 34.5–37.5 | 36 | ‖ | 1 | 90 |

DEFINITION 2-6. The endpoints of the classes (7.5, 10.5, 13.5, 16.5, etc. in Table 2-4) are called *class limits* or *class boundaries*.

DEFINITION 2-7. The midpoint between the upper and lower class boundaries of a class is called the *class mark* or *class midpoint*.

DEFINITION 2-8. The difference between the largest and smallest class boundaries is called the *range* of the table. (In Table 2-4 the range is $37.5 - 7.5 = 30$.)

DEFINITION 2-9. The number of variates falling within a given class interval is called the *class frequency*, or simply, *frequency*.

DEFINITION 2-10. The set of frequencies with their respective classes or class midpoints is called a *frequency distribution*.

In classifying data in a frequency table, experience indicates that for most data 10–20 classes are desirable. With fewer than 10 classes too much accuracy is lost; with more than 20 classes too extensive a summary is obtained.

The class interval therefore should be about $\frac{1}{10}$ to $\frac{1}{20}$ of the difference between the largest and smallest variate, which in the example above is $36.1 - 7.8 = 28.3$. Therefore, for 10 classes some convenient number in the neighborhood of 2.83 should be selected for the class interval. The value of

3.0 was used in Table 2-4. Since the first class should contain the smallest variate, it must begin with 7.8 or less. The value of 7.5 was chosen for the smallest class boundary.

Various procedures are used in tallying a variate falling on a class boundary. We shall adopt the method of always tabulating such a variate in the higher class, which means that in the above example 10.5 was recorded in the class having 10.5 and 13.5 as boundaries. Another method used to avoid having variates falling on class boundaries is to express the boundaries to one-half unit beyond the accuracy of the measurement. If the data are accurate to tenths, the class limits should then be expressed to twentieths; if data are measured to the nearest quarter of an inch, the class limits should be arranged in eighths of an inch. Therefore in the example above we might choose as the first class limit 7.45 or 7.55, and the remaining class limits would be obtained by repeatedly adding 3.00 until the largest measurement is included. Some statisticians use the method of assigning for a variate falling on a class boundary a count of one-half to the lower class and one-half to the higher class. Often, especially for discrete data, noncontiguous boundaries are used; i.e., for scores in an examination, based on a total of 100 points, the following would be appropriate class boundaries, assuming the lowest score to be a 43 and all scores to be integers: 40-49, 50-59, etc. Clearly, a score of 50 would be placed in the second class.

**DEFINITION 2-11.** The *cumulative frequency* for a given class is the sum of the frequencies of all classes up to and including the given class, assuming that the class with smallest class boundaries is written first.

Cumulative frequencies for each class in the example are listed in the last column of Table 2-4.

Several types of graphical representations are used as aids in the study of frequency distributions. A few important ones will be discussed.

### 2.3.1. Histogram

A histogram is a vertical bar graph, with no space between bars, having, for frequency distributions with contiguous boundaries, class boundaries as points on the horizontal axis and the frequencies as units on the vertical axis. The frequency corresponding to a class is represented by the height of a rectangle (bar) whose base is the class interval. The histogram for the data of Table 2-4 is shown in Figure 2-10. For frequency distributions with noncontiguous boundaries the vertical lines of the bars are drawn at the midpoints between the upper class boundaries of one class and the lower boundaries of the next class.

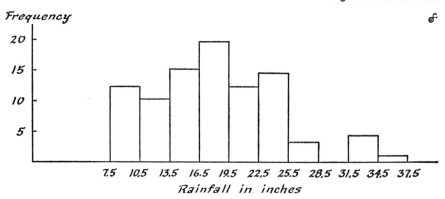

Fig. 2-10. Histogram for the data of Table 2-4.

### 2.3.2.  Frequency Polygon

A frequency polygon is a broken-line graph having class midpoints represented on the horizontal axis and frequencies on the vertical axis. The frequency corresponding to each class midpoint is marked by a point, and
consecutive points are connected by straight lines. This procedure is equivalent to joining the midpoints of the tops of the rectangles of a histogram by
straight lines. The frequency polygon for the data of Table 2-4 is shown in
Figure 2-11.

Fig. 2-11. Frequency polygon for the data of Table 2-4.

### 2.3.3.  Frequency Curve

If the class intervals are made smaller and smaller while at the same time
the total number of measurements or counts is increased further and further,
the histogram may approach a curve, which is called a frequency curve. It
is approximated by fitting a smooth curve to the points of the frequency
polygon.

### 2.3.4. Cumulative Frequency Polygon or Ogive

A cumulative frequency polygon or ogive is a broken-line graph having the upper class boundaries represented on the horizontal axis and the cumulative frequencies on the vertical axis. The cumulative frequency corresponding to each upper class boundary is marked by a point, and consecutive points are connected by straight lines. The cumulative frequency polygon for the data of Table 2-4 is shown in Figure 2-12.

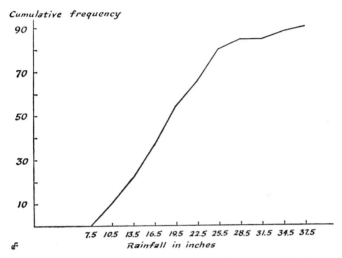

Fig. 2-12. Cumulative frequency polygon for the data of Table 2-4.

## Exercises

1. The urban and rural populations in the United States at 20-year intervals from 1800 to 1940 were as follows:

| Year | Urban | Rural |
|------|-------|-------|
| 1800 | 322,371 | 4,986,112 |
| 1820 | 693,255 | 8,945,198 |
| 1840 | 1,845,055 | 15,224,398 |
| 1860 | 6,216,518 | 25,226,803 |
| 1880 | 14,129,735 | 36,026,048 |
| 1900 | 30,159,921 | 45,834,654 |
| 1920 | 54,157,973 | 51,552,647 |
| 1940 | 74,423,702 | 57,245,573 |

Construct for these data

(a) a component-part bar graph;    (c) a broken-line graph;

(b) a grouped bar graph;    (d) a curve-line graph.

2. For the rural population data of Exercise 1 construct an ideograph.

3. The numbers of television stations on the air in the United States and its territories for the period 1945–1957 were as follows:

| Year | Number | Year | Number | Year | Number |
|------|--------|------|--------|------|--------|
| 1945 | 6 | 1950 | 97 | 1954 | 356 |
| 1946 | 6 | 1951 | 107 | 1955 | 439 |
| 1947 | 7 | 1952 | 108 | 1956 | 482 |
| 1948 | 17 | 1953 | 129 | 1957 | 511 |
| 1949 | 50 | | | | |

(a) Construct a bar graph for the 8-year data from 1950 to 1957.

(b) Construct a broken-line graph for all the data.

4. Of the life insurance policy dividends paid in the United States in 1957, 21% were taken in cash, 31% were used to pay premiums, 18% were used to purchase additional paid-up life insurance, and 30% were left with the life insurance companies to earn interest. Construct a pie diagram showing these different uses of policy dividends.

5. The data for total seasonal rainfall at Davis, California, for the 70-year period 1870–1940 (read horizontally) are given below to the nearest tenth of an inch.

| | | | | | | | | | |
|------|------|------|------|------|------|------|------|------|------|
| 19.2 | 12.0 | 18.3 | 11.2 | 18.7 | 5.1 | 20.0 | 12.9 | 17.0 | 18.8 |
| 11.6 | 15.8 | 18.8 | 9.8 | 24.5 | 12.2 | 12.0 | 20.1 | 37.4 | 21.4 |
| 12.4 | 24.3 | 15.2 | 22.6 | 21.7 | 18.8 | 9.0 | 13.2 | 13.3 | 17.8 |
| 15.7 | 16.2 | 18.5 | 22.8 | 24.5 | 23.9 | 13.2 | 22.1 | 11.8 | 23.2 |
| 9.5 | 8.7 | 28.7 | 20.0 | 20.9 | 14.1 | 9.7 | 19.4 | 8.9 | 17.2 |
| 16.6 | 17.9 | 9.0 | 19.2 | 18.4 | 19.0 | 14.8 | 10.8 | 13.9 | 8.7 |
| 15.2 | 9.6 | 11.0 | 18.7 | 17.8 | 17.9 | 25.8 | 7.0 | 20.4 | 31.5 |

(a) Construct a frequency table for these data (use approximately 10 classes).

For the above frequency table draw

(b) the histogram;

(c) the frequency polygon;

(d) the cumulative frequency polygon.

6. An industrial organization gives to all applicants for employment an aptitude test. The results in the case of 145 people taking the test are as follows:

| Score | Frequency | Score | Frequency |
|-------|-----------|-------|-----------|
| 9     | 5         | 4     | 21        |
| 8     | 10        | 3     | 15        |
| 7     | 19        | 2     | 11        |
| 6     | 23        | 1     | 6         |
| 5     | 35        |       |           |

(a) Draw a histogram for the frequency distribution, and on the same graph draw the frequency polygon.

(b) Draw the cumulative frequency polygon.

# 3   Summation Notation

In statistics the sums of large numbers of terms frequently occur, and it is desirable to have a simplified notation for the summation of these terms. If a variable is denoted by $X$, then successive observations of that variable are written as $X_1$ (read "$X$ sub one"), $X_2$, $X_3$, and so on. In general, the $i$th observation is written as $X_i$, and if there are $N$ observations the last one is denoted by $X_N$. The Greek letter sigma $\Sigma$ is used to indicate the sum of these $N$ observations, i.e.,

(3-1)
$$\sum_{i=1}^{N} X_i = X_1 + X_2 + X_3 + \cdots + X_N.$$

The symbol $\sum_{i=1}^{N} X_i$ is read "summation of $X$ sub $i$ (or sigma $X$ sub $i$), where $i$ assumes all integral values from 1 to $N$ inclusive," or more simply "summation of $X$ sub $i$, where $i$ goes from 1 to $N$."

> DEFINITION 3-1.   The letter below a summation sign $\Sigma$ is called the *summation index.*

In the summation in equation (3-1) the summation index is $i$.

*Example 3-1.*   If $X_1 = 3$, $X_2 = 9$, $X_3 = 11$, find $\sum_{i=1}^{3} X_i$.

*Solution.*   $\sum_{i=1}^{3} X_i = X_1 + X_2 + X_3 = 3 + 9 + 11 = 23.$

An explicit definition of the summation notation is as follows:

> DEFINITION 3-2.   The Greek letter sigma, $\Sigma$, placed before a term signifies the sum of all terms the first one of which is obtained by putting for $i$ (or for whatever other summation index is used) in the term being summed the integer listed below the $\Sigma$-sign, the second by putting $i$ equal to the next larger integer, and so on, until finally the last term results from putting $i$ equal to the integer indicated above the $\Sigma$-sign.

The number of terms in the summation is one more than the difference between the integers appearing above and below the summation sign.

*Example 3-2.*   If $X_1 = 9$, $X_2 = 6$, $X_3 = 5$, $X_4 = 8$, $X_5 = 12$, find

(a) $\displaystyle\sum_{i=1}^{5} (X_i - 5)^2$;   (b) $\displaystyle\left(\sum_{i=3}^{4} X_i\right)^2$;   (c) $\displaystyle\sum_{i=1}^{3} (X_i^2 - 2X_i)$.

*Solution.*

(a) $\displaystyle\sum_{i=1}^{5} (X_i - 5)^2 = (X_1 - 5)^2 + (X_2 - 5)^2 + (X_3 - 5)^2$

$$+ (X_4 - 5)^2 + (X_5 - 5)^2$$
$$= (9 - 5)^2 + (6 - 5)^2 + (5 - 5)^2 + (8 - 5)^2$$
$$+ (12 - 5)^2 = 75.$$

(b) $\displaystyle\left(\sum_{i=3}^{4} X_i\right)^2 = (X_3 + X_4)^2 = (5 + 8)^2 = 13^2 = 169.$

(c) $\displaystyle\sum_{i=1}^{3} (X_i^2 - 2X_i) = (X_1^2 - 2X_1) + (X_2^2 - 2X_2) + (X_3^2 - 2X_3)$

$$= (81 - 18) + (36 - 12) + (25 - 10)$$
$$= 63 + 24 + 15 = 102.$$

*Example 3-3.*   Prove that

$$\sum_{i=1}^{N} (aX_i + b) = a \sum_{i=1}^{N} X_i + Nb.$$

*Solution.*

$$\sum_{i=1}^{N} (aX_i + b) = (aX_1 + b) + (aX_2 + b) + (aX_3 + b) + \cdots + (aX_N + b)$$
$$= aX_1 + aX_2 + aX_3 + \cdots + aX_N + \underbrace{b + b + b + \cdots + b}_{N \text{ terms}}$$
$$= a(X_1 + X_2 + X_3 + \cdots + X_N) + Nb$$
$$= a \sum_{i=1}^{N} X_i + Nb.$$

From the preceding examples it is evident that:
1. The summation of an expression which is the sum of two or more terms is equal to the sum of the summations of the separate terms. For the case of an expression consisting of three terms this means

(3-2)          $\displaystyle\sum_{i=1}^{N} (X_i + Y_i + Z_i) = \sum_{i=1}^{N} X_i + \sum_{i=1}^{N} Y_i + \sum_{i=1}^{N} Z_i;$

2. The summation of a constant multiplied by a variable is the same as the constant multiplied by the summation of the variable,

(3-3)
$$\sum_{i=1}^{N} aX_i = a \sum_{i=1}^{N} X_i;$$

3. The summation of a constant is $N$ multiplied by the constant,

(3-4)
$$\sum_{i=1}^{N} b = Nb.$$

*Example 3-4.*  Prove that

$$\sum_{i=1}^{N} (X_i - m)^2 = \sum_{i=1}^{N} X_i^2 - \frac{1}{N} \left( \sum_{i=1}^{N} X_i \right)^2,$$

where

$$m = \frac{\sum_{i=1}^{N} X_i}{N}.$$

*Solution.*

$$\sum_{i=1}^{N} (X_i - m)^2 = \sum_{i=1}^{N} (X_i^2 - 2mX_i + m^2) = \sum_{i=1}^{N} X_i^2 - 2m \sum_{i=1}^{N} X_i + Nm^2$$

$$= \sum_{i=1}^{N} X_i^2 - 2 \left[ \frac{\sum_{i=1}^{N} X_i}{N} \right] \sum_{i=1}^{N} X_i + N \left[ \frac{\sum_{i=1}^{N} X_i}{N} \right]^2$$

$$= \sum_{i=1}^{N} X_i^2 - \frac{2}{N} \left( \sum_{i=1}^{N} X_i \right)^2 + \frac{1}{N} \left( \sum_{i=1}^{N} X_i \right)^2$$

$$= \sum_{i=1}^{N} X_i^2 - \frac{1}{N} \left( \sum_{i=1}^{N} X_i \right)^2.$$

In proving results of the type of Example 3-4 involving the quantity $m = \left( \sum_{i=1}^{N} X_i \right)/N$ it is important to carry out the procedure in the order indicated above. This means that the following sequence of steps should be used.

1. Perform the algebraic operations indicated after the summation sign and simplify (in Example 3-4 this operation consisted in squaring the binomial $X_i - m$).
2. Take the summation of the separate terms in accordance with the principle stated in formula (3-2); at the same time place any constants before the summation signs in accordance with formula (3-3) and replace the summation of a constant by $N$ times the constant in accordance with formula (3-4).

3. Replace $m$ by $\left(\sum\limits_{i=1}^{N} X_i\right)/N$ in the result obtained in step 2 if the final result is to be expressed in terms of $\sum\limits_{i=1}^{N} X_i$; if the final result is to be expressed in terms of $m$, replace $\sum\limits_{i=1}^{N} X_i$ by $Nm$.

4. Simplify the result obtained in step 3 as far as possible.

Frequently, where no confusion is possible, the summation index is omitted, and it is then understood that the summation includes all values under discussion.

*Example 3-5.* If $X_1 = 3$, $X_2 = 9$, $X_3 = 5$, find (a) $\Sigma X^2$; (b) $\sqrt{\Sigma 2X}$.
*Solution.*

(a) $\Sigma X^2 = X_1^2 + X_2^2 + X_3^2 = 9 + 81 + 25 = 115.$
(b) $\sqrt{\Sigma 2X} = \sqrt{2\Sigma X} = \sqrt{2(3 + 9 + 5)} = \sqrt{34}.$

## Exercises

1. Write out in full the sums represented by each of the following expressions:

(a) $\sum\limits_{i=2}^{6} X_i;$

(b) $\sum\limits_{i=7}^{9} X_i^2;$

(c) $\left(\sum\limits_{i=1}^{7} X_i\right)^2;$

(d) $\sum\limits_{i=1}^{3} (X_i - 2)^2;$

(e) $\left[\sum\limits_{i=1}^{4} (X_i + 3)X_i\right]^2;$

(f) $\sum\limits_{i=1}^{4} cX_i;$

(g) $\sum\limits_{j=2}^{5} (Y_j + 7);$

(h) $\sum\limits_{k=1}^{4} W_k^3;$

(i) $\sum\limits_{i=1}^{4} f_i X_i^2.$

2. Write each of the following expressions, using a summation sign and appropriate limits:
   (a) $X_1 + X_2 + X_3 + X_4;$
   (b) $X_2^2 + X_3^2 + X_4^2;$
   (c) $[(X_3 - 4) + (X_4 - 4) + (X_5 - 4)]^2;$
   (d) $y_9^2 + y_{10}^2 + y_{11}^2 + y_{12}^2 + y_{13}^2;$
   (e) $kn_2 + kn_3 + kn_4 + kn_5;$
   (f) $(X_1 - m)^2 + (X_2 - m)^2 + (X_3 - m)^2.$

3. If $X_1 = 3$, $X_2 = 9$, $X_3 = -7$, $X_4 = -3$, find the numerical values of the following:

(a) $\sum\limits_{i=2}^{4} (X_i + 1)^2;$

(b) $\sum\limits_{i=1}^{3} X_i(X_i - 7).$

4. If $X_1 = 7$, $X_2 = -5$, $X_3 = 4$, $X_4 = 2$, find

    (a) $\sum\limits_{i=1}^{4} (X_i - 10)^2$;

    (b) $\sqrt{\sum\limits_{i=2}^{4} X_i(X_i + 4)}$.

5. If $X_1 = 8$, $X_2 = 4$, $X_3 = -4$, $X_4 = 0$, find

    (a) $\left[ \sum\limits_{i=2}^{4} (X_i + 3) \right]^2$;

    (b) $\sum\limits_{i=1}^{4} (X_i - m)^2$, where $m = \dfrac{\sum\limits_{i=1}^{4} X_i}{4}$.

6. If $X_1 = 1$, $X_2 = 4$, $X_3 = 9$, find numerical values of the following:

    (a) $\left[ \sum\limits_{i=1}^{2} (X_i + 1) \right]^2$;

    (b) $\Sigma(\sqrt{X} + 1)^2$.

7. If $X_1 = -1$, $X_2 = 3$, $X_3 = -5$, $X_4 = 6$, evaluate $\Sigma(X^2 + 2X - 3)$.

8. If $X_1 = 7$, $X_2 = 8$, $X_3 = 0$, $X_4 = -7$, find

    (a) $\sqrt{\sum\limits_{j=2}^{4} (X_j + 5)}$;

    (b) $\Sigma(X + m)^2$, where $m = \dfrac{\Sigma X}{4}$.

9. If $X_1 = 4$, $X_2 = -5$, $X_3 = 11$, $X_4 = 0$, find

    (a) $\Sigma(X^2 - 3)$;

    (b) $\sum\limits_{j=1}^{3} \sqrt{X_j + 5}$.

10. If $X_1 = 9$, $X_2 = 3$, $X_3 = -2$, $X_4 = 0$, $X_5 = 4$, find

    (a) $\sum\limits_{i=1}^{5} (X_i^2 - 3X_i)$;

    (b) $\sqrt{\sum\limits_{i=2}^{4} (X_i - 2)^2}$.

11. Find

    (a) $\sum\limits_{i=1}^{n} 1$;

    (b) $\sum\limits_{i=1}^{6} 3$.

In the following exercises suppose that a set of numbers $X_1, X_2, X_3, \cdots, X_N$ is given and that $m = \left( \sum\limits_{i=1}^{N} X_i \right)/N$. Prove the relationships.

12. $\sum\limits_{i=1}^{N} [(X_i - 3m)^2 - 2mX_i] = \sum\limits_{i=1}^{N} X_i^2 + \dfrac{\left( \sum\limits_{i=1}^{N} X_i \right)^2}{N}$.

13. $\Sigma[(X - m)^2 + X(m - 1)] = \Sigma X^2 - Nm$.

14. $\sum\limits_{j=1}^{N} [X_j(X_j - m) + m^2] = \sum\limits_{j=1}^{N} X_j^2$.

15. $\Sigma[X(X + m) - m^2(X + 1)] = \Sigma X^2 - \dfrac{(\Sigma X)^3}{N^2}$.

16. $\sum\limits_{i=1}^{N} [(X_i + m)(X_i - 3m) - mX_i] = \sum\limits_{i=1}^{N} X_i^2 - 6 \dfrac{\left( \sum\limits_{i=1}^{N} X_i \right)^2}{N}$.

17. $\Sigma[(X - 2m)^2 + X - m] = \Sigma[X(X - m) + m^2]$.

18. $\Sigma[X(X - m) + m - X] = \Sigma X^2 - \dfrac{(\Sigma X)^2}{N}$.

19. $\displaystyle\sum_{i=1}^{N} [4mX_i + (X_i - 2m)(X_i + 2m)] = \sum_{i=1}^{N} X_i^2$.

20. $\displaystyle\sum_{j=1}^{N} (X_j - m)(X_j - 2m) + \sum_{j=1}^{N} m(X_j - 1) = \sum_{j=1}^{N} X_j^2 - \sum_{j=1}^{N} X_j$.

21. $\Sigma(X - 3m)(X - m) + \Sigma(3m^2 - mX) = \Sigma X^2 + \dfrac{(\Sigma X)^2}{N}$.

22. $\Sigma\left[(X - m)^2 + \dfrac{1}{N}\right] = \Sigma X^2 - Nm^2 + 1$.

23. $\displaystyle\sum_{i=1}^{N} [X_i(X_i + m) + (X_i - m)^2] = 2\sum_{i=1}^{N} X_i^2$.

# 4 Analysis of Data

## 4.1. Introduction

In order to reduce a mass of data to an understandable form which can be quickly grasped, we construct a frequency table for the data and draw the corresponding histogram or frequency curve. It is useful to simplify the presentation further by defining certain measures which describe important features of the distribution.

DEFINITION 4-1. Any measure indicating a center of the distribution is called a *measure of central tendency*.

In studying frequency distributions, however, it is also important to know the extent to which the data vary or scatter about a central point; the data may be closely packed about a central point as in (a) of Figure 4-1, they may be uniform as in (b), or there may be a relatively large number of extreme cases as in (c).

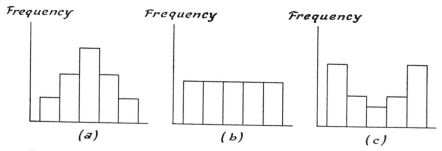

Fig. 4-1. Various frequency distributions having the same center.

DEFINITION 4-2. A numerical value indicating the amount of scatter about a central point is called a *measure of dispersion*.

Definitions of the more important measures of central tendency and of dispersion, along with their relative merits, are set forth in this chapter.

## 4.2. Measures of Central Tendency

### 4.2.1. The Mean (or Arithmetic Mean)

DEFINITION 4-3. For a set of $N$ numbers, $X_1, X_2, \cdots, X_N$, the *mean* (or *arithmetic mean*), denoted by $m$, is defined as

(4-1)
$$m = \frac{X_1 + X_2 + \cdots + X_N}{N} = \frac{\sum\limits_{i=1}^{N} X_i}{N}.$$

*Example 4-1.* Find to two decimal places the mean of 11, 14, 17, 20, 16, 10.
*Solution.*
$$m = \frac{11 + 14 + 17 + 20 + 16 + 10}{6} = 14.67.$$

It will be observed that the arithmetic mean is what is frequently called the average. However, the term "average" is also used for other measures of central tendency; consequently, whenever this term appears the reader will have to decide from the context which measure of central tendency is meant.

If the data are presented in a frequency table, we do not know the exact values of the variates but only the classes in which they lie. However, it seems reasonable to assume that the data within a class are uniformly distributed about the class midpoint, so for the purpose of calculating the mean we shall assume that all data within a class actually occur at the midpoint, which results in the following definition.

DEFINITION 4-4. If in a frequency table with $h$ classes the class midpoints are $X_1, X_2, \cdots, X_h$ and the respective frequencies are $f_1, f_2, \cdots, f_h$, then the mean is defined as

(4-2)
$$m = \frac{X_1 f_1 + X_2 f_2 + \cdots + X_h f_h}{f_1 + f_2 + \cdots + f_h} = \frac{\sum\limits_{i=1}^{h} X_i f_i}{\sum\limits_{i=1}^{h} f_i}.$$

If we denote the total number of variates by $N$, then, since $\sum\limits_{i=1}^{h} f_i = N$, we can rewrite (4-2) as

(4-3)
$$m = \frac{\sum\limits_{i=1}^{h} X_i f_i}{N}.$$

*Example 4-2.* Find to two decimal places the mean for the data given in Table 2-4.

*Solution.* In this case $X_1 = 9, f_1 = 12, X_2 = 12, f_2 = 10, \cdots, X_{10} = 36,$ $f_{10} = 1$; consequently,

$m =$

$$\frac{9(12) + 12(10) + 15(15) + 18(19) + 21(12) + 24(14) + 27(3) + 30(0) + 33(4) + 36(1)}{90}$$

$$= \frac{1632}{90} = 18.13.$$

However, it is more convenient to arrange this calculation in tabular form, as shown in Table 4-1 where the fourth column (the other columns are not needed for this example) gives the values of $Xf$, and the total of that column is equal to the numerator of $m$.

If $h$, the number of classes, is large, the above method for calculating the mean may be lengthy. We shall therefore consider a faster method of calculating the mean from a frequency table.

Let

$A = $ any class midpoint (called the *assumed mean*),

$c = $ the difference between two consecutive class midpoints,

$d_i = \dfrac{X_i - A}{c}$, i.e., $d_i$ is the number of classes that $X_i$ is away from the assumed mean. It is positive if $X_i$ is greater than $A$ and negative if $X_i$ is less than $A$.

Then $m$ can be calculated by the following formula:

(4-4)
$$m = A + c \frac{\sum\limits_{i=1}^{h} d_i f_i}{N}.$$

TABLE 4-1. Calculation of the Mean and Standard Deviation for the Data of Table 2-4

| (1) Class Boundaries | (2) X | (3) f | (4) Xf | (5) d | (6) df | (7) d²f |
|---|---|---|---|---|---|---|
| 7.5–10.5 | 9 | 12 | 108 | −3 | −36 | 108 |
| 10.5–13.5 | 12 | 10 | 120 | −2 | −20 | 40 |
| 13.5–16.5 | 15 | 15 | 225 | −1 | −15 | 15 |
| 16.5–19.5 | 18 | 19 | 342 | 0 | 0 | 0 |
| 19.5–22.5 | 21 | 12 | 252 | +1 | +12 | 12 |
| 22.5–25.5 | 24 | 14 | 336 | +2 | +28 | 56 |
| 25.5–28.5 | 27 | 3 | 81 | +3 | +9 | 27 |
| 28.5–31.5 | 30 | 0 | 0 | +4 | 0 | 0 |
| 31.5–34.5 | 33 | 4 | 132 | +5 | +20 | 100 |
| 34.5–37.5 | 36 | 1 | 36 | +6 | +6 | 36 |
|  |  | 90 | 1632 |  | +4 | 394 |

*Example 4-3.* Find the mean of Example 4-2 by using an assumed mean.

*Solution.* Table 4-1, using an assumed mean, $A = 18$, shows in the fifth and sixth columns the quantities required in the calculation. (Note: The last column in Table 4-1 is not used in this example, but will be used in Example 4-14).

Since $\sum_{i=1}^{h} d_i f_i = +4$, we have

$$m = 18 + 3 \left( \frac{4}{90} \right) = 18.13.$$

*Proof of formula (4-4).* Since $d_i = (X_i - A)/c$, we find $X_i = A + cd_i$, and substituting this value of $X_i$ into the definition of $m$ as given by (4-3) we have

$$m = \frac{\sum_{i=1}^{h} X_i f_i}{N} = \frac{\sum_{i=1}^{h} (A + cd_i) f_i}{N} = \frac{\sum_{i=1}^{h} (A f_i + cd_i f_i)}{N} = \frac{\sum_{i=1}^{h} A f_i + \sum_{i=1}^{h} cd_i f_i}{N}$$

$$= \frac{A \sum_{i=1}^{h} f_i + c \sum_{i=1}^{h} d_i f_i}{N} = \frac{AN + c \sum_{i=1}^{h} d_i f_i}{N} = A + c \frac{\sum_{i=1}^{h} d_i f_i}{N}.$$

Although (4-4) is valid no matter what class midpoint is assumed for $A$, in order to simplify calculations it is advisable to choose $A$ near the value where the mean is expected to occur.

**THEOREM 4-1.** If a set of $N_1$ variates has mean $m_1$ and a set of $N_2$ variates has mean $m_2$, then the mean of the set of $N_1 + N_2$ variates obtained by combining these two sets is given by

(4-5)
$$m = \frac{m_1 N_1 + m_2 N_2}{N_1 + N_2}.$$

*Proof.* For the set of $N_1$ variates let the class midpoints be $X_1, X_2, \cdots, X_h$, and the corresponding frequencies be $f_1, f_2, \cdots, f_h$; for the set of $N_2$ variates let the class midpoints be $X'_1, X'_2, \cdots, X'_k$, and the corresponding frequencies be $f'_1, f'_2, \cdots, f'_k$. Then

$$m = \frac{\sum_{i=1}^{h} X_i f_i + \sum_{i=1}^{k} X'_i f'_i}{N_1 + N_2}.$$

Since

$$m_1 = \frac{\sum_{i=1}^{h} X_i f_i}{N_1} \quad \text{and} \quad m_2 = \frac{\sum_{i=1}^{k} X'_i f'_i}{N_2},$$

we obtain. by solving the first equation for $\sum_{i=1}^{h} X_i f_i$, the second equation for $\sum_{i=1}^{k} X'_i f'_i$,

$$\sum_{i=1}^{h} X_i f_i = m_1 N_1 \quad \text{and} \quad \sum_{i=1}^{k} X_i' f_i' = m_2 N_2.$$

Substituting these values into the numerator of the formula for $m$ yields (4-5).

The value of $m$ given by formula (4-5) is frequently called a *weighted mean*, since the means $m_1$ and $m_2$ are weighted according to the number of variates in each set. A weighted mean is only equal to the ordinary mean of $m_1$ and $m_2$ if the two sets of data contain the same number of variates.

Theorem 4-1 can be generalized to the case of combining more than two sets of data (see exercise 15).

*Example 4-4.* A mathematics class is divided into two sections, both of which are given the same test. Section 1 (41 students) has a mean score of 62; and section 2 (52 students) has a mean score of 68. Find the mean of the whole class correct to two decimal places.

*Solution.* Since $N_1 = 41$, $m_1 = 62$, $N_2 = 52$, $m_2 = 68$, we find

$$m = \frac{62(41) + 68(52)}{93} = 65.35.$$

### 4.2.2. The Median

The median of a set of $N$ numbers arranged in order of ascending or descending magnitude is the middle number of the set if $N$ is odd, and the mean of the two middle numbers if $N$ is even.

**DEFINITION 4-5.** For a set of $N$ numbers, $X_1, X_2, \cdots, X_N$, written in increasing order of magnitude, the median, denoted by $M_d$, is defined as

$$X_{\frac{N+1}{2}}$$

if $N$ is odd, and as

$$\frac{X_{\frac{N}{2}} + X_{\frac{N}{2}+1}}{2}$$

if $N$ is even.

*Example 4-5.* Find the median of 6, 7, 9, 12, 16, 20.
*Solution.*

$$M_d = \frac{X_3 + X_4}{2} = \frac{9 + 12}{2} = 10.5.$$

**DEFINITION 4-6.** For a frequency distribution the *median class* is defined as the lowest class for which the cumulative frequency exceeds $N/2$.

To obtain a formula for calculating the median from a frequency distribution with $h$ classes we introduce the following notation:

Let

$$N = \text{total number of variates} = \sum_{i=1}^{h} f_i,$$

$c$ = the difference between two consecutive class midpoints,

$L$ = the mean of the lower boundary of the median class and the upper boundary of the next lower class,

$f_m$ = the frequency of the median class,

$F_c$ = the cumulative frequency for the class next lower than the median class, which also equals the number of variates less than $L$.

Then assuming that the data in the median class are distributed uniformly throughout the interval, by linear interpolation

$$c\,\frac{\dfrac{N}{2} - F_c}{f_m}$$

is the distance from $L$ to the median as shown in Figure 4-2. It might appear that this expression should assume different forms depending upon whether $N$ is even or odd; this, however, is not the case if the data are uniformly distributed throughout the median class.

Fig. 4-2.   Location of median in median class.

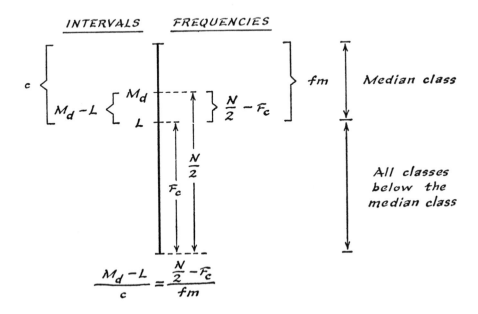

We therefore have the following definition:

**DEFINITION 4-7.** For a frequency distribution the *median* is defined as

$$(4\text{-}6) \qquad M_d = L + c \, \frac{\dfrac{N}{2} - F_c}{f_m}.$$

*Example 4-6.* Find to two decimal places the median for the data of Table 4-1.

*Solution.* The median class is the 16.5–19.5 class. Therefore,

$$M_d = 16.5 + 3 \left( \frac{\dfrac{90}{2} - 37}{19} \right) = 16.5 + 3 \left( \frac{8}{19} \right) = 16.5 + 1.26 = 17.76.$$

*Example 4-7.* Find the median and median class of the data in Table 4-2, which represent the grades on an examination given to a class of 66 students.

**TABLE 4-2.** Frequency Table for Grades on an Examination

| Class Boundaries | Frequency |
|:---:|:---:|
| 30–39 | 6 |
| 40–49 | 12 |
| 50–59 | 15 |
| 60–69 | 15 |
| 70–79 | 8 |
| 80–89 | 6 |
| 90–99 | 4 |
| | 66 |

*Solution.* Here the median falls between 59 and 60. Therefore, by Definition 4-6 the 60–69 class is the median class, and since $N/2 = 33$ and $F_c = 33$ we have $M_d = 59.5$, which is obvious without the use of (4-6) since it is the value on both sides of which equal frequencies fall.

### 4.2.3. The Mode

**DEFINITION 4-8.** The class (or classes) for which the frequency is greatest is called the *modal class* (or *modal classes*).

In Table 4-1 the modal class is the 16.5–19.5 class; for the data of Table 4-2, the modal classes are the 50–59 class and 60-69 class.

**DEFINITION 4-9.** The class midpoint of a modal class is called a *crude mode*. If there are several modal classes, there will be several crude modes, as in Table 4-2.

The true mode is easy to define but very difficult to determine.

**DEFINITION 4-10.** If a frequency curve has been fitted to a set of data, a *true mode* is the value on the horizontal axis for which the frequency curve reaches a maximum value.

### 4.2.4. The Geometric Mean

The geometric mean is less frequently used than are the measures of central tendency discussed so far.

**DEFINITION 4-11.** For a set of $N$ nonnegative numbers, $X_1, X_2, \cdots,$ $X_N$, the *geometric mean*, denoted by $M_g$, is defined as

$$(4\text{-}7) \qquad M_g = \sqrt[N]{X_1 \cdot X_2 \cdot X_3 \cdots X_N}.$$

It is convenient to express this in logarithmic form; thus,

$$(4\text{-}8) \qquad \log M_g = \frac{\log X_1 + \log X_2 + \cdots + \log X_N}{N} = \frac{\sum\limits_{i=1}^{N} \log X_i}{N}.$$

The geometric mean is applied to data for which the ratio of any two consecutive numbers is either constant (in which case the data form a geometric progression) or nearly constant. This occurs, for example, in data representing the size of a population at consecutive time intervals or the value of a sum of money which is increasing at compound interest.

*Example 4-8.* An amount of $1000 is invested at 4% on January 1, 1960. If interest is added annually on January 1 to this amount, use the geometric mean to calculate the average amount of money invested between January 1, 1960 and December 31, 1963.

*Solution.* Table 4-3 shows the amount of money invested on January 1 of each year from 1960 to 1963.

Since the amounts invested form a geometric progression (the ratio of any two consecutive numbers is 1.04), the geometric mean is the appropriate measure to use for averaging these data. Using (4-8) we list the logarithm of each value of $X$ in the last column of Table 4-3 and find

$$\log M_g = \frac{12.09220}{4} = 3.02305,$$

$$M_g = 1054.50.$$

TABLE 4-3.  Amount of Money Invested on January 1

|  | Amount Invested | |
| Year | (X) | Log X |
| --- | --- | --- |
| 1960 | 1000.00 | 3.00000 |
| 1961 | 1040.00 | 3.01703 |
| 1962 | 1081.60 | 3.03407 |
| 1963 | 1124.86 | 3.04110 |
|  |  | 12.09220 |

The arithmetic mean for Example 4-8 is 1061.61. The geometric mean is never greater than the arithmetic mean.

For data presented in a frequency table the following definition applies.

**DEFINITION 4-12.** If in a frequency table the class midpoints are nonnegative and are denoted by $X_1$, $X_2$, $\cdots$, $X_h$ and the respective frequencies are denoted by $f_1$, $f_2$, $\cdots$, $f_h$, then the geometric mean is defined as

(4-9)
$$M_g = \sqrt[N]{X_1^{f_1} \cdot X_2^{f_2} \cdots X_h^{f_h}},$$
where

$$N = \sum_{i=1}^{h} f_i.$$

## 4.2.5.  The Harmonic Mean

Another measure of central tendency, which is only occasionally used, is the *harmonic mean*.

**DEFINITION 4-13.** For a set of $N$ numbers, $X_1$, $X_2$, $\cdots$, $X_N$, the *harmonic mean*, denoted by $M_h$, is defined as

(4-10)
$$M_h = \frac{N}{\dfrac{1}{X_1} + \dfrac{1}{X_2} + \dfrac{1}{X_3} + \cdots + \dfrac{1}{X_N}} = \frac{N}{\sum\limits_{i=1}^{N} \dfrac{1}{X_i}}.$$

The harmonic mean is used most frequently in averaging speeds where the distances for which each speed is applicable are the same. Let us assume that a car travels first $d$ miles at speed $r_1$, then $d$ miles at speed $r_2$, and finally $d$ miles at speed $r_3$. Then the average speed is equal to the total distance traveled divided by the total time, or

$$\text{average speed} = \frac{d + d + d}{t_1 + t_2 + t_3}.$$

Now since $t_1$, the time at which the car traveled at speed $r_1$, equals

$$t_1 = \frac{d}{r_1}$$

and $t_2$ and $t_3$ are obtained similarly, we find

$$\text{average speed} = \frac{3d}{\dfrac{d}{r_1} + \dfrac{d}{r_2} + \dfrac{d}{r_3}} = \frac{3d}{d\left(\dfrac{1}{r_1} + \dfrac{1}{r_2} + \dfrac{1}{r_3}\right)} = \frac{3}{\dfrac{1}{r_1} + \dfrac{1}{r_2} + \dfrac{1}{r_3}},$$

which is the harmonic mean of the three speeds.

Thus, for example, if a car travels a certain distance with an average speed of 20 miles per hour and returns over the same route with an average speed of 30 miles per hour, the average speed for the round trip is given by

$$\frac{2}{\dfrac{1}{20} + \dfrac{1}{30}} = \frac{2}{\dfrac{30 + 20}{600}} = \frac{1200}{50} = 24 \text{ miles per hour},$$

and is not equal to 25 miles per hour, as might have been guessed.

*Example 4-9.*  An airplane travels a distance of 900 miles. If it covers the first third and last third distance of the trip at 250 miles per hour and the middle third at 300 miles per hour, find its average speed.

*Solution.*  Since the distances traveled at each speed are the same, we need to determine the harmonic mean. Using (4-10) we find

$$M_h = \frac{3}{\dfrac{1}{250} + \dfrac{1}{300} + \dfrac{1}{250}} = \frac{3}{\dfrac{6 + 5 + 6}{1500}} = \frac{4500}{17} = 264.71 \text{ miles per hour}.$$

However, if an average speed is to be calculated where the *times* (but not the distances) for which each speed is applicable are the same, the appropriate average is the arithmetic mean.

### 4.2.6.  Relative Merits of Mean, Median, and Mode

The most frequently used measure of central tendency is the arithmetic mean. It is easy to compute, easy to define, takes all measurements into consideration, and is well designed for algebraic manipulation. From the arithmetic means of different sets of data the arithmetic mean of the combined group may easily be calculated, as shown in Theorem 4-1. One of the chief advantages of the mean is its reliability in sampling. If we regard a set of data as being a sample taken from a certain population and then take another sample from the same population, the means of the two samples will in general show closer agreement than will the two medians, i.e., generally speaking, the mean is more stable than the median. For these reasons the mean is the most widely used measure of central tendency in statistics.

The median, although easy to calculate and easy to define, is not influenced by extreme measurements, which for certain situations may prove to be advantageous. In economic statistics it is often desirable to disregard extreme variates, which may be due to unusual circumstances. The median is particularly useful when the magnitude of the extreme data is not given but when their number is known. In this case, the mean cannot be calculated.

The mode is even less important than the median because of its ambiguity. It is possible that two nonadjacent classes will have the same maximum frequency, thereby yielding two modal values, which may be purely accidental because of the particular choice of the class interval. On the other hand, the mode, like the median, is easy to understand and is not greatly influenced by extreme cases.

## 4.3.  Measures of Dispersion

Although the arithmetic mean is a satisfactory measure of central tendency, it does not in itself give a clear picture of a set of variates or their distribution. Figure 4-1 shows very different frequency distributions having identical means, and Table 4-4 shows three sets of variates having the same mean values.

Obviously, the mean value, $m = 4$, does not describe the three sets in Table 4-4 equally well. It represents set (2) perfectly and set (3) the least well. We need, therefore, some measure of the spread or dispersion of a set of variates about their mean. The first measure that might occur to us is the difference between the largest and smallest values. This is known as the *range*.

### 4.3.1.  The Range

DEFINITION 4-14.  For a set of numbers the *range* is the difference between the largest and smallest numbers.

DEFINITION 4-15.  For a frequency table the range is the difference between the upper boundary of the highest class and the lower boundary of the lowest class.

Although the range does give some indication of the spread of the data about the mean, it depends solely on extreme values, which may be purely

TABLE 4-4.  Three Sets of Variates Having Identical Means

| | (1) | | | | (2) | | | | (3) | | |
|---|---|---|---|---|---|---|---|---|---|---|---|
| X | X − m | \|X − m\| | (X − m)² | Y | Y − m | \|Y − m\| | (Y − m)² | Z | Z − m | \|Z − m\| | (Z − m)² |
| 3 | −1 | 1 | 1 | 4 | 0 | 0 | 0 | 10 | 6 | 6 | 36 |
| 5 | 1 | 1 | 1 | 4 | 0 | 0 | 0 | 1 | −3 | 3 | 9 |
| 6 | 2 | 2 | 4 | 4 | 0 | 0 | 0 | 0 | −4 | 4 | 16 |
| 3 | −1 | 1 | 1 | 4 | 0 | 0 | 0 | 0 | −4 | 4 | 16 |
| 3 | −1 | 1 | 1 | 4 | 0 | 0 | 0 | 9 | 5 | 5 | 25 |
| 20 | 0 | 6 | 8 | 20 | 0 | 0 | 0 | 20 | 0 | 22 | 102 |

| | | | |
|---|---|---|---|
| Mean | 4 | 4 | 4 |
| Range | 3 | 0 | 10 |
| Mean Deviation | 1.2 | 0 | 4.4 |
| Variance | 1.6 | 0 | 20.4 |
| Standard Deviation | 1.26 | 0 | 4.52 |

accidental, and tells us nothing about the distribution of the variates between these two extremes or the concentration of the variates about the center.

### 4.3.2. The Mean Deviation

A second measure which immediately suggests itself is the sum of the deviations of a set of variates from their mean. From Table 4-4 it appears that this expression, $\Sigma(X - m)$, may always be zero. This is easily shown to be the case for any set of $N$ variates.

**THEOREM 4-2.** The sum of the deviations of a set of variates from their mean is equal to zero.

*Proof.*

$$\sum_{i=1}^{N} (X_i - m) = \sum_{i=1}^{N} X_i - Nm = \sum_{i=1}^{N} X_i - N\left[\frac{\sum_{i=1}^{N} X_i}{N}\right] = \sum_{i=1}^{N} X_i - \sum_{i=1}^{N} X_i = 0.$$

Similarly, for a frequency distribution $\sum_{i=1}^{h} f_i(X_i - m) = 0$. (See exercise 26.) Although, as follows from Theorem 4-2, this expression is of no value in measuring the dispersion, it furnishes a useful device for checking the accuracy of a calculated mean.

Since for purposes of describing the dispersion it is immaterial whether a variate is at a certain distance above or below the mean, the sign of the deviation can be ignored. The average of the deviations, all taken as positive, therefore measures the dispersion of the data about the mean, and is called the *mean deviation*. Its definition involves the concept of *absolute value*, which for a number $a$ is denoted by $|a|$ and is defined as

$$|a| = \begin{cases} a \text{ if } a \geq 0 \\ -a \text{ if } a < 0 \end{cases}.$$

This means that $|a|$ is always nonnegative. Thus, for example, $|-7| = 7$, $|6| = 6$, $|0| = 0$.

**DEFINITION 4-16.** For a set of $N$ numbers, $X_1, X_2, X_3, \cdots, X_N$, whose mean is $m$, the *mean deviation*, denoted by $M.D.$ is defined as

(4-11) $$M.D. = \frac{\sum_{i=1}^{N} |X_i - m|}{N}.$$

More accurately, this measure should be called the mean absolute deviation, since the absolute values of the deviations from the mean are used in its calculation. In accordance with common usage we shall refer to it hereafter merely as the mean deviation.

*Example 4-10.*   Find the mean deviation of 11, 14, 17, 20, 16, 10.
*Solution.*   Since $m = 14.67$,

$M.D. =$

$$\frac{|11 - 14.67| + |14 - 14.67| + |17 - 14.67| + |20 - 14.67| + |16 - 14.67| + |10 - 14.67}{6}$$

$$= \frac{3.67 + 0.67 + 2.33 + 5.33 + 1.33 + 4.67}{6} = \frac{18.00}{6} = 3.00.$$

In this case, therefore, we can say that, on the average, the variates differ by 3.00 from the mean.

It is customary to denote the difference $X_i - m$ by $x_i$; i.e.,

$$(4\text{-}12) \qquad\qquad x_i = X_i - m.$$

The mean deviation may then be written as

$$(4\text{-}13) \qquad\qquad M.D. = \frac{\sum\limits_{i=1}^{N} |x_i|}{N}.$$

**DEFINITION 4-17.**   If in a frequency table the class midpoints are $X_1, X_2, \cdots, X_h$, and the respective frequencies are $f_1, f_2, \cdots, f_h$, then the mean deviation is defined as

$$(4\text{-}14) \qquad M.D. = \frac{\sum\limits_{i=1}^{h} |X_i - m| f_i}{N} = \frac{\sum\limits_{i=1}^{h} |x_i| f_i}{N},$$

where

$$N = \sum_{i=1}^{h} f_i.$$

*Example 4-11.*   Find the mean deviation for the data of Table 4-1.
*Solution.*   Since $m = 18.13$, we find the absolute values of the deviations as listed in the fourth column of Table 4-5, and the products of these values with their respective frequencies in the fifth column. (The last two columns of Table 4-5 are not needed in this example.)

Consequently,

$$M.D. = \frac{440.86}{90} = 4.90.$$

The mean deviation includes all the variates, is easy to define, and is easy to compute. It gives due weight to extreme cases. Its disadvantage is its unsuitability for algebraic manipulations, since signs must be adjusted in its definition. For example, there is no shorter method of calculating the mean

TABLE 4-5.    Calculation of Mean Deviation and Standard Deviation for the Data of Table 4-1

| (1) | (2) | (3) | (4) | (5) | (6) | (7) |
|---|---|---|---|---|---|---|
| Class Boundaries | X | f | $\|X - m\|$ | $\|X - m\|f$ | $(X - m)^2$ | $(X - m)^2 f$ |
| 7.5–10.5 | 9 | 12 | 9.13 | 109.56 | 83.3569 | 1000.2828 |
| 10.5–13.5 | 12 | 10 | 6.13 | 61.30 | 37.5769 | 375.7690 |
| 13.5–16.5 | 15 | 15 | 3.13 | 46.95 | 9.7969 | 146.9535 |
| 16.5–19.5 | 18 | 19 | 0.13 | 2.47 | 0.0169 | 0.3211 |
| 19.5–22.5 | 21 | 12 | 2.87 | 34.44 | 8.2369 | 98.8428 |
| 22.5–25.5 | 24 | 14 | 5.87 | 82.18 | 34.4569 | 482.3965 |
| 25.5–28.5 | 27 | 3 | 8.87 | 26.61 | 78.6769 | 236.0307 |
| 28.5–31.5 | 30 | 0 | 11.87 | 0.00 | 140.8969 | 0.0000 |
| 31.5–34.5 | 33 | 4 | 14.87 | 59.48 | 221.1169 | 884.4676 |
| 34.5–37.5 | 36 | 1 | 17.87 | 17.87 | 319.3369 | 319.3369 |
|  |  |  |  | 440.86 |  | 3544.4010 |

deviation, as was the case for the mean. Also, if the means and mean deviations of two sets of variates are known, there is no formula allowing the calculation of the mean deviation of the combined set without going back to the original data.

### 4.3.3.   The Variance and Standard Deviation

A method of converting positive and negative quantities into quantities which are all positive is the process of squaring. The average of the squared deviations from the mean, called the *variance,* is used as a measure of dispersion.

DEFINITION 4-18.   For a set of $N$ numbers, $X_1, X_2, X_3, \cdots, X_N$, whose mean is $m$, the *variance,* denoted by $\sigma^2$, is defined as

(4-15)
$$\sigma^2 = \frac{\sum\limits_{i=1}^{N} (X_i - m)^2}{N} = \frac{\sum\limits_{i=1}^{N} x_i^2}{N},$$

where

$$x_i = X_i - m.$$

The variance is a widely used measure of dispersion in statistical analysis. It is expressed in units which are the squares of the original units. For many purposes it is desirable that a measure of dispersion be expressed in the same units as the original variates and their mean. Such a measure of dispersion is the standard deviation, which is obtained by taking the square root of the variance.

**DEFINITION 4-19.** The square root of the variance is called the *standard deviation* and is defined as

(4-16)
$$\sigma = \sqrt{\frac{\sum\limits_{i=1}^{N}(X_i - m)^2}{N}} = \sqrt{\frac{\sum\limits_{i=1}^{N} x_i^2}{N}}.$$

*Example 4-12.* If $X_1 = 3$, $X_2 = 6$, $X_3 = 12$, find the standard deviation.
*Solution.* Since $m = 7$,

$$\sigma = \sqrt{\frac{(3-7)^2 + (6-7)^2 + (12-7)^2}{3}} = \sqrt{\frac{42}{3}} = \sqrt{14} = 3.74.$$

**DEFINITION 4-20.** If in a frequency table the class midpoints are $X_1, X_2, \cdots, X_h$, and the respective frequencies are $f_1, f_2, \cdots, f_h$, then the standard deviation is defined as

(4-17)
$$\sigma = \sqrt{\frac{\sum\limits_{i=1}^{h}(X_i - m)^2 f_i}{N}} = \sqrt{\frac{\sum\limits_{i=1}^{h} x_i^2 f_i}{N}},$$

where

$$N = \sum_{i=1}^{h} f_i.$$

*Example 4-13.* Find the standard deviation for the data of Table 4-1.
*Solution.* The values of $(X - m)^2$ and $(X - m)^2 f$ needed for the calculation of $\sigma$ are listed in the last two columns of Table 4-5; we find

$$\sigma = \sqrt{\frac{3544.4010}{90}} = \sqrt{39.38} = 6.28.$$

It is not as easy to grasp the meaning of a standard deviation as that of a mean deviation, since the standard deviation is not the mean of a set of deviations. On the other hand, the standard deviation has the very remarkable property that in many frequency distributions (in particular the so-called normal distribution, which is discussed in Chapter 7) approximately two-thirds of the variates fall between $m - \sigma$ and $m + \sigma$. Thus, for example, if this property is true for the data of Table 2-4, approximately 60 (which is two-thirds of 90) variates should fall between $18.13 - 6.28 = 11.85$ and $18.13 + 6.28 = 24.41$. It can easily be verified from Table 2-3 that actually 58 variates fall within this range.

For many purposes it is convenient to write the standard deviation in the alternate forms

(4-18)
$$\sigma = \sqrt{\frac{\sum\limits_{i=1}^{h} X_i^2 f_i - \dfrac{\left(\sum\limits_{i=1}^{h} X_i f_i\right)^2}{N}}{N}},$$

or

(4-19)
$$\sigma = \frac{1}{N} \sqrt{N \sum_{i=1}^{h} X_i^2 f_i - \left( \sum_{i=1}^{h} X_i f_i \right)^2}.$$

*Proof of formulae (4-18) and (4-19).*

$$\sigma^2 = \frac{1}{N} \sum_{i=1}^{h} (X_i - m)^2 f_i = \frac{1}{N} \sum_{i=1}^{h} (X_i^2 f_i - 2m X_i f_i + m^2 f_i)$$

$$= \frac{1}{N} \left( \sum_{i=1}^{h} X_i^2 f_i - 2m \sum_{i=1}^{h} X_i f_i + Nm^2 \right)$$

$$= \frac{1}{N} \left[ \sum_{i=1}^{h} X_i^2 f_i - 2 \left( \frac{\sum_{i=1}^{h} X_i f_i}{N} \right) \left( \sum_{i=1}^{h} X_i f_i \right) + N \left( \frac{\sum_{i=1}^{h} X_i f_i}{N} \right)^2 \right]$$

$$= \frac{1}{N} \left[ \sum_{i=1}^{h} X_i^2 f_i - 2 \frac{\left( \sum_{i=1}^{h} X_i f_i \right)^2}{N} + \frac{\left( \sum_{i=1}^{h} X_i f_i \right)^2}{N} \right]$$

$$= \frac{1}{N} \left[ \sum_{i=1}^{h} X_i^2 f_i - \frac{\left( \sum_{i=1}^{h} X_i f_i \right)^2}{N} \right],$$

from which (4-18) is obtained by taking the square root of both sides. For-mula (4-19) follows from (4-18) by multiplying numerator and denominator of the fraction under the radical by $N$.

Formulae (4-18) and (4-19) are particularly suitable for machine calcula-tion of the standard deviation, since these formulae require only one subtrac-tion whereas formula (4-17) requires $h$ subtractions. They are, therefore, sometimes referred to as the *computing forms* of the standard deviation.

Since the calculation of $\sigma$ from its definition may be tedious if the number of classes is large, a faster method of calculation, employing an assumed mean, will be given. Let $A$ represent a class midpoint, to be used as assumed mean. Then $\sigma$ may be calculated by

(4-20)
$$\sigma = c \sqrt{\frac{\sum_{i=1}^{h} d_i^2 f_i - \frac{\left( \sum_{i=1}^{h} d_i f_i \right)^2}{N}}{N}},$$

or by

(4-21)
$$\sigma = \frac{c}{N} \sqrt{N \sum_{i=1}^{h} d_i^2 f_i - \left( \sum_{i=1}^{h} d_i f_i \right)^2},$$

where $c$ and $d_i$ have the same meanings as those given in the calculation of the mean by formula (4-4).

*Example 4-14.* Solve Example 4-13, using an assumed mean.

*Solution.* Using an assumed mean, $A = 18$, refer to the last column of

Table 4-1 for the values of $d^2f$. Substituting the total of this column and that of the $df$-column into (4-21) we obtain

$$\sigma = \frac{3}{90} \sqrt{90(394) - 16} = \frac{1}{30} \sqrt{35444} = 6.28.$$

The entries in the $d^2f$-column are most easily obtained by multiplying the respective numbers in the $d$- and $df$-columns together, e.g., $d_1^2 f_1 = d_1(d_1 f_1) = (-3)(-36) = 108$.

*Proof of formula (4-21).* As in the proof of (4-4), $X_i = A + cd_i$. Substituting this into (4-19) we obtain

$$\sigma^2 = \frac{1}{N^2}\left[ N \sum_{i=1}^{h} X_i^2 f_i - \left( \sum_{i=1}^{h} X_i f_i \right)^2 \right]$$

$$= \frac{1}{N^2}\left\{ N \sum_{i=1}^{h} (A + cd_i)^2 f_i - \left[ \sum_{i=1}^{h} (A + cd_i)f_i \right]^2 \right\}$$

$$= \frac{1}{N^2}\left\{ NA^2 \sum_{i=1}^{h} f_i + 2NAc \sum_{i=1}^{h} d_i f_i + Nc^2 \sum_{i=1}^{h} d_i^2 f_i - \left[ A \sum_{i=1}^{h} f_i + c \sum_{i=1}^{h} d_i f_i \right]^2 \right\}$$

$$= \frac{1}{N^2}\left[ N^2 A^2 + 2NAc \sum_{i=1}^{h} d_i f_i + Nc^2 \sum_{i=1}^{h} d_i^2 f_i - N^2 A^2 \right.$$

$$\left. - 2NAc \sum_{i=1}^{h} d_i f_i - c^2 \left( \sum_{i=1}^{h} d_i f_i \right)^2 \right]$$

$$= \frac{c^2}{N^2}\left[ N \sum_{i=1}^{h} d_i^2 f_i - \left( \sum_{i=1}^{h} d_i f_i \right)^2 \right],$$

from which (4-21) is obtained by taking the square root of both sides.

The variance and standard deviation have all the advantages of the mean deviation, and in addition are suitable for algebraic work. This, for example, explains the existence of a short method for calculating the standard deviation. It also makes possible the derivation of a formula (see exercise 31) which allows the calculation of the standard deviation of a set of variates, obtained by combining two sets of variates, whose respective means and standard deviations (or variances) are known. The variance and standard deviation are therefore by far the most frequently used measures of dispersion.

# Exercises

1. For the set of numbers 6.5, 8.3, 4.7, 9.2, 11.3, 8.5, 9.5, 9.2, calculate to two decimal places

(a) the mean;                              (c) the mean deviation;
(b) the median;                            (d) the standard deviation.

2. Given the following frequency distribution:

| Class Boundaries | Frequencies |
| --- | --- |
| 10– 30 | 5 |
| 30– 50 | 8 |
| 50– 70 | 12 |
| 70– 90 | 18 |
| 90–110 | 3 |
| 110–130 | 2 |

Find to two decimal places
(a) the mean, using the definition;
(b) the mean, using an assumed mean;
(c) the median;
(d) the modal class;
(e) the mean deviation;
(f) the standard deviation, using the definition;
(g) the standard deviation, using an assumed mean.

3. Measurements of the lengths, in feet, of 50 iron rods are distributed as
follows:

| Class Boundaries | Frequencies |
| --- | --- |
| 2.35–2.45 | 1 |
| 2.45–2.55 | 4 |
| 2.55–2.65 | 7 |
| 2.65–2.75 | 15 |
| 2.75–2.85 | 11 |
| 2.85–2.95 | 10 |
| 2.95–3.05 | 2 |

Answer the questions given for exercise 2.

4. A set of 6 cards is shaken in a box and dropped on a table 100 times. The
number of cards ($X$) falling face up and the corresponding frequencies ($f$)
are as follows:

| $X$ | 0 | 1 | 2 | 3 | 4 | 5 | 6 |
| --- | --- | --- | --- | --- | --- | --- | --- |
| $f$ | 2 | 10 | 24 | 35 | 22 | 6 | 1 |

Find (a) the mean, and (b) the standard deviation, for this distribution.

5. Given the following frequency distribution:

| Class Boundaries | Frequencies |
|:---:|:---:|
| 15–25 | 4 |
| 25–35 | 11 |
| 35–45 | 19 |
| 45–55 | 14 |
| 55–65 | 0 |
| 65–75 | 2 |

Find to two decimal places
(a) the mean, without using an assumed mean;
(b) the mean, using an assumed mean;
(c) the median class;
(d) the median;
(e) the modal class;
(f) the mean deviation;
(g) the standard deviation, using an assumed mean.

6. From the frequency table obtained in exercise 5, Chapter 2, find to two decimal places
(a) the mean, using the definition;
(b) the mean, using an assumed mean;
(c) the median;
(d) the modal class;
(e) the mean deviation;
(f) the standard deviation, using the definition;
(g) the standard deviation, using an assumed mean.

7. Given the frequency distribution

| Class Boundaries | Frequencies |
|:---:|:---:|
| 0.5– 3.5 | 2 |
| 3.5– 6.5 | 3 |
| 6.5– 9.5 | 6 |
| 9.5–12.5 | 7 |
| 12.5–15.5 | 1 |
| 15.5–18.5 | 0 |
| 18.5–21.5 | 1 |

Find
(a) the mean, without using an assumed mean;
(b) the mean, using an assumed mean;

(c)  the median class;
(d)  the modal class;
(e)  the mean deviation;
(f)  the variance, without using an assumed mean;
(g)  the variance, using an assumed mean.

8. In two sections of a mathematics course the following distributions of grades are obtained:

| Section 1 | | Section 2 | |
|---|---|---|---|
| Range of Grades | Frequencies | Range of Grades | Frequencies |
| 80–89 | 4 | 90–99 | 2 |
| 70–79 | 10 | 80–89 | 6 |
| 60–69 | 18 | 70–79 | 12 |
| 50–59 | 9 | 60–69 | 20 |
| 40–49 | 5 | 50–59 | 10 |
| 30–39 | 2 | 40–49 | 2 |

Note: Any class not listed indicates that there are no scores in that class.

Find
(a)  the mean of Section 1;
(b)  the mean of Section 2;
(c)  the mean of the whole group, using formula (4-5).

9. Make up a frequency table for the whole group consisting of the two sections in exercise 8, and from this table find for the whole group
(a)  the mean;
(b)  the mean deviation;
(c)  the standard deviation.

10. If the mean of 75 items is 52.6 gallons and the mean of 25 items is 48.4 gallons, find the mean of the 100 items.

11. Of 500 freshmen, whose mean height is 67.8 inches, 150 are girls. If the mean height of the 150 girls is 62.0 inches, what is the mean height of the boys?

12. A group of 200 students whose mean height is 60.96 inches is divided into two groups, one having a mean height of 63.4 inches, the other having a mean height of 57.3 inches. How many students are there in each of the two groups?

13. In a test given to two sections of a mathematics course the average grade is 60.98. Section 1 has a mean of 57.30, section 2 a mean of 65.30. If there are 27 students in section 1, how many students are there in section 2?

14. In an athletic competition in which 45 participants are entered, 20 compete on the first day, the others on the second day. If the group of 20 participants on the first day scores an average of 48.4 points, what is the smallest average number of points the remaining group of participants has to score on the second day in order for the average score of the 45 participants to be at least equal to 55.0?

15. Three sets of data having $N_1$, $N_2$, $N_3$ variates, respectively, and means $m_1$, $m_2$, $m_3$, respectively, are combined into a single set. Prove that the mean $m$ of this set is

$$m = \frac{m_1 N_1 + m_2 N_2 + m_3 N_3}{N_1 + N_2 + N_3}.$$

16. A group of 100 athletes is transported across the country on two airplanes. The first airplane carries 40 athletes, the second the remaining 60. It is known that the average weight of all the athletes is 186.3 pounds, and that the average weight of the athletes on the second airplane is 10 pounds less than the average of those on the first airplane. What is the average weight of the athletes on each of the two airplanes?

17. In a final examination given to three sections of a mathematics class totaling 91 students the average grade of all students was 69.3. The averages for sections 1 and 2 were 70.4 and 64.2, respectively. Records giving the number of students in each section and the average grade of section 3 were lost, but the instructors of sections 1 and 2 remember that they had exactly the same number of students while the instructor of section 3 recalls that he had 5 students less than section 1. What was the average grade for section 3?

18. On a certain examination the average grade of all students in class $A$ is 68.4 and of all students in class $B$ is 71.2. If the average of both classes combined is 70.0, what is the ratio of the number of students in class $A$ to the number in class $B$?

19. The population of the United States from 1910 to 1950 is given in the following table.

| Year | Population (in millions) |
|------|--------------------------|
| 1910 | 92.0 |
| 1920 | 105.7 |
| 1930 | 122.8 |
| 1940 | 131.7 |
| 1950 | 150.7 |

Calculate the geometric mean of these data.

20. The amount of $2000 is invested at 5% on January 1, 1959. If interest is added annually on January 1 to this amount, calculate the average amount invested between January 1, 1959, and December 31, 1963.

21. On July 1, 1960, $5000 is placed into a savings account at 4% interest, compounded semiannually. Find the average amount deposited in the savings account between July 1, 1960, and December 31, 1962, if no withdrawal is made from the account in this period.

22. A man makes an automobile trip lasting 4 days. Each day he travels 8 hours. If the first day he drives at 50 miles per hour, the second day at 52, the third day at 58, and the last day at 60 miles per hour, what is his average speed for the trip?

23. A salesman makes a trip by car lasting 4 days. If he travels 200 miles each day, but drives the first and last days at 50 miles per hour, the second at 55, and the third at 60 miles per hour, what is his average speed on the trip?

For a set of $N$ numbers, $X_1, X_2, X_3, \cdots, X_N$, whose mean is $m$, prove in exercises 24 and 25 that

24. $\Sigma(X + 2m)^2 - 8Nm^2 = \Sigma X^2$.

25. $\Sigma X(X - m)^2 - m\Sigma(m - 2X)X = \Sigma X^3$.

26. In a frequency distribution $X_1$ occurs with frequency $f_1$, $X_2$ occurs with frequency $f_2$, and so on. Prove that

$$\sum_{i=1}^{h} (X_i - m)f_i = 0,$$

where $m$ is the mean and $h$ is the number of classes.

27. If for a set of $N$ values of $X$ it is known that $\Sigma X = 10$, $\Sigma X^2 = 260$, and $\sigma^2 = 25$, find $N$. (Hint: See Example 3-4.)

28. The mean of a set of 10 variates is 3 and the sum of their squares is 100. Find the standard deviation of the set.

29. For a set of $N$ values of $X$, it is known that $\Sigma X^2 = 1360$, $\Sigma X = 40$, $N\sigma^2 = 1280$; find $N$.

30. Prove that the geometric mean of two nonnegative numbers is never greater than their arithmetic mean.

31. A set of $N_1$ variates has mean $m_1$ and standard deviation $\sigma_1$, while another set of $N_2$ variates has mean $m_2$ and standard deviation $\sigma_2$. If the two sets are combined into a single set, prove that the variance of this set, which we shall denote by $\sigma^2$, is given by

$$\sigma^2 = \frac{N_1\sigma_1^2 + N_2\sigma_2^2 + N_1(m_1 - m)^2 + N_2(m_2 - m)^2}{N_1 + N_2},$$

where $m$ is the mean of the combined set.

# 5    Elementary Probability, Permutations, and Combinations

## 5.1.   Definition of Probability

Experience resulting from repeated experiments or from recurrent observations is frequently used to predict the outcome of future events. If we toss a properly balanced coin we can predict with certainty that, excluding the possibility of the coin-on-edge event, it will fall with either a head or a tail showing. We say that the chance of its showing heads for a single toss is 50:50, or that it will probably show heads about one-half of the time. From past and present knowledge of weather conditions in a particular locality we may say that it will probably be warm tomorrow or that there is a probability of rain. In this sense we are using the word probability to denote a belief founded on a certain amount of evidence and in many cases, no doubt, influenced by considerable wishful thinking. In mathematical usage the meaning of the word probability is established by definition and is not connected with beliefs or any form of wishful thinking.

Statistics and probability are so fundamentally interrelated that it is impossible to discuss statistics without an understanding of the meaning of probability. A knowledge of probability theory makes it possible to interpret statistical results, since many statistical procedures involve conclusions based on samples which are always affected by random variation, and it is by means of probability theory that we can express numerically the inevitable uncertainties in the resulting conclusions.

Before defining probability let us consider an example. In studying the effect of seed treatments on emergence of cotton seedlings it is necessary to know the per cent of emergence or viability of untreated seed. To find this we might start by planting 100 untreated cotton seeds and counting the seedlings which emerge. If 49 seeds germinate, that is, if there are 49 successes (by *success* in statistics we mean the occurrence of the event under discussion) in 100 trials, we say that the relative frequency of success (number of successes divided by number of trials) is 0.49. Next let us plant 200 seeds, and suppose that out of these 103 germinate, resulting in a relative frequency of $103 \div 200 = 0.515$. If we continue by planting more and more seeds, a whole sequence of values for the respective relative frequencies is obtained. If these relative frequencies approach a limiting value, we call this limit the probability of success in a single trial. From the data of Table 5-1 it appears that the relative frequencies are approaching the value 0.52, which we would then call the probability of a cotton seedling emerging from an untreated seed.

TABLE 5-1.   Relative Frequency of Emergence of Cotton Seedlings from Untreated Seed

| Number of Trials (n) | Number of Successes (s) | Relative Frequency (s/n) |
|---|---|---|
| 100 | 49 | 0.49 |
| 200 | 103 | 0.515 |
| 500 | 262 | 0.524 |
| 1000 | 517 | 0.517 |
| 10,000 | 5193 | 0.5193 |

We now can formulate a definition of probability.

> DEFINITION 5-1.   If the number of successes in $n$ trials is denoted by $s$, and if the sequence of relative frequencies $s/n$ obtained for larger and larger values of $n$ approaches a limit, then this limit is defined as the *probability of success in a single trial*.

In actual practice a probability is frequently taken as the relative frequency for the largest number of trials for which the experiment has been performed. Thus, for the data of Table 5-1, if the experiment was performed for 10,000 untreated cotton seeds, but not for any larger number, we might take the corresponding relative frequency 0.5193 as the probability of a cotton seedling emerging from an untreated seed. We will also find it convenient for other purposes--for example, for the understanding and proving of theorems on probability—to think of probability as the relative frequency applicable to a large, but finite, number of trials. While this is not strictly accurate, it will never lead us to a wrong conclusion, and will enable us to avoid a discussion of limits, which is beyond the scope of this text.

In many cases, notably in games of chance, the probability may be stated without collecting data on frequencies. Without making trials we can say that the probability of getting a head in tossing a properly balanced coin is $\frac{1}{2}$.

We make this statement since, in tossing a properly balanced coin, only two events are possible—namely head or tail—and both these events are equally likely to occur. Similarly, even before throwing an honest die, we can say that the probability of any particular face being on top is $\frac{1}{6}$, since, if we throw one, there are six equally likely events which can occur. For any such cases, in which successes or failures constitute a finite number of equally likely events, the following definition of probability is appropriate.

> **DEFINITION 5-2.** If an event can happen in $s$ ways and fail to happen in $f$ ways, and if each of these $s + f$ ways is equally likely to occur, the probability of success (the event happening) in a single trial is
>
> $$p = \frac{s}{s+f},$$
>
> and the probability of failure is
>
> $$q = \frac{f}{s+f}.$$

It should be pointed out that this definition is in a sense circular in nature, since the expression "equally likely to occur" itself involves the concept of probability. However, since this term is generally intuitively understood, the concept of "equally likely" will be left undefined. A precise definition of probability without this deficiency can be given in terms of elementary notions concerning sets. Since these notions may, however, not be familiar to the reader, this definition is omitted here.

Definition 5-2 clearly is a special case of Definition 5-1. Thus, the probability of getting a head in the toss of a well-balanced coin can be obtained from either of these definitions. Obviously it is much easier to obtain the probability from the second definition, since in a toss of a coin a head can occur only in $s = 1$ way and a tail in $f = 1$ way, and both ways are equally likely to occur; thus

$$p = \frac{1}{1+1} = \frac{1}{2}.$$

If we use Definition 5-1 we would have had to toss the coin many times and record the number of heads. Clearly, the limit of the ratio of the number of heads to the number of tosses would approach for a larger and larger number of trials the value $\frac{1}{2}$.

From Definition 5-2 we see that

$$p + q = \frac{s}{s+f} + \frac{f}{s+f} = \frac{s+f}{s+f} = 1.$$

Since an event either happens or fails to happen, certainty must be expressed by unity. From either of the definitions it should be observed that a probability is a number never greater than 1 nor less than 0. If $p = 0$, the event cannot happen at all.

*Example 5-1.*   From a bag containing 7 black balls and 4 white balls a ball is drawn at random. What is the probability that it is white?

*Solution.*   A white ball may be drawn in four different ways, and each of the 11 balls has an equal chance of being drawn; therefore

$$s = 4, f = 7, \text{ and } p = \tfrac{4}{11}.$$

Hence, the probability of drawing a white ball is $\tfrac{4}{11}$.

*Example 5-2.*   In a single throw of two dice what is the probability of getting

(a) a total of 9;

(b) a total different from 9?

*Solution.*   (a) A total of 9 can be obtained as follows: $6 + 3, 3 + 6, 5 + 4$, $4 + 5$, where the first number is the face showing on the first die and the second number is that on the second die. Therefore, there are four possible ways to get a total of 9 out of 36 equally likely ways in which two dice can fall, and the probability of getting a total of 9 is

$$p = \tfrac{4}{36} = \tfrac{1}{9}.$$

(b) It is certain that the faces of the two dice total 9 or a number different from 9, and therefore the probability of getting a total other than 9 is

$$q = 1 - \tfrac{1}{9} = \tfrac{8}{9}.$$

This result could have been obtained by enumeration. If there are four ways out of 36 of getting a total of 9, there must be 32 ways of getting a total different from 9, and therefore the probability of getting a total different from 9 is

$$q = \tfrac{32}{36} = \tfrac{8}{9}.$$

Although students of mathematics should always be encouraged to guess the answer to a problem before solving it, it should be pointed out that guessing answers to a probability problem is hazardous, since answers to such problems frequently are completely different from what intuition might indicate. The following example and Example 5-10 serve to illustrate this point. In both, the reader is advised not to look at the solution until he has made a guess or, to lend added emphasis to the point, let some of his friends make a guess.

*Example 5-3.*   A hat-check girl checks the hats of 100 men going to a theater. Accidentally she mixes these hats up completely. Not willing to admit her error, she hands back these 100 hats to the men as they leave the theater, completely at random, hoping that at least some will get their own hats back. What is the probability that at least one of these men gets his own hat back?

Solution. In order to understand this problem better, let us first solve it for the case in which 100 is replaced by 2 everywhere in the example, that is, where only 2 men go to the theater. To list successes and failures, let us denote by $A$ the first man leaving the theater, by $B$ the second man leaving the theater, by $H_A$ the hat belonging to $A$, and by $H_B$ the hat belonging to $B$. Then there are two equally likely possibilities when the hat-check girl returns the hats:

$$H_A H_B$$
$$H_B H_A.$$

In the first, since $A$ leaves the theater first, both $A$ and $B$ get their own hats back, in the second neither, so that $s = 1$, $f = 1$, and $p = \frac{1}{2}$.

Now let us look at the problem for the case in which 100 is replaced by 3 everywhere in the example. Again, let us denote by $A$ the first man leaving the theater, by $B$ the second, and by $C$ the third. Then there are the following equally likely possibilities when the girl returns the hats:

$$H_A H_B H_C$$
$$H_A H_C H_B$$
$$H_B H_A H_C$$
$$H_B H_C H_A$$
$$H_C H_A H_B$$
$$H_C H_B H_A.$$

Of these, the first, second, third, and sixth are successes, since in each of these at least one of the men receives his own hat back; for example, in the sixth, because $B$ leaves the theater second he receives his own hat back. Thus, there are four successes and two failures and

$$p = \tfrac{4}{6} = \tfrac{2}{3}.$$

At this stage, the reader is undoubtedly amazed at the high probabilities that were obtained and is prepared to guess that, since the probability has increased from $\frac{1}{2}$ to $\frac{2}{3}$ as we increased the number of men entering the theater from 2 to 3, it will increase further as we consider the case in which 4 men enter the theater. Not so, however. As the reader may verify himself (see Exercise 7), the probability for this case turns out to be lower than $\frac{2}{3}$. The following table shows the probability of at least one man getting his own hat back for increasing numbers of men entering the theater.

| Number of Men | *Probability of at Least One Man Getting His Own Hat Back* |
|:---:|:---:|
| 2 | 0.5000 |
| 3 | 0.6667 |
| 4 | 0.6250 |
| 5 | 0.6333 |
| 6 | 0.6319 |
| 7 | 0.6321 |
| 8 | 0.6321 |

As this table indicates, the probability alternately increases and decreases and stabilizes at a value of 0.6321, if we consider four-decimal accuracy. If these values were indicated to a higher degree of accuracy, it would be seen that the feature of alternating increases and decreases continues indefinitely.

It is clear that the solution of this problem for increasing numbers of men by the indicated procedure of listing all possible successes and failures becomes increasingly tedious. Methods that allow a much more rapid calculation of the solution are available.

## 5.2.   Expectation

DEFINITION 5-3.   If $p$ is the probability of the occurrence of an event in a single trial, then the *expected number of occurrences* or *expectation* of that event in $n$ trials is defined as $np$.

*Example 5-4.*   In 900 trials of a throw of two dice, what is the expected number of times that the sum will be less than 5?

*Solution.*   To find the probability $p$ of obtaining a total less than 5 in a single throw of two dice, we use Definition 5-2 and find that $s = 6$, $s + f = 36$, so $p = \frac{6}{36} = \frac{1}{6}$, and the expected number of times the total will be less than 5 in 900 trials is $\frac{1}{6} \cdot 900 = 150$.

The expectation is easily seen to be the most likely number of successes to occur in $n$ trials. Thus, in Example 5-4 the most likely event is that there will be 150 throws with sum less than 5. This, however, does not mean that this event must happen when two dice are thrown 900 times; in fact, it does not even mean that this event is very likely to happen. It does mean that this event (150 throws with sum less than 5) is more likely to occur than other events. If the probability $p$ has been determined as the relative frequency in $n$ trials, then the expectation in these $n$ trials is easily seen to equal the actual number of successes in these $n$ trials. Thus, if the probability of emergence of cotton seedlings from untreated seed, as taken from the last line of Table 5-1, is 0.5193, then the expectation in 10,000 trials is $0.5193 \cdot 10.000 = 5193$, which equals the actual number of seedlings which emerged.

**DEFINITION 5-4.** If $p$ is the probability that a person will win $m$ dollars, his *expectation* is defined as $mp$.

*Example 5-5.* What is the expectation of a person who is to receive $80 if he obtains 3 heads in a single toss of 3 coins?

*Solution.* In a single trial, if $H$ stands for head and $T$ for tail, the following possibilities exist: $HHH, HHT, HTH, THH, HTT, THT, TTH, TTT$. Therefore, $s = 1$, $s + f = 8$, and $p = \frac{1}{8}$. Then the expectation is $\frac{1}{8} \cdot 80 = \$10$.

We may say that a player's expectation $mp$ is the fair price to pay per game for the privilege of playing. When the player pays more per game than $mp$ he is sure to lose if he plays long enough, and if he pays less per game he is certain to come out ahead in the long run. The analysis of all games of chance requires the evaluation of the player's expectation.

## 5.3. Three Elementary Probability Laws

Probability laws are useful for faster calculation of probabilities. The first of these laws requires the following definition.

**DEFINITION 5-5.** If two or more events are such that not more than one of them can occur in a single trial, they are said to be *mutually exclusive*.

In a single draw from a deck of playing cards the two events of obtaining an ace and obtaining a king are mutually exclusive, whereas the two events of drawing an ace and drawing a spade are *not* mutually, exclusive since in a particular draw a card may be both an ace and a spade.

**THEOREM 5-1.** If $p_1, p_2, p_3, \cdots, p_r$ are the separate probabilities of the occurrence of $r$ mutually exclusive events, the probability $P$ that some *one* of these events will occur in a single trial is

(5-1)                         $P = p_1 + p_2 + p_3 + \cdots + p_r.$

*Example 5-6.*   Find the probability of drawing an ace, king, or queen from a regular 4-suit, 52-card deck of cards.

*Solution.*   The probability $p_1$ of drawing an ace in a single trial is $\frac{4}{52} = \frac{1}{13}$; the probability $p_2$ of drawing a king is $\frac{1}{13}$; and the probability of drawing a queen is $\frac{1}{13}$. Since these events are mutually exclusive, the probability of drawing an ace or a king or a queen is

$$P = \tfrac{1}{13} + \tfrac{1}{13} + \tfrac{1}{13} = \tfrac{3}{13},$$

which could also have been found directly from the definition of probability.

*Proof of Theorem 5-1.*   Consider a large number of trials $n$. For the purposes of this proof it is most convenient to think of $n$ as the number of trials from which the probabilities $p_1$, $p_2$, $\cdots$, $p_r$ have been determined as relative frequencies so that the expected numbers of occurrences (see Definition 5-3) of each of these $r$ events is equal to its actual number of occurrences. To determine the total number of successes we first indicate in the $n$ boxes of Figure 5-1 the results of the $n$ trials. The order of the trials is indicated by the numbers in the boxes; thus, the result of the first trial is marked in box number 1. A cross ($\times$) in a

Fig. 5-1.   Number of occurrences of $r$ mutually exclusive events in $n$ trials.

box indicates the occurrence of the first event, a circle (O) the occurrence of the second event, two horizontal lines (=) the occurrence of the third event, and so on.

Then the expected (or, in this case, also actual) number of occurrences for the first event, whose probability is $p_1$, is equal to $p_1 n$ or the number of boxes marked with a cross; similarly, the expected number of occurrences for the second event is $p_2 n$ or the number of boxes marked with a circle; and the expected number of occurrences for the third event is $p_3 n$ or the number of boxes marked with two horizontal lines, and so on. Note that no box will have more than one mark, i.e., a box will contain either one mark or no mark at all; this is guaranteed by the fact that the events are mutually exclusive.

Now the total number of successes (success in this case happens if some one of the events occurs) is equal to the total number of marked boxes, i.e., $s = p_1 n + p_2 n + \cdots + p_r n$; consequently, in accordance with the definition of probability,

$$P = \frac{s}{n} = \frac{p_1 n + p_2 n + \cdots + p_r n}{n} = p_1 + p_2 + \cdots + p_r.$$

This derivation makes it clear why Theorem 5-1 is not applicable if the events are not mutually exclusive. It also suggests how to modify this theorem for that case. Consider two events which are not mutually exclusive; let $p_1$ and $p_2$ be their separate probabilities and $p_{1,2}$ the probability that both events will occur together in a single trial. Then from a figure corresponding to Figure 5-1 the expected number of occurrences of either the first or the second event, or of both events, is given by the number of boxes marked with a cross plus the number of boxes marked with a circle minus the number of those which have been counted twice (i.e., those marked with a cross and a circle), or $s = p_1 n + p_2 n - p_{1,2} n$. Consequently, in this case

$$(5\text{-}2) \qquad P = \frac{s}{n} = \frac{p_1 n + p_2 n - p_{1,2} n}{n} = p_1 + p_2 - p_{1,2}.$$

Since we shall be primarily interested in events which are mutually exclusive, we shall make no further use of (5-2).

Before stating the second probability law we require the following definition.

**DEFINITION 5-6.** Two or more events are said to be *independent* if the probability of occurrence of any of them is not influenced by the occurrence of any other. Otherwise the events are *dependent*.

If a die is tossed twice, the occurrence of a 3 on the first throw and the occurrence of a 5 on the second throw are independent events. If, however, two cards are drawn in succession from a deck of cards without replacement, the appearance of an ace on the first draw and the appearance of a king on the second are not independent events, since the probability of getting a king on the second draw depends on what happened on the first draw. If after the first draw the card is replaced, then the outcome of the second draw is independent of the result of the first draw.

**THEOREM 5-2.** If $p_1$, $p_2$, $p_3$, $\cdots$, $p_r$ are the separate probabilities of the occurrence of $r$ independent events, the probability $P$ that *all* of these events will occur in a single trial is

$$(5\text{-}3) \qquad\qquad\qquad P = p_1 p_2 p_3 \cdots p_r.$$

*Example 5-7.* What is the probability of obtaining three heads in a single toss of three coins?

*Solution.*   The probability of obtaining a head with the first coin is $p_1 = \frac{1}{2}$; similarly, $p_2 = \frac{1}{2}$, and $p_3 = \frac{1}{2}$. These events are independent, and the probability of tossing three heads with three coins is

$$P = \tfrac{1}{2} \cdot \tfrac{1}{2} \cdot \tfrac{1}{2} = \tfrac{1}{8}.$$

Compare the result with that in Example 5-5.

*Proof of Theorem 5-2.*   Again let $n$ be a large number of trials, most conveniently thought of as the number of trials from which the probabilities $p_1, p_2, \cdots, p_r$ have been determined as relative frequencies. As in the proof of Theorem 5-1, we first indicate in the $n$ boxes of Figure 5-2 the results of the $n$ trials, again using crosses, circles, or two horizontal lines to mark the boxes for which the first, second, third, and so on, event occurred.

Fig. 5-2.  Number of occurrences of $r$ independent events in $n$ trials.

The expected (or actual) number of occurrences of the first event is again equal to $p_1 n$. Since success in this case requires that all events occur, we can exclude from further consideration all boxes except those marked with a cross, since for all boxes without a cross the first event did not occur and therefore cannot be included among the successes. Now among the $p_1 n$ boxes marked with a cross we must single out those for which also the second event occurred, i.e., those which also are marked with a circle. Since the probability of occurrence of the second event, $p_2$, is the same for boxes marked with a cross and for boxes without a cross (here we use the fact that the events are independent), we find the expected number of occurrences of the second event among the $p_1 n$ boxes to be $p_2(p_1 n) = p_1 p_2 n$, which equals the expected number of occurrences of the first two events. Clearly, the expected number of occurrences of the third event among these $p_1 p_2 n$ boxes is $p_3(p_1 p_2 n) = p_1 p_2 p_3 n$. Continuing this process, it is seen that the expected number of occurrences of all $r$ events is $s = p_1 p_2 \cdots p_r n$; thus, in accordance with the definition of probability,

$$P = \frac{s}{n} = \frac{p_1 p_2 \cdots p_r n}{n} = p_1 p_2 \cdots p_r.$$

Note that the main distinction between Theorems 5-1 and 5-2 is that in the former we are interested in the occurrence of the first *or* the second *or* the third, and so on, event, whereas in the latter we desire the occurrence of the first *and* the second *and* the third, and so on, event. Generally, therefore, a probability problem involving *or* requires the addition of the probabilities of the events (provided of course that they are mutually exclusive); a problem involving *and*, on the other hand, requires the multiplication of the probabilities of the events (provided that they are independent).

**THEOREM 5-3.** In the case of $r$ dependent events, if the probability of the occurrence of a first event is $p_1$, and if, after this event has occurred, the probability of the occurrence of a second event is $p_2$, and if, after the first and second events have occurred, the probability of the occurrence of a third event is $p_3$, and so on, the probability $P$ that all events will occur in the specified order is

(5-4) $$P = p_1p_2p_3 \cdots p_r.$$

*Example 5-8.* From a deck of 52 cards a card is withdrawn at random and not replaced. A second card is then drawn. What is the probability that the first card is an ace and the second a king?

*Solution.* The probability of getting an ace on the first draw is $p_1 = \frac{1}{13}$ and of getting a king on the second draw, after an ace has been withdrawn, is $p_2 = \frac{4}{51}$. Therefore, the desired probability is

$$P = \frac{1}{13} \cdot \frac{4}{51} = \frac{4}{663}.$$

This means that in a long run of drawing two cards in a row, when the first card drawn is not replaced, an ace followed by a king will occur only 4 in 663 times or about once in 166 trials.

*Proof of Theorem 5-3.* The proof of this theorem is almost identical to that of Theorem 5-2. Again using Figure 5-2, we consider the $p_1n$ boxes marked with a cross, i.e., those for which the first event occurred. As before, all boxes not marked with a cross can be ruled out from further consideration. Restricting ourselves therefore to the $p_1n$ boxes with a cross, we need to determine the expected number among them for which the second event occurred. Since $p_2$ in this case was defined exactly for these boxes, i.e., those for which the first event had occurred, we find the expected number of occurrences of the second event among these $p_1n$ boxes to be $p_2(p_1n) = p_1p_2n$. The completion of this proof is now evident.

Frequently Theorem 5-2 is considered a special case of Theorem 5-3. Obviously, Theorem 5-3 is applicable also to independent events, since in that case $p_2$, for example, is the same whether or not the first event has occurred, and so, for independent events, Theorem 5-3 becomes Theorem 5-2. In general, however, it is more convenient to think of these two theorems as two separate probability laws.

In solving probability problems the work will be greatly simplified if we proceed as follows:

1. List all mutually exclusive events which are successes for the problem.
2. For each of the above listed events determine the probability.
3. Add all of the probabilities obtained in step 2.
4. If desirable, check the result by listing the failures for the problem.

This procedure is illustrated in the following three examples.

*Example 5-9.* The probability that a certain beginner at golf gets a good shot if he uses the correct club is $\frac{1}{3}$, and the probability of a good shot with an incorrect club is $\frac{1}{4}$. In his bag are 5 different clubs, only one of which is correct for the shot in question. If he chooses a club at random and takes a stroke, what is the probability that he gets a good shot?

*Solution.* In accordance with step 1 of the procedure stated above, we list the two events which are successes; next we list on the same lines their corresponding probabilities.

(a) Right club, good shot:  $p_1 = \frac{1}{5} \cdot \frac{1}{3} = \frac{1}{15} = \frac{1}{15}.$
(b) Wrong club, good shot:  $p_2 = \frac{4}{5} \cdot \frac{1}{4} = \frac{1}{5} = \frac{3}{15}.$
$$\frac{4}{15}$$

Since either of these cases will result in a good shot, i.e., success, we need to add the probabilities of the two events:

$$P = \tfrac{1}{15} + \tfrac{3}{15} = \tfrac{4}{15}.$$

We can now check this result by listing the cases which are failures together with their respective probabilities.

(c) Right club, poor shot:  $p_3 = \frac{1}{5} \cdot \frac{2}{3} = \frac{2}{15} = \frac{2}{15}.$
(d) Wrong club, poor shot:  $p_4 = \frac{4}{5} \cdot \frac{3}{4} = \frac{3}{5} = \frac{9}{15}.$
$$\frac{11}{15}$$

Since the probability of failure, $\frac{11}{15}$, and the probability of success, $\frac{4}{15}$, total 1, our result checks.

In some problems the number of situations which are failures may be considerably less than the number of situations which are successes. In such cases it is more convenient to determine the probability of failure and subtract it from 1 to obtain the probability of success. The following is a typical example.

*Example 5-10.*   What is the probability that among 23 randomly selected people at least two have birthdays falling on the same day, that is, on the same month and day (not necessarily the same year)?

*Solution.*   Here failure occurs only if all 23 people have birthdays falling on different days of the year. Let us, therefore, calculate this probability. We shall assume that each year has 365 days and that the probability of a person having a birthday on any of these days is the same. Now all 23 people will have different birthdays if all of the following 23 dependent events occur: the first person has a birthday on any day of the year, which occurs, of course, with probability 1; the second person has a birthday on any day of the year except the one on which the first person has his birthday, for which the probability is $\frac{364}{365}$; the third person has a birthday on any day of the year except those of the first two, for which the probability is $\frac{363}{365}$, and so on. Therefore the probability $Q$ that all 23 people have different birthdays, in accordance with Theorem 5-3, is found to be

$$Q = 1 \cdot \tfrac{364}{365} \cdot \tfrac{363}{365} \cdot \tfrac{362}{365} \cdots \tfrac{343}{365} = 0.493,$$

so that the desired probability $P$ that at least two people have birthdays falling on the same day is given by

$$P = 1 - 0.493 = 0.507.$$

This means that the chance is better than even that among 23 people in a room at least two have the same birthday, a result few people would guess. Even more surprising is the fact that this probability increases very rapidly with increasing numbers of people in the room, as shown in the following table.

| Number of People | Probability of at Least 2 People Having the Same Birthday |
|:---:|:---:|
| 20 | 0.411 |
| 21 | 0.444 |
| 22 | 0.476 |
| 23 | 0.507 |
| 24 | 0.569 |
| 30 | 0.706 |
| 40 | 0.891 |
| 50 | 0.970 |
| 60 | 0.994 |

These probabilities were all calculated on the assumption that the probability of a person's birthday falling on any one day of the year is equal to that for any other day. In reality, this is not true, and the actual probabilities involved are even larger than those given in the table.

There are also problems in which there are infinitely many situations that are successes, such as the following.

*Example 5-11.* $A$, $B$, and $C$ in order toss a coin. The first one to throw a head wins. What are their respective chances of winning?

*Solution.* Let us first determine the probability that $A$ will win; we shall denote this probability by $P_A$. If $H$ stands for head and $T$ for tail, then the following situations will mean success for $A$ (note that $TTTH$ means that $A$, $B$, and $C$ all obtained tails on their first throws, but $A$ obtained a head on the second round):

$$
\begin{aligned}
H \qquad\qquad & p_1 = \tfrac{1}{2} \\
TTTH \qquad\qquad & p_2 = \tfrac{1}{2}\cdot\tfrac{1}{2}\cdot\tfrac{1}{2}\cdot\tfrac{1}{2} = \tfrac{1}{16} \\
TTTTTTH \qquad\qquad & p_3 = \tfrac{1}{2}\cdot\tfrac{1}{2}\cdot\tfrac{1}{2}\cdot\tfrac{1}{2}\cdot\tfrac{1}{2}\cdot\tfrac{1}{2}\cdot\tfrac{1}{2} = \tfrac{1}{128} \\
\vdots \qquad\qquad & \vdots
\end{aligned}
$$

To obtain the desired probability we need to add the probabilities of these mutually exclusive events, i.e.,

$$ P_A = \tfrac{1}{2} + \tfrac{1}{16} + \tfrac{1}{128} + \cdots. $$

This is an infinite geometric series and we recall that for such a series

$$ a + ar + ar^2 + ar^3 + \cdots = \frac{a}{1-r}, $$

where $r$, the ratio between any two consecutive numbers, is between $-1$ and $1$. In this case, therefore, since $a = \tfrac{1}{2}$, $r = \tfrac{1}{8}$,

$$ P_A = \frac{\tfrac{1}{2}}{1 - \tfrac{1}{8}} = \frac{\tfrac{1}{2}}{\tfrac{7}{8}} = \tfrac{1}{2}\cdot\tfrac{8}{7} = \tfrac{4}{7}. $$

The calculation of $P_B$ and $P_C$ is left as an exercise (see exercise 97).

## 5.4. Conditional Probability

We have seen how Theorem 5-3 can be applied to calculate the probability $P$ of the occurrence of two dependent events, say $A$ and $B$, if we know the probability $p_1$ of the occurrence of the event $A$, and the probability $p_2$ of the occurrence of the event $B$ after the event $A$ has occurred. Thus, in Example 5-8, we found the probability of obtaining an ace and a king when withdrawing two cards from a deck of 52 cards to be

$$ P = p_1 p_2 = \tfrac{1}{13}\cdot\tfrac{4}{51} = \tfrac{4}{663}. $$

Now consider the problem in which we are given the fact that the event $A$ has occurred and we wish to find the probability $p_2$ of the occurrence of the event $B$. For example, let us find the probability $p_2$ of withdrawing a king after an ace has been withdrawn. This problem can be solved in two ways: either by noting that after an ace has been withdrawn, there are 4 kings left among the remaining 51 cards so that $p_2 = \frac{4}{51}$ or by solving the equation

$$P = p_1 p_2$$

for $p_2$, so that

(5-5)
$$p_2 = \frac{P}{p_1},$$

from which we obtain

$$p_2 = \frac{\frac{4}{663}}{\frac{1}{13}} = \frac{4}{51}.$$

**DEFINITION 5-7.** The probability of the occurrence of an event $B$, given that an event $A$ has occurred, is called the *conditional probability* of the occurrence of the event $B$.

To indicate the events involved we shall now use $P(B|A)$, instead of $p_2$, as notation for the probability of the occurrence of an event $B$, given that an event $A$ has occurred. To indicate the probability of the occurrence of an event $B$, when we do not know whether another event has occurred, we shall simply write $P(B)$.

The probability $P(B)$, therefore, is the probability of the occurrence of an event $B$ before any experiments have taken place; accordingly it is called a *prior* or an *a priori* probability. On the other hand, the probability $P(B|A)$ represents the probability of the occurrence of an event $B$ after some experimentation has taken place—namely, after it has become known that the event $A$ has occurred—accordingly, it is called a *posterior* or an *a posteriori* probability.

In terms of the notation just introduced, formula (5-5) can be written as

(5-6)
$$P(B|A) = \frac{P(AB)}{P(A)},$$

where $P(AB)$ denotes the probability of the occurrence of both events $A$ and $B$.

In many problems, it is of interest to calculate an *a posteriori* probability from given *a priori* probabilities. Such a formula was first stated by the English clergyman Thomas Bayes, who died in 1761, but whose now famous formula was not published until 1763. It is stated in the following theorem.

**THEOREM 5-4.** If $B_1, B_2, \cdots, B_n$ are $n$ mutually exclusive events, of which some one must occur in a given trial, that is, $P(B_1) + P(B_2) + \cdots + P(B_n) = 1$, and $A$ is any event for which $P(A) \neq 0$, then the conditional probability $P(B_i|A)$ for any one of the events $B_i$, given that the event $A$ has occurred, is given by

$$P(B_i|A) = \frac{P(B_i)P(A|B_i)}{P(B_1)P(A|B_1) + P(B_2)P(A|B_2) + \cdots + P(B_n)P(A|B_n)}.$$

This formula is known as *Bayes' theorem, Bayes' law,* or *Bayes' formula.* It is a useful formula, but its applicability is limited by the fact that in many cases the *a priori* probabilities involved in the formula are unknown.

*Example 5-12.* In Example 5-9, if it is known that a good shot has resulted, what is the probability that the right club was used?

*Solution.* Let $A$ represent the event of obtaining a good shot, $B_1$ the event of selecting the right club, and $B_2$ that of selecting the wrong club. Then $P(B_1) = \frac{1}{5}$, $P(B_2) = \frac{4}{5}$, $P(A|B_1) = \frac{1}{3}$, $P(A|B_2) = \frac{1}{4}$ and, using Bayes' formula,

$$P(B_1|A) = \frac{P(B_1)\,P(A|B_1)}{P(B_1)\,P(A|B_1) + P(B_2)\,P(A|B_2)} = \frac{\frac{1}{5} \cdot \frac{1}{3}}{\frac{1}{5} \cdot \frac{1}{3} + \frac{4}{5} \cdot \frac{1}{4}} = \frac{\frac{1}{15}}{\frac{4}{15}} = \frac{1}{4}.$$

One can conclude that only one out of four good shots can be attributed solely to use of the right club.

This example might have been solved, without use of Bayes' formula, as follows. In $n$ trials, the expected number of good shots with the right club is $\frac{1}{5} \cdot \frac{1}{3}\,n = \frac{1}{15}\,n$, and the expected number of all good shots is $(\frac{1}{5} \cdot \frac{1}{3} + \frac{4}{5} \cdot \frac{1}{4})n = \frac{4}{15}\,n$. Therefore, the probability that the right club was used is that proportion of the expected number of good shots in which the right club was used, namely

$$P(B_1|A) = \frac{\frac{1}{15}\,n}{\frac{4}{15}\,n} = \frac{1}{4}.$$

In this case, knowledge that the shot was good has increased the probability from $P(B_1) = \frac{1}{5}$ to $P(B_1|A) = \frac{1}{4}$. In other problems, the added information may result in a decrease in the probability obtained.

*Proof of Theorem 5-4.* The probability of the joint occurrence of two events $A$ and $B_i$, where $B_i$ is any one of the events $B_1, B_2, \cdots, B_n$, in accordance with formula (5-6), may be written as

$$P(AB_i) = P(A)\,P(B_i|A) = P(B_i)\,P(A|B_i),$$

from which it follows, if $P(A) \neq 0$, that

(5-7)
$$P(B_i|A) = \frac{P(B_i)\,P(A|B_i)}{P(A)}.$$

Now, since $B_1$, $B_2$, $\cdots$, $B_n$ are $n$ mutually exclusive events of which some one must occur in a given trial, we have

(5-8) $P(A) = P(AB_1) + P(AB_2) + \cdots + P(AB_n)$
$$= P(B_1)\,P(A|B_1) + P(B_2)\,P(A|B_2) + \cdots + P(B_n)\,P(A|B_n).$$

Substituting this value of $P(A)$ in the denominator of formula (5-7) yields Bayes' Theorem.

Formula (5-7) is, of course, an alternative version of Bayes' formula and one which is easier to remember. Indeed, it is usually best to calculate $P(A)$ separately first by use of formula (5-8) and then substitute the result into formula (5-7). This is illustrated in Example 5-13.

*Example 5-13.* Three automatic machines produce similar automotive parts. Machine $A$ produces 40% of the total, machine $B$, 25%, and machine $C$, 35%. On the average, 10% of the parts turned out by machine $A$ do not conform to the specification, and for machines $B$ and $C$ the corresponding percents are 5% and 1%, respectively. If one part is selected at random from the combined output and is found not to conform to the specifications, what is the probability that it was produced by machine $A$?

*Solution.* Let $D$ represent the event of selecting a defective part. We need to determine the probability, $P(A|D)$, of the part having been selected from machine $A$, assuming that the part was defective, which, according to formula (5-7), is given by

$$P(A|D) = \frac{P(A)\,P(D|A)}{P(D)}.$$

Now, $P(D)$, the probability of obtaining a defective part, is given—just as was shown in Section 5.3—as the sum of the following probabilities:

$$P(DA) = P(A)\,P(D|A) = (0.40)(0.10) = 0.0400$$
$$P(DB) = P(B)\,P(D|B) = (0.25)(0.05) = 0.0125$$
$$P(DC) = P(C)\,P(D|C) = (0.35)(0.01) = \underline{0.0035}$$
$$0.0560.$$

Therefore,

$$P(A|D) = \frac{(0.40)(0.10)}{0.0560} = 0.714,$$

which shows that on the average machine $A$ produces 71.4% of the defective parts.

## 5.5.  Combinations and Permutations

Combinations and permutations deal with the grouping and arrangement of objects, and in calculating probabilities they are useful in determining the number of favorable cases as well as the total number of possible cases.

**DEFINITION 5-8.** Each of the sets which can be made by using all or part of a given collection of objects, without regard to order of the objects in the set, is called a *combination*.

**DEFINITION 5-9.** Each different ordering or arrangement of all or part of a set of objects is called a *permutation*.

*Example 5-14.*  Find
(a) the number of combinations,
(b) the number of permutations
of the letters $A, B, C, D$ in sets of 3.

*Solution.*  (a) The letters $A, B, C, D$ can be taken in sets of 3, without regard to order, in the following ways: $ABC, ABD, ACD$, and $BCD$. Therefore, there are four such combinations, i.e., there are four combinations of four objects taken 3 at a time.

(b) If ordering is considered also, there are the following permutations of the letters $A, B, C, D$ in sets of 3: $ABC, ACB, BAC, BCA, CAB, CBA, ABD,$ $ADB, BAD, BDA, DAB, DBA, ACD, ADC, CAD, CDA, DAC, DCA, BCD,$ $BDC, CBD, CDB, DBC, DCB$. Therefore, there are 24 such permutations; i.e., there are 24 permutations of four objects taken 3 at a time.

*Example 5-15.*  Find
(a) the number of combinations,
(b) the number of permutations
of four objects taken four at a time.

*Solution.*  (a) Since all 4 objects have to be used in the set, there is only one such combination in this case.

(b) The number of orderings of the 4 letters $A, B, C, D$ is easily found to be 24, thus there are 24 permutations of 4 objects taken four at a time.

To find simple formulae for the number of combinations and permutations, we shall first consider the special case of finding the number of permutations of $n$ objects (say letters) in sets of $n$ items.

To write all such permutations we observe that we have $n$ choices for the first letter; to each of these corresponds one of the "trees" of Figure 5-3, which represents the case $n = 4$. After having chosen the first letter

Fig. 5-3.   The permutations of A, B, C, D.

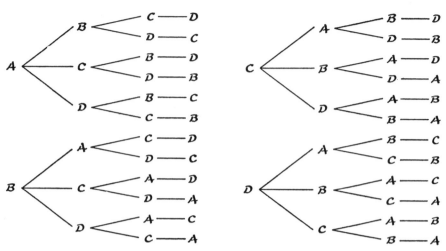

(say, for example, $A$) we have $n - 1$ choices left for the second letter; thus, for the first two letters there are $n(n - 1)$ possible choices, i.e., as many choices as there are branches emanating from the left tips of the trees of Figure 5-3. Now, after the first two letters have been chosen there remain $n - 2$ choices for the third letter, so there are $n(n - 1)(n - 2)$ choices for the first three letters. Continuing this process, we see that there is only one choice left for the $n$th letter; consequently, the $n$ letters can be arranged in $n(n - 1)(n - 2) \cdots (2)(1)$ ways.

If the symbol $n!$ (read "$n$ *factorial*") denotes the product of the first $n$ integers, i.e.,

(5-9)                     $$n! = n(n - 1)(n - 2) \cdots (2)(1),$$

and $P_{n,n}$ denotes the number of permutations of $n$ objects arranged in sets of $n$, we have shown that

(5-10)                     $$P_{n,n} = n!$$

*Example 5-16.*   Solve part (b) of Example 5-15 by use of formula (5-10).

*Solution.*   In this case we need the number of permutations of 4 objects in sets of 4, i.e., $P_{4,4}$, and we find

$$P_{4,4} = 4! = 4 \cdot 3 \cdot 2 \cdot 1 = 24,$$

which agrees with the result found directly from the definition of permutations in the solution to Example 5-15 (b).

To develop a formula for the number of permutations of $n$ things taken $r$ at a time, we consider the special case of 4 objects arranged in sets of 3. In this case there are 4 choices for the first letter (again see Figure 5-3), and after the first letter has been chosen there are 3 choices left for the second letter; thus, for the first 2 letters there are $(4)(3) = 12$ possible choices. Now, for the third letter there remain 2 choices, so there are $(4)(3)(2) = 24$ choices of 3 letters out of a total of 4. This shows that, in general, if we denote the number of permutations of $n$ objects taken $r$ at a time by $P_{n,r}$, we need to take the product of the $r$ numbers $n, n - 1, n - 2, \cdots$ , or

$$\overbrace{}^{r \text{ factors}}$$

(5-11)        $P_{n,r} = \overbrace{n(n - 1)(n - 2) \cdots (n - r + 1)}.$

If we multiply and divide the right-hand side of (5-11) by

$$(n - r)(n - r - 1) \cdots (2)(1),$$

the numerator becomes $n!$; thus we can write

(5-12)        $P_{n,r} = \dfrac{n!}{(n - r)!}.$

*Example 5-17.* Solve part (b) of Example 5-14 by use of formula (5-11).
*Solution.* Here $n = 4$, $r = 3$, so

$$P_{4,3} = \frac{4!}{1!} = 4 \cdot 3 \cdot 2 = 24,$$

which agrees with the result found directly from the definition in the solution to Example 5-14 (b).

To develop a formula for the number of combinations of $n$ things taken $r$ at a time, we note that for every set of $r$ letters there is just one combination if all $r$ letters are to be used, whereas there are $r!$ permutations of these $r$ letters. Thus, there are $r!$ times as many permutations of $n$ objects taken $r$ at a time as there are combinations of $n$ objects taken $r$ at a time. This shows that, if we denote the number of combinations of $n$ objects taken $r$ at a time by $C_{n,r}$, we have

(5-13)        $C_{n,r} = \dfrac{n!}{r!(n - r)!},$

or, if we divide numerator and denominator by $(n - r)!$,

(5-14)        $C_{n,r} = \dfrac{n(n - 1)(n - 2) \cdots (n - r + 1)}{r!}.$

The following notations are also used for $C_{n,r}$: $C_r{}^n$, $C_r^n$, $^nC_r$, $_nC_r$, $C(n,r)$, $\binom{n}{r}$.
*Example 5-18.* Solve part (a) of Example 5-14 by use of formula (5-13).
*Solution.* Here $n = 4$, $r = 3$, so by use of formula (5-13)

$$C_{4,3} = \frac{4!}{3!1!} = \frac{4 \cdot 3 \cdot 2 \cdot 1}{3 \cdot 2 \cdot 1 \cdot 1} = 4,$$

which agrees with the result found directly from the definition in the solution to Example 5-14 (a).

The main difficulty encountered in problems involving permutations and combinations is deciding whether the problem involves the number of permutations or the number of combinations. In solving such problems it is advisable to determine first whether a change of order in the objects would make a difference in the desired result; if it does, the number of permutations is desired; if it does not, the number of combinations is wanted.

*Example 5-19.* A student body president is asked to appoint a committee consisting of 5 boys and 3 girls. He is given a list of 10 boys and 7 girls from which to make the appointments. From how many possible committees must he make his selection?

*Solution.* In a particular committee, if the order of the appointees is changed, the result would still be the same committee, so this is a problem involving combinations. From 10 boys the student body president can select

$$C_{10,5} = \frac{10!}{5!5!} = 252$$

groups of 5 boys. From 7 girls he can select

$$C_{7,3} = \frac{7!}{3!4!} = 35$$

groups of 3 girls. Therefore, for each of the 252 selections of boys there are 35 possible choices of girls; thus the total number of possible committees is equal to

$$(252)(35) = 8820.$$

Note that in Example 5-19 we assumed no distinction between the various positions in the committee. However, if the committee is to consist of a president, vice-president, secretary, treasurer, etc., that is, if each of the eight positions of the committee has a different designation and we wish to differentiate also between the various possible assignments of the members of the committee to these positions, we must, of course, calculate the number of permutations.

## 5.6. Repeated Trials

If, during repeated trials, the probability of success in a single trial remains fixed, the calculation of the probability of obtaining a given number, say $r$,

of successes in these $n$ trials can be greatly simplified. We shall demonstrate
this for the case where we toss a coin several times (or toss several coins once)
by listing the probabilities involved as in Table 5-2, where $H$ represents a

**TABLE 5-2.   Results of Repeated Trials in Coin Tossing**

| Number of Tosses | Enumeration of Possible Results | Probabilities Corresponding to These Results | Expansion Whose Terms Correspond to These Probabilities |
|---|---|---|---|
| 1 | T, H | $q, p$ | $(q + p)^1 = q + p$ |
| 2 | TT, TH, HT, HH | $q^2, qp, qp, p^2$ | $(q + p)^2 = q^2 + 2qp + p^2$ |
| 3 | TTT, TTH, THT, HTT, THH, HTH, HHT, HHH | $q^3, q^2p, q^2p, q^2p, qp^2, qp^2, qp^2, p^3$ | $(q + p)^3 = q^3 + 3q^2p + 3qp^2 + p^3$ |
| . | | | |
| . | | | |
| . | | | |
| $n$ | | | $(q + p)^n = q^n + nq^{n-1}p + \cdots + p^n$ |

head, $T$ a tail, and $p = \frac{1}{2}$ the probability of obtaining a head, $q = \frac{1}{2}$ the probability of obtaining a tail.

Table 5-2 clearly suggests that, in $n$ tosses of a coin, the probabilities of
the various possible events (i.e., obtaining 0, 1, 2, $\cdots$ , $n$ heads) are given by
the successive terms of the binomial expansion of $(q + p)^n$, which is

$$(q + p)^n = q^n + C_{n,1}q^{n-1}p + C_{n,2}q^{n-2}p^2 + \cdots + C_{n,r}q^{n-r}p^r + \cdots + p^n.$$

The coefficient $C_{n,r}$ represents the number of ways in which $n$ tosses of a
coin can produce exactly $r$ heads and $n - r$ tails, which, of course, is precisely
the same as the number of combinations of $n$ things taken $r$ at a time. The
term

$$C_{n,r}q^{n-r}p^r = C_{n,r}(\tfrac{1}{2})^{n-r}(\tfrac{1}{2})^r,$$

then, represents the probability that exactly $r$ heads and $n - r$ tails occur in
the $n$ tosses.

Thus, for example, the probability of obtaining exactly 2 heads in 3 tosses
of a coin is given by

$$C_{3,2}q^{3-2}p^2 = 3(\tfrac{1}{2})(\tfrac{1}{2})^2 = \tfrac{3}{8},$$

where the coefficient $C_{3,2} = 3$ corresponds to the 3 cases $THH, HTH, HHT$
(see Table 5-2) in which 2 heads can be obtained in 3 tosses of a coin.

Theorem 5-5 is a generalization of this discussion applying to any case involving a sample or series of $n$ trials, in each of which the probability of success
is fixed and remains fixed during the entire procedure.

**THEOREM 5-5.** If $p$ is the probability of the success of an event in a single trial and $q$ is the probability of its failure, then the probability $P$ that there will be exactly $r$ successes in $n$ trials is the term in the binomial expansion of $(q + p)^n$ for which the exponent of $p$ is $r$, i.e., $C_{n,r}q^{n-r}p^r$.

Recall that

$$(q + p)^n = q^n + nq^{n-1}p + \frac{n(n-1)}{2}\, q^{n-2}p^2 + \frac{n(n-1)(n-2)}{2 \cdot 3}\, q^{n-3}p^3 + \cdots$$

$$+ \frac{n(n-1)(n-2) \cdots (n-r+1)}{2 \cdot 3 \cdots r}\, q^{n-r}p^r + \cdots + p^n$$

$$= q^n + C_{n,1}q^{n-1}p + C_{n,2}q^{n-2}p^2 + \cdots + C_{n,r}q^{n-r}p^r + \cdots + C_{n,n}p^n.$$

A convenient way to obtain the coefficients of the binomial expansion is to note that each coefficient of the expansion can be obtained from the previous term as follows: Multiply the coefficient of the previous term by the exponent of $q$ and divide the result by one more than the exponent of $p$.

Thus, for example, in the expansion

$$(q + p)^8 = q^8 + 8q^7p + 28q^6p^2 + 56q^5p^3 + 70q^4p^4 + 56q^3p^5$$
$$+ 28q^2p^6 + 8qp^7 + p^8,$$

we obtain the coefficient of $q^6p^2$ from the term $8q^7p$ as $(8)(7)/2 = 28$, or the coefficient of $q^5p^3$ as $(28)(6)/3 = 56$, etc.

*Example 5-20.* Find the probability of getting 5 exactly twice in 7 throws of a die.

*Solution.* The probability of success (getting a 5) in a single trial is $p = \frac{1}{6}$, from which $q = \frac{5}{6}$. Since the number of trials $n$ is 7, and the required number of successes $r$ is 2, the desired probability is the term containing $p^2$ in the expansion of $(q + p)^7$, i.e., $C_{7,2}q^5p^2$.

Since

$$(q + p)^7 = q^7 + 7q^6p + 21q^5p^2 + \cdots + p^7,$$

we find

$$P = 21q^5p^2 = 21\left(\frac{5}{6}\right)^5\left(\frac{1}{6}\right)^2 = \frac{21875}{93312}.$$

*Example 5-21.* Find the probability of throwing at most 2 sixes in 6 throws with a single die.

*Solution.* To throw at most 2 sixes means that we must throw 0, 1, or 2 sixes. Therefore, the desired probability is the sum of the terms in the binomial expansion of $(q + p)^6$ for which the exponents of $p$ are 0, 1, and 2. Since

$$(q + p)^6 = q^6 + 6q^5p + 15q^4p^2 + \cdots + p^6,$$

we find

$$P = \left(\frac{5}{6}\right)^6 + 6\left(\frac{5}{6}\right)^5\left(\frac{1}{6}\right) + 15\left(\frac{5}{6}\right)^4\left(\frac{1}{6}\right)^2 = \frac{21875}{23328}.$$

*Example 5-22.*  It is known that 10% of certain articles manufactured are defective. What is the probability that in a random sample of 12 such articles at least 9 are defective?

*Solution.*  In this case $p = \frac{1}{10}$, $q = \frac{9}{10}$, $n = 12$. Since we are interested in at least 9 defective articles, we need the terms for which the exponents of $p$ are 9, 10, 11, and 12. In the expansion of $(q + p)^{12}$, these terms will occur at the end. In order to obtain these terms at the beginning of the expansion we note that $(q + p)^{12} = (p + q)^{12}$ and find

$$(p + q)^{12} = p^{12} + 12p^{11}q + 66p^{10}q^2 + 220p^9q^3 + \cdots + q^{12},$$

thus

$$P = \left(\frac{1}{10}\right)^{12} + 12\left(\frac{1}{10}\right)^{11}\left(\frac{9}{10}\right) + 66\left(\frac{1}{10}\right)^{10}\left(\frac{9}{10}\right)^2 + 220\left(\frac{1}{10}\right)^9\left(\frac{9}{10}\right)^3$$

$$= \frac{165835}{10^{12}} = \frac{33167}{(2)(10)^{11}}.$$

*Proof of Theorem 5-5.*  First determine the probability of obtaining $r$ consecutive successes, followed by $n - r$ consecutive failures. These $n$ events are independent; therefore, the desired probability is

$$\overbrace{p\cdot p \,\cdots\, p}^{r} \cdot \overbrace{q\cdot q \,\cdots\, q}^{n-r} = p^r q^{n-r}.$$

Since the $r$ successes and $n - r$ failures may occur in any order, it is necessary to count the number of such orders, which is the same as finding the number of ways of writing the product of $n$ factors, $r$ of which are $p$, and $n - r$ of which are $q$. This is precisely the number of combinations of $n$ things taken $r$ at a time, and it equals $C_{n,r}$. The desired probability is therefore

$$C_{n,r}p^r q^{n-r},$$

which is the term in the binomial expansion of $(q + p)^n$ for which the exponent of $p$ is $r$.

Note that Theorem 5-5 is not applicable if, during the repeated trials, the probability of success does not remain constant. This is the case if the probability of success in a trial is dependent upon the result of one of the previous trials, which makes the events dependent.

## Exercises

Express all answers representing probabilities as fractions in lowest terms.

1. A card is drawn at random from a deck of 52 playing cards. What is the probability that it is an ace or a face card?

2. If a die is rolled, what is the probability that the roll yields a 3 or 4?

3. If a die is rolled twice, what is the probability that the first roll yields a 5 or a 6, and the second anything but 3?

4. In a single throw of two dice, what is the probability that a doublet (two of the same number) or a 9 will appear?

5. In a single throw of two dice, what is the probability that neither a doublet nor a 9 will appear?

6. In a single throw of two dice, what is the probability that neither a doublet nor an 8 will appear?

7. Solve Example 5-3 for the case in which 4 men go to the theater.

8. Ten balls, numbered 1 to 10, are placed in a bag. One ball is drawn and not replaced, and then a second ball is drawn. What is the probability that
   (a) the balls numbered 3 and 7 are drawn;
   (b) neither of these two balls is drawn?

9. An urn contains 52 balls numbered 1 to 52. Suppose that numbers 1 through 13 are considered "lucky." Two balls are drawn from the urn without replacement. Find the probability that
   (a) both balls drawn are "lucky";
   (b) neither ball drawn is "lucky";
   (c) at least one of the balls drawn is "lucky";
   (d) exactly one of the balls drawn is "lucky."

10. In a bag there are 6 white and 5 black balls. If they are drawn out one by one without replacement, what is the chance that the first will be white, the second black, and so on alternately?

11. A bag contains 4 red, 3 green, and 5 black balls. We draw 5 balls in succession, replacing each ball before the next is drawn. Find the probability that we draw 2 red and 3 green balls.

12. On a slot machine there are three reels with the ten digits 0, 1, 2, 3, 4, 5, 6, 7, 8, 9, plus a star on each reel. When a coin is inserted and the handle is pulled, the three reels revolve independently several times and come to rest.
    (a) What is the probability of getting 3 stars?
    (b) What is the probability of getting a particular sequence of numbers?
    (c) What is the probability of getting the same number on each reel?

13. One man draws three cards from a well-shuffled deck without replacement, and at the same time another man tosses a coin. What is the probability of obtaining three cards of the same suit and a head?

14. Four men in turn each draw a card from a deck of 52 cards without replacing the card drawn. What is the probability that the first man draws the ace of spades, the second the king of diamonds, the third a king, and the fourth an ace?

15. A man owns a house in town and a cabin in the mountains. In any one year the probability of the house being burglarized is 0.01, and the probability of the cabin being burglarized is 0.05. For any one year what is the probability that
    (a) both will be burglarized;
    (b) one or the other (but not both) will be burglarized;
    (c) neither will be burglarized?

16. From a box containing 6 white balls and 4 black balls, 3 balls are drawn at random. Find the probability that 2 are white and 1 is black
    (a) if each ball is returned before the next is drawn;
    (b) if the 3 balls are drawn successively without replacement.

17. A person draws 3 balls in succession without replacement from a box containing 8 black, 8 white, and 8 red balls. If he is to receive $5 if he does not draw a black ball, what is his expectation?

18. Three people work independently at deciphering a message in code. The respective probabilities that they will decipher it are $\frac{1}{5}$, $\frac{1}{4}$, and $\frac{1}{3}$. What is the probability that the message will be deciphered?

19. The respective chances of three men to survive for one year are 0.9, 0.8, and 0.7. What is the probability that at least two will survive for one year?

20. The probability that a certain door is locked is $\frac{1}{2}$. The key to the door is one of 12 keys in a cabinet. If a person selects two keys at random from the cabinet and takes them to the door with him, what is the probability that he can open the door without returning for another key?

21. A father and son practice shooting at a target. If, on the average, the father hits the target 3 times out of 4, and the son hits it 4 times out of 7, what is the probability, when both shoot simultaneously, that the target is hit at least once?

22. A pair of dice is tossed twice. What is the probability that either a 7 or a 12 appears on the first throw, and that neither a doublet nor an 8 appears on the second throw?

23. Two like-appearing but genetically different flower seeds are planted, one in each of two pots numbered 1 and 2. The genetic models involved lead us to expect 3 red-flowered plants to 1 white-flowered plant from one of the seeds, and 1 red-flowered plant to 1 white-flowered plant from the other. Find the probability that
    (a) pot number 1 contains a white flower;
    (b) both pots contain red flowers;
    (c) pot number 1 contains a red flower and pot number 2 a white flower.

24. If 3 dice are thrown, find the probability that
    (a) all 3 will show fours;
    (b) all 3 will be alike;
    (c) 2 will show fours and the third something else;
    (d) only 2 will be alike;
    (e) all 3 will be different.

25. What is the probability of throwing at least 4 sevens in 5 throws of a pair of dice?

26. A bag contains 50 envelopes of which 10 contain $5 each, 10 contain $1 each, and the others are empty. What is our expectation in drawing a single envelope?

27. A, B, and C in the order named are allowed one throw each with three dice. The first one, if any, who throws an 11 gets $583.20. If each pays an amount equal to his expectation to participate in the game, how much should each pay?

28. A class in mathematics is composed of 15 juniors, 30 seniors, and 5 graduate students; 3 of the juniors, 5 of the seniors, and 2 of the graduate students received an A grade in the course. If a student is selected at random from the class and is found to have received an A grade, what is the probability that he is a junior?

29. Of 100 boxes of fuses, 5 fuses per box, 20 boxes contain fuses from factory

$A$, 30 boxes from factory $B$, and 50 boxes from factory $C$. Fuses from factory $A$ are, on the average, 5% defective; from factory $B$, 4%; and from factory $C$, 2%. The fuses and boxes all look alike and are piled without regard to place of manufacture. A box is selected at random, and a fuse in it is tested and found to be defective. What is the probability that it was produced at factory $B$?

30. Of the freshmen in a certain college, it is known that 18% attended private secondary schools and 82% attended public schools. The Dean's office reports that 30% of all students who attended private secondary schools and 15% of those who attended public schools attained grades high enough to be entered on the honors list. If one student is chosen at random from the freshman class and is found to be on the honors list, what is the probability that the student attended a public school?

31. Of those people voting in an election, 45% are registered Republicans, 40% Democrats, and 15% Independents. There are three candidates for office, a Republican $R$, a Democrat $D$, and an Independent $I$, and the party votes were distributed as follows:

|         | Republican | Democrat | Independent |
|---------|------------|----------|-------------|
| For $R$ | 80%        | 10%      | 15%         |
| For $D$ | 5%         | 85%      | 10%         |
| For $I$ | 15%        | 5%       | 75%         |

(a) If a voter is selected at random and is found to have voted for $I$, what is the probability that he is a Republican?
(b) Which candidate received the largest percentage of the vote?

32. Tests employed in the detection of a particular disease are 90% effective; they fail to detect it in 10% of the cases. In persons free of the disease, the tests indicate 1% to be affected and 99% not to be affected. From a large population, in which only 0.2% have the disease, one person is selected at random, is given the tests, and presence of the disease is indicated. What is the probability that the person is affected?

33. An urn contains 3 red marbles and 7 white marbles. A marble is drawn from the urn and a marble of the other color is then put into the urn. A second marble is drawn from the urn. If the two marbles drawn in this process are of the same color, what is the probability that they are both white?

34. Urn $A$ contains 3 red and 5 white marbles; urn $B$ contains 2 red and 1 white marble; urn $C$ contains 2 red and 3 white marbles. An urn is se-

lected at random, and a marble is drawn from the urn. If the marble is red, what is the probability that it came from urn $A$?

35. Suppose that the probability of a student passing an examination is $\frac{4}{5}$, that of the student sitting to his left $\frac{2}{3}$, and that of the student sitting to his right $\frac{1}{5}$. Assuming that none of these students looks at his neighbor's paper, find the probability that, of these three students,
    (a) exactly two pass the examination;
    (b) the student sitting in the middle passes the examination, given that the student on his right passes it.

36. Suppose that 5% of a student body ride bicycles and have accidents. If 75% of that student body ride bicycles, what is the probability of a bicycle rider from that student body having an accident?

37. How many four-digit numbers can be formed from the digits 1, 3, 5, 7, 8, and 9 if none of these appears more than once in each number?

38. In how many ways can 3 identical jobs be filled by selections from 12 different people?

39. A girl has invited 5 friends to a dinner party. After locating herself at the table how many different seating arrangements are possible?

40. From a bag containing 7 black and 5 white balls, how many sets of 5 balls of which 3 are black and 2 are white can be drawn?

41. From 7 men and 4 women, how many committees can be selected consisting of
    (a) 3 men and 2 women;
    (b) 5 people of which at least 3 are men?

42. From a bag containing 5 black and 7 white balls, how many sets of balls can be selected which include
    (a) exactly 2 black balls;
    (b) at most 2 black balls?

43. A company has 7 men qualified to operate a machine which requires 3 operators for each shift.
    (a) How many shifts are possible?
    (b) In how many of these shifts will any one man appear?

44. How many committees consisting of 3 representatives and 5 senators can be selected from a group of 5 representatives and 8 senators?

45. In how many seating arrangements can 8 men be placed around a table

if there are 3 who insist on sitting together? Consider two seating arrangements different unless each man sits in the same chair in the two arrangements.

46. A certain college has only 3-unit courses in 13 of which a freshman may enroll. Find the number of 15-unit programs a freshman can consider if
    (a) there are no specific requirements;
    (b) English 1 and History 1 are required courses.

47. A delegation of 4 students is selected each year from a college to attend the National Student Association annual meeting.
    (a) In how many ways can the delegation be chosen if there are 12 eligible students?
    (b) In how many ways if there are 2 particular students among these 12 who refuse to attend the meeting together?
    (c) In how many ways if 2 of the eligible students are married and will attend the meeting only if they can both go together?

48. A committee of 10 is to be selected from 6 lawyers, 8 engineers, and 5 doctors. If the committee is to consist of 4 lawyers, 3 engineers, and 3 doctors, how many such committees are possible?

49. In how many ways can a set consisting of 5 different books on mathematics, 3 on physics, and 2 on chemistry be arranged on a straight shelf that has space for 10 books if the books on each subject are to be kept together?

50. A stamp collector has 8 different Canadian stamps and 9 different United States stamps, all of the same size. Find the number of ways in which he can select 4 Canadian stamps and 3 United States stamps and arrange them in 7 numbered spaces in his stamp album.

51. A railway coach has 12 seats facing backward and 12 facing forward. In how many ways can 10 passengers be seated if 2 of these people are known to refuse to ride facing forward and 4 refuse to ride facing backward?

52. A coin is tossed 6 times. Find the probability of getting
    (a) exactly 4 heads;
    (b) at most 4 heads.

53. Seven dice are rolled. Calling a 5 or 6 a success, find the probability of getting

    (a) exactly 4 successes;
    (b) at most 4 successes.

54. In the manufacture of a certain article it is known that 1 out of 10 of the articles is defective. What is the probability that a random sample of 4 of the articles will contain
(a) no defectives;                    (c) exactly 2 defectives;
(b) exactly 1 defective;              (d) not more than 2 defectives?

55. If a man having a batting average of 0.40 comes to bat 5 times in a game, what is the probability that he will get
(a) exactly 2 hits;
(b) less than 2 hits?

56. In tossing 8 coins, what is the probability of obtaining less than 6 heads?

57. According to records in the registrar's office, 5% of the students in a certain course fail. What is the probability that out of 6 randomly selected students who have taken the course less than 3 failed?

58. Hospital records show that 10% of the cases of a certain disease are fatal. If 5 patients suffer from this disease, find the probability that
(a) all will recover;      (c) exactly 3 will die;
(b) at least 3 will die;   (d) a particular 3 will die and the others survive.

59. A student can solve on the average half the problems given him. In order to pass he is required to solve 7 out of 10 problems on an examination. What is the probability that he will pass?

60. In target practice a man is able, on the average, to hit a target 9 times out of 10. Find the probability that he
(a) hits exactly 4 times in 10 shots;
(b) hits the first 4 shots and misses all the rest.
(c) If 10,000 men, of skill equal to that of the man in parts (a) and (b), each have 4 shots, how many of them would you expect to make at least 3 hits?

61. Find the probability of obtaining the most probable number of heads, if a coin is tossed 6 times.

62. Find the probability of obtaining the most probable number of sixes if a die is rolled 5 times.

63. One bag contains 6 oranges and 5 grapefruit, and a second bag contains 8 grapefruit and 6 oranges. If a bag is selected at random and then one fruit is chosen at random, find the probability that an orange will be selected.

64. $A$ and $B$ play a game in which the probability that $A$ wins is $\frac{3}{8}$ and the probability that $B$ wins is $\frac{5}{8}$. $A$ and $B$ play a series of games, and the winner is to be the one who first wins 4 games. If $A$ and $B$ have each won twice, find the probability that $A$ wins the series.

65. In the World Series, teams $A$ and $B$ play until one team has won 4 games. If team $A$ has probability $\frac{2}{3}$ of winning against team $B$ in a single game, what is the probability that the Series will end only after 7 games are played?

66. $A$ plays in a series of games against $B$ such that the first to win 4 games wins the series. If $A$'s chance of winning a game against $B$ is $\frac{2}{3}$, and if $B$ has already won 2 games, find the probability that $A$ will win the series.

67. One bag contains 6 white balls and 3 black balls, and a second bag contains 7 white balls and 4 black balls. Two balls are selected at random, one from each of the bags, and are placed in a third bag containing 3 white and 3 black balls. One ball is now selected from this third bag; what is the probability that it is white?

68. You are given the option of drawing a bill from one of two boxes. In one box are 9 one-dollar bills, and 1 ten-dollar bill, and in the other box are 5 one-dollar bills, 3 ten-dollar bills, and 7 five-dollar bills. What is the probability that you will draw a ten-dollar bill?

69. Fourteen white and 14 black balls are distributed on two trays. A blindfolded man selects a tray at random and picks a ball from the tray. Under which of the following two arrangements are his chances of obtaining a white ball better: on each tray there are as many black as white balls, or on one tray there are 2 white balls and all other balls are on the other tray?

70. Urn $A$ contains 5 red balls and 5 black balls, urn $B$ contains 4 red balls and 8 black balls, and urn $C$ contains 3 red balls and 6 black balls. A ball is drawn from $A$, color unknown, and put into $B$. Then a ball is drawn from $B$, color unknown, and put into $C$. What is the probability that a ball now drawn from $C$ will be red?

71. One urn contains 4 red balls and 1 black ball. A second urn contains 2 white balls. Three balls are drawn at random from the first urn and placed in the second, and then 4 balls are drawn at random from the second urn and placed in the first. Find the probability that the black ball is in the first urn after these transfers are completed.

72. A bag contains 2 white balls and 3 black balls. A second bag contains 3 white balls and 2 black balls. A ball is drawn at random from the first bag and placed in the second, then a ball is drawn at random from the second bag and placed in the first. This entire operation is repeated. What is the probability that after these two exchanges the first bag will contain only black balls?

73. Six red poker chips and 2 white ones, all the same size, are thoroughly mixed and placed at random in a pile. What is the probability that
    (a) the 2 white ones are on top;
    (b) the white ones are third and fourth from the top;
    (c) the white ones are together;
    (d) the white ones are not together?

74. Find the probability that of the first 5 persons encountered on a given day at least 3 of them were born on a Saturday.

75. The probability that each of 5 fishermen will catch limits on any particular fishing trip is $\frac{1}{3}$.
    (a) What is the probability that at least 3 of these fishermen on any particular trip will return with limits?
    (b) What is the probability that the first 3 returning will each have a limit, and the others will not have limits?

76. On a certain multiple-choice examination, each question has 5 listed answers, of which one and only one is correct. There are 6 questions, all of equal weight, and a grade of $66\frac{2}{3}\%$ is required for passing. If a student selects the answer for each question at random, what is the probability that he will pass the examination?

77. A coin is tossed repeatedly. Find the probability that the fourth head appears on the eleventh toss.

78. Two dice are rolled repeatedly and a record is kept of the number of times a 9 is obtained. Find the probability that the third time a 9 is obtained occurs on the seventh roll of the two dice.

79. A die is rolled until a 1 occurs. What is the probability that
    (a) the first 1 occurs on the fourth toss;
    (b) more than two tosses are required.

80. A coin is tossed repeatedly. Find the probability that during this tossing it so happens that the fourth head appears on the eighth toss and the eighth head on the sixteenth toss.

81. A family has 6 children. Find the probability that there are fewer boys than girls. Assume that the probability of the birth of either sex is $\frac{1}{2}$.

82. Four statisticians arrange to meet at the Grand Hotel in Paris. It happens that there are 4 hotels with that name in the city. What is the probability that all the statisticians will choose different hotels?

83. If a die is rolled three times what is the probability of obtaining at least one 4 and at least one 5?

84. Six married couples are standing in a room. If 2 people are chosen at random, find the probability that
   (a) they are married to each other;
   (b) one is male and the other is female.

85. A committee of 5 is chosen at random from 6 married couples. What is the probability that the committee will not include 2 people who are married to each other?

86. A boy stands on a street corner and tosses a coin. If it falls heads, he walks one block east; if it falls tails, he walks one block west. At his new position he repeats the procedure. What is the probability that after having tossed the coin 6 times he is
   (a) at his starting point;
   (b) 2 blocks from his starting point;
   (c) 4 blocks from his starting point?

87. Five red books and 3 green books are placed at random on a shelf. Find the probability that the green books will all be together.

88. In a roll of 5 dice, what is the probability of getting exactly 4 faces alike?

89. At golf, $A$ defeats $B$ on the average of 2 times out of 5; $A$ defeats $C$ 5 times out of 6; $A$ defeats $D$ 7 times out of 10; and $C$ defeats $D$ 3 times out of 8. To win a tournament $A$ must defeat $B$ and the winner of a match between $C$ and $D$. If the prize for winning the tournament is $1000, what is $A$'s expectation?

90. At the end of the season a nursery puts on sale 10 peach trees from which the tags have fallen. It is known that 4 of the trees are of one variety and the rest are of another variety. A customer purchases 3 of the trees. What is the probability that the 3 are the same variety?

91. It is known that 4 out of 5 zebra-finch eggs hatch, 6 out of 7 fire-finch eggs hatch, and 11 out of 12 mallard eggs hatch. If one egg each is incubated, what is the probability that something will hatch?

92. Two zebra-finch eggs are in one nest, and 2 fire-finch eggs are in another nest. An egg is taken at random from each nest simultaneously and placed in the other nest. This exchange is performed once more. What is the probability that both eggs in the first nest hatch? (Use the data of Exercise 91.)

93. A bag contains 5 white balls and 4 black balls. $A$ and $B$ take turns in drawing one ball at a time without replacement until all balls are drawn. If $A$ draws first, what is the probability that $A$ will be the first to draw a black ball?

94. A bag contains 3 white marbles and 4 black ones. $A$, $B$, and $C$ in order withdraw a marble, without replacing it. The first to draw a white marble wins. What is $A$'s probability of winning the game?

95. Suppose two bad light bulbs get mixed up with five good ones and that you start testing the bulbs, one by one, until you have found both defectives. What is the probability that you will find the second defective bulb on the seventh testing?

96. Suppose we have four courts $c_1$, $c_2$, $c_3$, and $c_4$. An accused person must start in court $c_1$. If he is convicted in a lower court, he has the possibility of being heard in a higher court in the order $c_1$, $c_2$, $c_3$, $c_4$, but he cannot by-pass any court. The probabilities of winning a case are $\frac{1}{4}$, $\frac{1}{3}$, $\frac{1}{2}$, $\frac{1}{4}$ in the courts $c_1$, $c_2$, $c_3$, $c_4$, respectively. If a person loses his case in a court, the probabilities of a hearing in the next higher court are as follows: $\frac{1}{5}$ in $c_2$, $\frac{1}{4}$ in $c_3$, and $\frac{1}{8}$ in $c_4$. What is the probability that a person will be cleared of an accusation in these courts?

97. In Example 5-11, find the chances of each of $B$ and $C$ winning.

98. $A$, $B$, $C$, and $D$ in order toss a coin. The first one to throw a head wins. What are their respective chances of winning?

99. $A$ and $B$ in order toss a pair of dice. The first to obtain a 10 wins. What are their respective chances of winning?

100. $A$, $B$, and $C$ in order toss a pair of dice. The first to obtain a 7 wins. What are their respective chances of winning?

101. A professional tennis player, $A$, plays for a long period of time alternately against two amateurs, $B$ and $C$. If he has a chance of $\frac{15}{16}$ of winning against $B$, and $\frac{9}{10}$ against $C$, what is the probability that $C$ will be the first among the two amateurs to win against $A$, provided that the professional starts the series by playing against $B$?

102. If a die is thrown repeatedly, what is the probability that a 6 is obtained before a 1 turns up?

103. If two dice are thrown repeatedly, find the probability of obtaining a 9 before a 6 turns up.

104. The probability that a fertile egg hatches is $\frac{11}{12}$. Three eggs are taken for incubation from a box of 12 eggs, 4 of which are fertile and 8 infertile. What is the probability that something hatches from the 3 eggs?

105. The rules of the game of craps are the following: A player using two dice wins if he throws a 7 or 11 on the first throw. He loses if he throws 2, 3, or 12 on the first throw. If he throws 4, 5, 6, 8, 9, 10 on the first throw, then he wins if he repeats the result of his first throw before throwing a 7. What is the probability of winning in the game of craps?

# 6  The Binomial Distribution

For our present purposes it is convenient to restate Theorem 5-5 in the following form.

**THEOREM 6-1.** If $p$ is the probability of the success of an event in a single trial and $q$ is the probability of its failure, then the successive terms of the binomial expansion of $(q + p)^n$ give the respective probabilities of $0, 1, 2, \cdots, n$ successes in $n$ trials.

By means of Theorem 6-1 it is possible to construct a "theoretical frequency table" and the corresponding histogram for cases where the number of successes is obtained by the binomial theorem.

**DEFINITION 6-1.** If a frequency distribution is obtained by use of the binomial expansion, it is called a *binomial distribution*.

*Example 6-1.* If 9 coins are tossed $N$ times ($N$ a given number), construct the theoretical frequency table and the corresponding histogram for $0, 1, 2, \cdots, 9$ heads.

*Solution.* The expected frequencies for $0, 1, 2, \cdots, 9$ heads in $N$ tosses are listed in the second column of Table 6-1.

In the third column, the expected frequencies for $N = 512$ are listed ($N = 512$ was arbitrarily chosen in order to obtain simple numbers, i.e., integers), and in the fourth column are shown the actual frequencies obtained when 9 coins were tossed 512 times. It can be seen that there is good agreement between the actual and theoretical frequencies. The corresponding histogram for the theoretical frequencies is shown in Figure 6-1.

It should be noted that the histogram for a binomial distribution is symmetric if and only if $p = q = \frac{1}{2}$.

Since the widths of the rectangles in the histogram of a binomial distribution are equal to unity, the areas of the rectangles are equal in magnitude to their altitudes and, consequently, are measures of the frequencies of the

TABLE 6-1. Expected (binomial) and Actual Frequencies Obtained in Tossing 9 Coins N Times

| X | f | Expected f for N = 512 | Actual f for N = 512 |
|---|---|---|---|
| 0 | $\frac{1}{512} N$ | 1 | 2 |
| 1 | $\frac{9}{512} N$ | 9 | 11 |
| 2 | $\frac{36}{512} N$ | 36 | 37 |
| 3 | $\frac{84}{512} N$ | 84 | 88 |
| 4 | $\frac{126}{512} N$ | 126 | 131 |
| 5 | $\frac{126}{512} N$ | 126 | 119 |
| 6 | $\frac{84}{512} N$ | 84 | 82 |
| 7 | $\frac{36}{512} N$ | 36 | 32 |
| 8 | $\frac{9}{512} N$ | 9 | 9 |
| 9 | $\frac{1}{512} N$ | 1 | 1 |

Fig. 6-1. Histogram for expected (binomial) frequencies in 512 tosses of 9 coins.

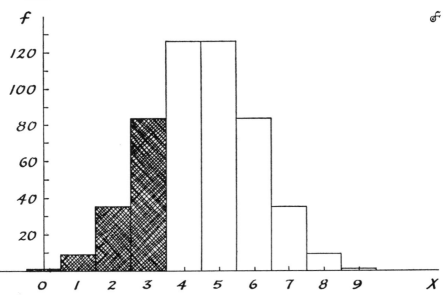

classes. For example, the shaded area in Figure 6-1 represents the expected number of times of getting at most 3 heads in 512 tosses of 9 coins. This concept of an area being a measure of a frequency will be used in Chapter 7.

*Example 6-2.* Calculate the mean and standard deviation for the binomial frequency distribution of Example 6-1.

*Solution.* The values of $X_i f_i$, $X_i^2 f_i$, and their sums, needed in this calculation, are shown in Table 6-2.

TABLE 6-2. Frequency Table for Calculation of Mean and Standard Deviation of Binomial Distribution of Example 6-1.

| $X_i$ | $f_i$ | $X_i f_i$ | $X_i^2 f_i$ |
|-------|-------|-----------|-------------|
| 0 | 1 | 0 | 0 |
| 1 | 9 | 9 | 9 |
| 2 | 36 | 72 | 144 |
| 3 | 84 | 252 | 756 |
| 4 | 126 | 504 | 2016 |
| 5 | 126 | 630 | 3150 |
| 6 | 84 | 504 | 3024 |
| 7 | 36 | 252 | 1764 |
| 8 | 9 | 72 | 576 |
| 9 | 1 | 9 | 81 |
|   | 512 | 2304 | 11520 |

Then

$$m = \frac{\sum\limits_{i=1}^{h} X_i f_i}{N} = \frac{2304}{512} = 4.50,$$

and using formula (4-18)

$$\sigma^2 = \sqrt{\frac{\sum\limits_{i=1}^{h} X_i^2 f_i - \frac{\left(\sum\limits_{i=1}^{h} X_i f_i\right)^2}{N}}{N}} = \sqrt{\frac{11520 - \frac{(2304)^2}{512}}{512}} = \sqrt{\frac{1152}{512}}$$

$$= \sqrt{2.25} = 1.50.$$

We shall now state a theorem by means of which the mean and standard deviation of a binomial distribution may be calculated directly from $n$, $p$, and $q$, without the need of calculating any summations such as those shown in Table 6-2.

**THEOREM 6-2.** If $p$ is the probability of the success of an event in a single trial and $q$ the probability of its failure, then the binomial distribution giving the expected frequencies for $0, 1, \cdots, n$ successes in $n$ trials has as its mean

$$m = np,$$

and as its standard deviation

$$\sigma = \sqrt{npq}.$$

*Example 6-3.* Calculate the mean and standard deviation for the binomial frequency distribution of Example 6-1 by use of Theorem 6-2.

*Solution.*

$$m = 9 \cdot \tfrac{1}{2} = 4.50, \ \sigma = \sqrt{9 \cdot \tfrac{1}{2} \cdot \tfrac{1}{2}} = \sqrt{\tfrac{9}{4}} = \tfrac{3}{2} = 1.50.$$

These results agree with those obtained in Example 6-2.

*Proof of Theorem 6-2.* To prove Theorem 6-2, we need to make the calculations that were made in Example 6-2 for certain given values of $n$, $p$, and $q$, so that they are applicable for any $n$, $p$, and $q$. Table 6-3 shows the values of $X_i f_i$ and $X_i^2 f_i$ needed in the calculation of the mean and standard deviation. The totals of these two columns are listed in the last row of the table. Thus the total of the $X_i f_i$ column is found as

$$\sum_{i=1}^{h} X_i f_i = Nnp \left[ q^{n-1} + (n-1)q^{n-2}p + \frac{(n-1)(n-2)}{2} q^{n-3}p^2 \right.$$

$$\left. + \cdots + (n-1)qp^{n-2} + p^{n-1} \right]$$

$$= Nnp(q+p)^{n-1} = Nnp,$$

since $q + p = 1$.

In order to find the total of the $X_i^2 f_i$ column, the algebra is greatly simplified if each value of $X_i^2 f_i$ is written as the sum of two terms, the first one of which is $X_i f_i$. Consequently, in the $X_i^2 f_i$ column of Table 6-3, each entry is written as the sum of two terms whose separate sums are then shown at the bottom of the column.

Using the sums of the $X_i f_i$ and $X_i^2 f_i$ columns, respectively, as shown in Table 6-3, we find for the mean of the binomial distribution

$$m = \frac{\sum\limits_{i=1}^{h} X_i f_i}{N} = \frac{Nnp}{N} = np,$$

TABLE 6-3. Frequency Table for Calculation of Mean and Standard Deviation of Binomial Distribution

| $i$ | $X_i$ | $f_i$ | $X_i f_i$ | $X_i^2 f_i$ |
|---|---|---|---|---|
| 1 | 0 | $Nq^n$ | 0 | $0 \qquad\qquad = X_1 f_1$ |
| 2 | 1 | $Nnq^{n-1}p$ | $Nnq^{n-1}p$ | $Nnq^{n-1}p \qquad = X_2 f_2$ |
| 3 | 2 | $\dfrac{Nn(n-1)q^{n-2}p^2}{2}$ | $Nn(n-1)q^{n-2}p^2$ | $2Nn(n-1)q^{n-2}p^2 = X_3 f_3 + Nn(n-1)p^2[q^{n-2}]$ |
| 4 | 3 | $\dfrac{Nn(n-1)(n-2)q^{n-3}p^3}{2\cdot 3}$ | $\dfrac{Nn(n-1)(n-2)q^{n-3}p^3}{2}$ | $\dfrac{3Nn(n-1)(n-2)q^{n-3}p^3}{2} = X_4 f_4 + Nn(n-1)p^2[(n-2)q^{n-3}p]$ |
| . | . | . | . | . |
| . | . | . | . | . |
| . | . | . | . | . |
| $h-1$ | $n-1$ | $Nnqp^{n-1}$ | $Nn(n-1)qp^{n-1}$ | $Nn(n-1)^2qp^{n-1} = X_{h-1}f_{h-1} + Nn(n-1)p^2[(n-2)qp^{n-3}]$ |
| $h$ | $n$ | $Np^n$ | $Nnp^n$ | $Nn^2p^n \qquad\quad = X_h f_h + Nn(n-1)p^2[p^{n-2}]$ |

$$N(q+p)^n = N \qquad Nnp(q+p)^{n-1} = Nnp \qquad \sum_{i=1}^{h} X_i f_i + Nn(n-1)p^2(q+p)^{n-2} = Nnp + Nn(n-1)p^2$$

and for the standard deviation, again using formula (4-18),

$$\sigma^2 = \frac{\sum\limits_{i=1}^{h} X_i^2 f_i - \dfrac{\left(\sum\limits_{i=1}^{h} X_i f_i\right)^2}{N}}{N} = \frac{Nnp + Nn(n-1)p^2 - \dfrac{N^2 n^2 p^2}{N}}{N}$$

$$= np + n^2 p^2 - np^2 - n^2 p^2 = np - np^2 = np(1-p) = npq.$$

Hence

$$\sigma = \sqrt{npq}.$$

## Exercises

1. Draw the histogram for the binomial distribution obtained in rolling 6 dice 46,656 times, considering a 1 a success, everything else a failure; i.e., construct the histogram for 0, 1, 2, $\cdots$, 6 successes.

2. Five coins are tossed 64 times.
   (a) Construct the theoretical frequency table for 0, 1, $\cdots$, 5 heads.
   (b) Draw the corresponding histogram.
   (c) Find the expected number of times of getting at least 3 heads.
   (d) In the histogram shade the area which is a measure of the result in part (c).
   (e) Toss 5 coins 64 times and record the actual frequencies of 0, 1, $\cdots$, 5 heads.
   (f) Calculate the mean and standard deviation of the frequency distribution obtained in part (a) by finding the values of $Xf$ and $X^2 f$, as was done in Table 6-2.
   (g) Calculate the mean and standard deviation of part (f) by use of Theorem 6-2.

3. (a) Toss 6 coins 128 times and record the observed frequencies of 0, 1, 2, $\cdots$ heads.
   (b) Calculate the expected frequencies for 128 trials, and compare with the observed frequencies of part (a).
   (c) Draw the histogram for the expected frequencies.

4. Four dice are rolled 81 times. If a 1 or a 6 on a die is considered a success and everything else a failure,

   (a) construct the theoretical frequency table for 0, 1, 2, 3, 4 successes;

   (b) draw the corresponding histogram;

   (c) find the expected number of times of obtaining at least 3 successes among the 4 dice.

   (d) In the histogram shade the area which is a measure of the result in part (c).

   (e) Roll 4 dice 81 times and record the actual frequencies for 0, 1, 2, 3, 4 successes.

   (f) Calculate the mean and standard deviation of the frequency distribution obtained in part (a) by finding the values of $Xf$ and $X^2f$, as was done in Table 6-2.

   (g) Calculate the mean and standard deviation of part (f) by use of Theorem 6-2.

5. In a seed viability test 450 seeds are placed on filter paper in rows of 5. The number of seeds that germinated in each row were counted, and the results are shown below.

| Number of Seeds Germinating per Row | Observed Frequencies of Rows |
|:---:|:---:|
| 0 | 0 |
| 1 | 1 |
| 2 | 11 |
| 3 | 30 |
| 4 | 38 |
| 5 | 10 |
| | — |
| | 90 |

   If the germinating seeds are distributed at random among the rows, we could expect a binomial distribution with $n = 5$. Find an estimate of

   (a) the average number of seeds germinating per row;

   (b) the probability of a single seed germinating.

   (c) Using the probability obtained in part (b), compute the expected frequencies of rows for each number of germinating seeds and compare with the observed frequencies.

   (d) Draw the histogram for the expected frequencies, and by means of dotted lines show the histogram for the observed frequencies.

6. Using any necessary information from Table 6-3, show that for a binomial distribution

$$\sum_{i=1}^{h} X_i(X_i - 1)(X_i - 2)f_i = Nn(n - 1)(n - 2)p^3.$$

# 7 The Normal Distribution

## 7.1. The Normal Distribution as an Approximation of the Binomial Distribution

In Chapter 6 we saw that the expected frequencies of the occurrence of $r$ heads in tossing $n$ coins follow a binomial distribution. The histograms representing expected frequencies in 64 tosses of 1–6 coins are shown in Figure 7-1.

If the number of trials $n$ is large, the calculation of frequencies and probabilities by means of the binomial theorem becomes tedious. Since many practical problems involve large numbers of repeated trials, it is important to find a more rapid method of calculating probabilities. Such a method is furnished by the normal distribution, which is the most important continuous probability distribution and one on which much statistical theory is based. From Figure 7-1 it is apparent that as $n$ increases, the tops of the rectangles of the histograms approach a bell-shaped curve. This limiting frequency curve obtained as $n$ becomes larger and larger is called the *normal frequency curve*.

Fig. 7-1. Histograms for expected frequencies of heads in tossing 1–6 coins 64 times.

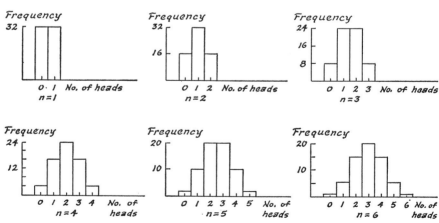

**THEOREM 7-1.**   In the binomial distribution for $N$ samples of $n$ trials each where the probability of success in a single trial is $p$, if the value of $n$ is increased, the histogram approaches a curve, called the *normal curve*, whose equation is

$$(7\text{-}1) \qquad\qquad Y = \frac{N}{\sigma\sqrt{2\pi}}\, e^{-(X-m)^2/2\sigma^2},$$

where

$m$ = mean of the binomial distribution = $np$,

$\sigma$ = standard deviation of the binomial distribution = $\sqrt{npq}$,

$e$ = base of the natural logarithms = $2.71828\cdots$,

$\pi$ = $3.14159\cdots$,

$Y$ = frequency with which any $X$ occurs.

The proof of this theorem is omitted, since it requires a knowledge of mathematical techniques beyond the scope of this text.

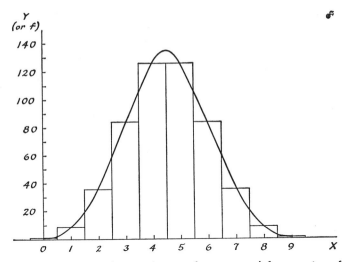

**Fig. 7-2.** Histogram and normal curve for expected frequencies of heads in tossing 9 coins 512 times.

In Figure 7-2 the histogram of Figure 6-1 has been approximated by the corresponding normal curve. A surprising agreement can be observed in spite of the fact that $n = 9$ is not a large number.

If the relative frequency (or probability) with which a variate $X$ occurs is denoted by $P$, then $P = Y/N$, and (7-1) can be written as

$$(7\text{-}2) \qquad\qquad P = \frac{1}{\sigma\sqrt{2\pi}}\, e^{-(X-m)^2/2\sigma^2},$$

the graph of which is called the *normal probability curve*.

If we multiply both sides of (7-2) by $\sigma$ and let $y = P\sigma$, thereby making $\sigma$ the unit of measurement on the vertical axis, we can rewrite (7-2) as

(7-3)                          $$y = \frac{1}{\sqrt{2\pi}} e^{-(X-m)^2/2\sigma^2}.$$

In order to measure also the deviations $X - m$ in terms of $\sigma$, we introduce a new variable

(7-4)                          $$z = \frac{X - m}{\sigma},$$

which represents a measure of the deviation in terms of the standard deviation or in so-called *standard units*. The expression given by (7-4) is also frequently referred to as the *normal deviate*.

By use of (7-4) we can now rewrite (7-3) as

(7-5)                          $$y = \frac{1}{\sqrt{2\pi}} e^{-z^2/2},$$

which is called the *standard normal probability curve*.

From (7-2) and its equivalent (7-5) it is evident that $y$ and $P$ reach their maximum values when $z = 0$, that is, when $X = m$. It is also clear from (7-5) that since $z$ is squared the substitution of $z$ or $-z$ into the equation results in the same value of $y$. This shows that the curve represented by equation (7-5) is symmetrical about the line drawn at $z = 0$ perpendicular to the horizontal axis. Furthermore, it is observed that as $X$ increases more and more, $y$ becomes smaller and smaller without, however, ever becoming equal to zero. This means that the curve approaches the horizontal axis but never touches it. The values of $y$ corresponding to given values of $z$ are listed in the Appendix

Fig. 7-3. Normal probability curve for expected frequencies of heads in tossing 9 coins 512 times.

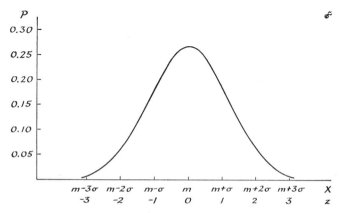

in Table Ia. In Figure 7-3 is shown the normal probability curve for $\sigma = 1.5$ corresponding to the normal curve of Figure 7-2. The $P$-values in this case can easily be obtained by dividing the values of $y$ obtained from Table Ia by $\sigma = 1.5$. Thus, the value of $P$ corresponding to $z = 1$ is found as

$$P = \frac{0.2420}{1.5} = 0.1613.$$

Since the normal frequency curve is always symmetric, whereas the binomial histogram is symmetric only if $p = q = \frac{1}{2}$, it is clear that the normal curve is a better approximation of the binomial histogram if both $p$ and $q$ are equal to or nearly equal to $\frac{1}{2}$. The more $p$ and $q$ differ from $\frac{1}{2}$, the worse is the approximation. In fact, if $p$ (or $q$) is very small even though $n$ is large, the normal approximation should not be used. It is generally suggested that if $p$ is so small that $np$ is less than 5 (or if $q$ is so small that $nq$ is less than 5), the normal approximation to the binomial distribution should ordinarily not be used. In this case, fortunately, there exists another distribution—the Poisson distribution—which serves as an excellent approximation of the binomial distribution; however, it will not be discussed here.

Let us suppose that the normal curve can be used to approximate a binomial distribution and that we wish to use the normal probability curve to find the probability that a variate $X$ will fall between two given integral values $A$ and $B$ ($A$ and $B$ both included and $B$ greater than $A$). We recall from Chapter 6 that the sum of the areas of the rectangles whose centers are at $X = A$, $A + 1, \cdots, B$ represents a measure of the expected frequency with which $X$ will fall between $A$ and $B$. We need then the area under the binomial histogram from $X = A - \frac{1}{2}$ to $X = B + \frac{1}{2}$ or, since the normal frequency curve is assumed to approximate the binomial distribution, the area between the same two values of $X$ under the normal frequency curve. Since, however, we are interested here in the probability (rather than the frequency), we need to divide the result by $N$, or, what is the same thing, we need to find the area under the curve where frequencies have already been divided by $N$, i.e., the area under the normal probability curve as given by (7-5). The areas under this curve in terms of $z$ are given in Appendix Table I where the first column gives the $z$-value, the second the area between the line of symmetry of the normal curve (i.e., where $z = 0$) and the given $z$-value. Since these areas are tabulated, the probabilities can be determined directly without making use of the formulae for the normal frequency (or probability) curves. The procedure is shown in Example 7-1. It should be noted of course that the total area under the normal probability curve, representing the probability that $X$ will fall anywhere, is equal to 1.

*Example 7-1.* Using the normal curve approximation, find the probability that 3-6 heads are obtained in a toss of 9 coins, i.e., that $X$ lies between and includes 3 and 6.

*Solution.* The area from $X = 2.5$ to $X = 6.5$ under the histogram of Figure 7-2 represents the expected number of times we would get 3-6 heads. To obtain the desired probability, we divide this area by $N = 512$. Since the normal curve approximates the binomial, we find the desired probability with a good degree of accuracy by finding the area under the corresponding normal probability curve (Figure 7-3) from $X = 2.5$ to $X = 6.5$. Since the areas in Appendix Table I are given in terms of $z$, we need to find the $z$-values corresponding to the two $X$-values. Since

$$m = np = 9 \cdot \tfrac{1}{2} = 4.5,$$

and

$$\sigma = \sqrt{9 \cdot \tfrac{1}{2} \cdot \tfrac{1}{2}} = 1.5,$$

we have for

$$X = 2.5: \quad z = \frac{2.5 - 4.5}{1.5} = \frac{-2}{1.5} = -1.33,$$

and for

$$X = 6.5: \quad z = \frac{6.5 - 4.5}{1.5} = \frac{2}{1.5} = 1.33.$$

We therefore need the area from $z = -1.33$ to $z = 1.33$. This we find by looking up the area from $z = 0$ to $z = +1.33$ (which is the same as the area from $z = 0$ to $z = -1.33$) and multiplying it by 2. The desired probability is therefore equal to

$$P = 0.4082 \cdot 2 = 0.8164.$$

From Table 6-1 we find that if we had used the binomial distribution for this example we would have obtained

$$\frac{84 + 126 + 126 + 84}{512} = 0.8203.$$

The discrepancy is not surprising, in view of the small value of $n$.

In order to be able to make use of the tables in the appendix without having to resort to interpolation, we shall calculate all standard deviations and $z$-values to two decimals only, which may occasionally cause a slight loss of accuracy in the result.

*Example 7-2.* If 12 dice are thrown, what is the probability, using the normal curve approximation, that 7 or more dice will show a 5?

*Solution.* Here, $p = \tfrac{1}{6}, q = \tfrac{5}{6}, n = 12$; thus

$$m = 12 \cdot \tfrac{1}{6} = 2,$$
$$\sigma = \sqrt{12 \cdot \tfrac{1}{6} \cdot \tfrac{5}{6}} = \sqrt{1.67} = 1.29.$$

We therefore need the area under the normal probability curve from $X = 6.5$ to $X = 12.5$, i.e., from

$$z = \frac{6.5 - 2}{1.29} = 3.49 \qquad \text{to} \qquad z = \frac{12.5 - 2}{1.29} = 8.14.$$

But since the area to the right of $z = 8.14$ is so small we can just as well include it without introducing any significant error. We find the area to the right of $z = 3.49$ by subtracting the area from $z = 0$ to 3.49 from 0.5, the total area to the right of the line $z = 0$, therefore,

$$P = 0.5 - 0.4998 = 0.0002.$$

From the solution of Example 7-2 it is evident why the following procedure is appropriate. If a normal curve approximates a binomial distribution, and the probability that $X$ is greater than or equal to $A$ (an integer) is desired, we simply take the total area under the normal probability curve to the right of $X = A - \tfrac{1}{2}$; on the other hand, if the probability that $X$ is less than or equal to $A$ (an integer) is desired, we take the total area under the normal probability curve to the left of $X = A + \tfrac{1}{2}$. The adoption of this procedure is also motivated by the desire to have the probabilities that $X$ is greater than or equal to $A$ and the probability that $X$ is less than $A$ add up to 1, which would not be true had we not accepted the preceding convention.

## 7.2. The Normal Distribution as a Limit of a Frequency Distribution of a Continuous Variable

The normal curve serves as a good approximation not only for a histogram obtained from the binomial distribution but for many other histograms as well. Frequently a histogram of a distribution with mean $m$ and standard deviation $\sigma$ is well approximated for a large number of data $N$ by the curve whose equation is

(7-6)
$$Y = \frac{Nc}{\sigma\sqrt{2\pi}} e^{-(X-m)^2/2\sigma^2},$$

where $c$ is the difference between two consecutive class midpoints. The smaller the value of $c$, the better the approximation usually will be.

The normal curve is indeed the most important frequency curve. Many measurements in science and industry follow distributions that can be approximated well by normal distributions.

Fig. 7-4. Histogram and normal curve for 90 years of rainfall at Sacramento, California.

In order to find from the normal curve the number of variates falling between $X = A$ and $X = B$, consider Figure 7-4, which shows the histogram and corresponding normal frequency curve for the total seasonal rainfall at Sacramento, California (see data of Table 2-4).

From Figure 7-4 the number of seasonal rainfall measurements falling between $X = A$ and $X = B$ is simply the shaded area divided by $c$, since the shaded area is $f_A c + f_P c + f_Q c + f_R c$, where $f_A$ is the frequency for the interval for which $X = A$ is the lower class boundary, i.e., the height of the rectangle whose base is $AP = c$, etc. The normal curve in Figure 7-4 is the graph of (7-6) for $m = 18.13$, $\sigma = 6.28$, and $Nc = 270$, or it can be considered as the result of increasing $N$ and decreasing $c$ in the histogram of Figure 7-4. To use the normal curve to determine the number of variates (rainfall measurements) falling between $X = A$ and $X = B$, we find the corresponding area under the normal curve of Figure 7-4 and divide by $c$, which is equivalent to finding the area under

$$Y = \frac{N}{\sigma\sqrt{2\pi}} e^{-(X-m)^2/2\sigma^2}$$

from $X = A$ to $X = B$.

In other words, for a normal distribution, to find the probability that a variate will fall between $X = A$ and $X = B$, it is necessary merely to find the area from $X = A$ to $X = B$ under the normal probability curve (7-2).

Similarly, for any probability curve (not necessarily normal) the probability that a variate will fall between $X = A$ and $X = B$ is the area under the curve from $X = A$ to $X = B$. Indeed, a probability curve representing a frequency distribution is frequently defined as a curve such that the area under the curve from $X = A$ to $X = B$ represents the probability that $X$ will fall between $A$ and $B$, no matter what $A$ and $B$ are. From this it follows immediately that the total area under any probability curve must be equal to 1.

*Example 7-3.*   Given a normal distribution of a continuous variable with $N = 2000$, $m = 20$, $\sigma = 5$. Find

(a) the number of variates between $X = 12$ and $X = 22$;

(b) the number of variates larger than $X = 30$.

*Solution.*   (a) We need first the area under the normal probability curve from $X = 12$ to $X = 22$, i.e., from

$$z = \frac{12 - 20}{5} = -1.6 \qquad \text{to} \qquad z = \frac{22 - 20}{5} = 0.4,$$

which is found from Appendix Table I to be

$$0.4452 + 0.1554 = 0.6006.$$

Therefore the desired number of variates is

$$0.6006 \cdot 2000 = 1201.$$

(b) We first find the total area to the right of $X = 30$, i.e., to the right of

$$z = \frac{30 - 20}{5} = 2,$$

which is 0.0227, and the desired number of variates is therefore

$$0.0227 \cdot 2000 = 45.$$

In a given problem the reader may have difficulty in deciding whether the normal curve arises as an approximation to a binomial distribution or as a frequency curve approximating a histogram of a continuous variable. But since the first case arises only for variables taking on only nonnegative integral values, there should be no difficulty in making a decision.

## 7.3.   Special Areas Under the Normal Curve

Because certain areas under the normal curve arise in so many applications we shall make special mention of them. The area under the normal probability curve from $X = m - \sigma$ to $X = m + \sigma$ (i.e., from $z = -1$ to $z = 1$) is found from Appendix Table I to be $0.3413 \cdot 2 = 0.6826$, or, from more extensive tables, 0.68268, which means that in a normal distribution 68.268% (or about two-thirds) of the data fall in this interval. This explains the property of the standard deviation referred to in Chapter 4 that in many frequency distributions (in particular, the normal distribution) about two-thirds of the data fall within one standard deviation on either side of the mean.

The area under the normal probability curve from $X = m - 2\sigma$ to $X = m + 2\sigma$ is 0.95450; thus about 95% of the data in a normal distribution fall within two standard deviations on either side of the mean. Finally, the

Fig. 7-5.  Special areas under the normal curve.

area from $X = m - 3\sigma$ to $X = m + 3\sigma$ is equal to 0.99730. These special areas are shown in Figure 7-5.

In many applications, notably in physics, it is of interest to determine the interval around the mean which contains 50% of the data of the distribution. Clearly, the $z$-value at the upper limit of this interval must be such that the corresponding area is equal to $\frac{1}{2}(0.50) = 0.25$. Determining then from Appendix Table I the value of $z$ corresponding to an area of 0.25, we find to two decimal places $z = 0.67$, or, from more extensive tables, $z = 0.6745$. Consequently, in a normal distribution, half of the data fall within $0.6745\sigma$ on either side of the mean.

> **DEFINITION 7-1.** The *probable error* (*P.E.*) is defined such that the interval from $m - P.E.$ to $m + P.E.$ will contain 50% of the data in the distribution.

From the discussion above it follows that for a normal distribution the probable error is given as

(7-7) $$P.E. = 0.6745\sigma.$$

## 7.4.   Grading on the Curve

As most readers undoubtedly are aware, many instructors, especially those teaching large classes, use a system of grading referred to as "grading on the curve," which of course refers to the normal curve. While there are many such systems which depend upon the percentage of $A$, $B$, $C$, $D$, and $F$ grades the instructor desires to give, the basic idea is the same in all of them. If the grades are assumed to be normally distributed and if intervals of the distribution (given in terms of the mean and standard deviation) are assigned to each of the various grades, the percentage for each grade is specified. Example 7-4 illustrates the procedure for a system which is, perhaps, most frequently used.

*Example 7-4.* An instructor assigns grades in an examination according to the following procedure:

A   if score exceeds $m + 1.5\sigma$;
B   if score is between $m + 0.5\sigma$ and $m + 1.5\sigma$;
C   if score is between $m - 0.5\sigma$ and $m + 0.5\sigma$;
D   if score is between $m - 1.5\sigma$ and $m - 0.5\sigma$;
F   if score is less than $m - 1.5\sigma$.

What percentage of each grade does this instructor give, assuming that the scores are normally distributed?

*Solution.* To determine the percentage of $A$'s we need to determine the area under the normal probability curve to the right of $z = 1.5$, which from Appendix Table I is found to be

$$P_A = 0.5000 - 0.4332 = 0.0668.$$

Consequently, the instructor is assigning 6.68% $A$'s. To determine the percentage of $B$'s, we determine the area under the normal probability curve from $z = 0.5$ to $z = 1.5$ from Appendix Table I and find

$$P_B = 0.4332 - 0.1915 = 0.2417;$$

thus, he gives 24.17% $B$'s. Similarly, we find that he assigns 38.30% $C$'s, 24.17% $D$'s, and 6.68% $F$'s.

Note that in Example 7-4 it was assumed that the intervals are arranged symmetrically with respect to the mean. This, however, need not always be the case. Sometimes instructors might wish to use a system in which the lower limit of the $C$'s is farther removed from the mean than the upper limit.

## Exercises

Calculate standard deviations and $z$-values to two decimal places.

1. A coin is tossed 100 times. Use the normal curve approximation to find the probability of obtaining
   (a) exactly 50 heads, and compare the result with the value 0.0796 obtained from the binomial distribution;
   (b) 60 or more heads. The actual value from the binomial distribution is 0.028.

2. Use the normal curve approximation to find the probability of obtaining exactly 16 sixes in 96 tosses of a die. Compare the result with the value 0.110 obtained from the binomial distribution.

3. Assume that one-half the people in a certain community are regular viewers of television. Of 100 investigators, each interviewing 10 individuals regarding their viewing habits, how many would you expect to report that 3 people or fewer were regular television viewers?
   (a) Calculate by an exact method (using binomial distribution).
   (b) Calculate by an approximate method (using normal distribution).

4. For a binomial frequency distribution for which $p = \frac{1}{4}$, find the probability of obtaining 25 or more successes in 80 trials.

5. A manufacturer of light bulbs finds that on the average 2% are defective. What is the probability that out of 1000 such bulbs selected at random 15 or more are defective?

6. A pair of unbiased dice is rolled 45 times. What is the probability that a 6, 7, or 8 will appear 25 or more times?

7. According to American Experience Mortality Tables the probability of a man of age 41 dying within a year is 0.01. If an insurance company has 50,000 policies in force on men of this age, estimate by use of a normal curve the probability that the company will have to pay more than 525 death claims on this group of men within a year.

8. If a normal distribution of a continuous variable has $m = 21.2$ and $\sigma = 3.10$, find the probability that a variate selected at random will be larger than 30 or less than 15.

9. In a certain building trade the average wage is $3.60 per hour and the standard deviation is 45 cents. If the wages are assumed to follow a normal distribution, what per cent of the workers receive wages between $3.00 and $3.50 per hour?

10. The weight of grapefruit from a large shipment averages 15.00 ounces with a standard deviation of 1.62 ounces. If these weights are normally distributed, what per cent of all these grapefruit would be expected to weigh between 15.00 and 18.00 ounces?

11. If the average life of a certain make of storage battery is 30 months with a standard deviation of 6 months, what per cent of these batteries can be expected to last from 24 months to 36 months? Assume that the lifetimes follow a normal distribution.

12. Records indicate that the average life of television picture tubes is 3.0 years with a standard deviation of 1.5 years. Tubes lasting less than a year are replaced free. For every 100 sets (one tube to a set) sold, how many tubes can be expected to have to be replaced free?

13. A manufacturer knows that on the average 2% of his products are defective. Using the normal curve approximation, what is the probability that a lot of 100 pieces will contain exactly 5 defectives?

14. How many times do two dice have to be rolled so that there is a 50% chance of getting a total of 5 at least 3 times?

15. By use of the normal curve find how many throws with one die will be required in order that the probability of getting at least 5 sixes will have the value $\frac{1}{2}$.

16. The average seasonal rainfall in a certain town is 18.75 inches with a standard deviation of 6.50 inches. Assume that the seasonal rainfall for this town satisfies a normal distribution. In how many years out of a period of 50 years would we expect between 15.00 and 25.00 inches of rain?

17. If the heights of 10,000 college men closely follow a normal distribution with a mean of 69.0 inches and a standard deviation of 2.5 inches,
   (a) how many of these men would you expect to be at least 6 feet in height;
   (b) what range of heights would you expect to include the middle 75% of the men in this group?

18. Three students take different tests. $A$ gets a score of 72, $B$ one of 85, and $C$ one of 17. All students taking the test with $A$ had an average grade of 85, with $B$ an average of 90, and with $C$ an average of 25. The three standard deviations are 7, 3, and 7, respectively. Arrange the three students in order of excellence as you would judge them by these results, indicating your reasons.

19. In grading Satsuma plums whose weights are normally distributed, 20% are called small, 55% medium, 15% large, and 10% very large. If the mean weight of all Satsuma plums is 4.83 ounces with a standard deviation of 1.20 ounces, what are the lower and upper bounds for the weight of medium Satsuma plums?

20. In a normal distribution having a standard deviation of 2.00 the probability that a variate selected at random exceeds 28.00 is 0.03.
   (a) Find the mean of the distribution.
   (b) Find the variate above which lie 95% of all variates of this distribution.

21. On an examination the average grade was 70.0, and the standard deviation was 10.0. The instructor gave all students with grades from 61.0 to

79.0 the grade of $C$. There were 24 students who received a $C$ grade. If the grades are assumed to satisfy a normal distribution, how many students took the examination?

22. In a normal distribution with mean 15.00 and standard deviation 3.50 it is known that 647 variates exceed 16.25. What is the total number of variates in the distribution?

23. An instructor who assigns 10% $A$'s, 20% $B$'s, 40% $C$'s, 20% $D$'s, 10% $F$'s gives an examination on which the average is 68.0. If the borderline between the $C$'s and $B$'s is 78.0 on that examination and if the grades are normally distributed, what is the standard deviation of the class?

24. A physical education instructor announces that he will give an $A$ grade to 20% of his high-jump class based entirely on ability to jump. If experience in his classes has shown that the height of the jump is normally distributed with mean 4 feet 8 inches and standard deviation 4 inches, at least how high must a student jump if he is to get an $A$?

25. The heights of a number of students are normally distributed with a mean of 68.50 inches. If 12% are at least 71.20 inches tall,
    (a) what is the standard deviation of this distribution;
    (b) what is the probable error?

26. A set of 10,000 variates is found to be normally distributed with mean 450. If 1700 of them lie between 450 and 460,
    (a) what is the standard deviation;
    (b) what is the probable error?

27. The diameters of ball bearings are normally distributed with standard deviation 2 mm. If it is known that 4% of the bearings have diameters larger than 23.5 mm., what is the mean of the distribution?

28. In a normal distribution with mean 100 and standard deviation 53 there are 135 variates greater than 200. How many variates should we expect between 150 and 200?

29. In a restaurant on a particular morning the amounts spent for breakfast by all patrons follow a normal distribution with mean 87.2 cents and standard deviation 12.0 cents. On that morning if 420 people spend 85 cents or more for breakfast, what is the total number of people served?

30. In a normal distribution with mean 72.0 and standard deviation 12.0 there are 220 variates between 40.0 and 90.0. How many variates are there in the whole distribution?

31. In a normal distribution with mean 120.0 and standard deviation 30.0 there are 300 variates between 130 and 150. How many variates are there between 130 and 145?

32. It is known that a variate originates either from a normal population with mean 10 and standard deviation 2 or from a normal population with mean 11 and standard deviation 3. If it is considered twice as likely that the variate comes from the second population than from the first, find the probability that the variate exceeds 12.5.

33. In an examination 13% of the class receives a grade of $A$; 20% $B$; 48% $C$; 10% $D$; and 9% $F$. The $C$ grade ranges from 55 to 79. Assuming a normal distribution, what are the mean and the standard deviation of the grades?

34. In a certain cross of two varieties of peas, genetic theory indicates that half the seeds obtained will be smooth and half will be wrinkled. How many seeds have to be examined in order that at least 100 smooth seeds are obtained with a probability of 90%?

35. According to Mendelian inheritance theory, certain crosses of peas give yellow and green peas in the ratio of 3:1. How many seeds from this cross have to be planted in order that there is a 95% probability that at least 50 green peas are obtained?

# 8 Random Sampling. Large Sample Theory

## 8.1. Introduction

Sampling is one of the most important concepts in the study of statistics. It is basic to statistical theory and to applications of statistical theory in all fields of the physical, biological, and social sciences, in economics, in medicine, in agriculture, and in business and industry. Before proceeding, we must clarify certain fundamental ideas about populations and samples.

> **DEFINITION 8-1.** A *population* (or universe) is the totality of the measurements or counts obtainable from all objects possessing some common specified characteristic.

In the statistical sense, therefore, a population is never a set of objects, but always a set of measurements or counts. A population may consist of finitely or infinitely many variates. For example, in a study of the size of a particular variety of fruit at some specified stage of development we may be interested only in the fruits on a certain limb of a tree; the sizes of these fruits, then, constitute the population. But if we are interested in all fruits on the tree, their sizes form the population. Or we may wish to study all the fruits on all the trees of a particular orchard; in this case the population consists of the sizes of all fruits in the orchard. Frequently, we wish to extend the applicability of our conclusions beyond such finite populations to encompass, say, all fruits at a specified stage of development on all such trees which now exist or will exist in the future. In this population the number of measurements of size may be inexhaustible, and this constitutes an infinite population.

Another example of a finite population is the set of "maximum blowing currents" of a lot of 1000 fuses, all manufactured under similar conditions. Since for each fuse there is one, and only one, maximum current at which it will blow, these currents constitute a finite population of 1000 items.

Since we can rarely investigate a whole population we are obliged to formulate conclusions regarding a population from samples selected from it.

**DEFINITION 8-2.** A *sample* is a set of measurements which constitute part or all of a population.

In Chapter 5, in evaluating probabilities, some exercises involved a series of drawings in which the object drawn was returned before the next drawing was made, while in other exercises the withdrawn objects were not returned. Sampling also can be carried out either with or without replacement. In studying the size of fruit on a particular limb of a tree, we might select 10 fruits for measurement. If the fruits are picked one by one and measured, the sampling is effected without replacement; if, however, the fruits are measured on the limb, without picking, the procedure is equivalent to sampling with replacement, since after each measurement the population remains the same as before and a fruit which has already been measured might be selected again. Much sampling is done with replacement; however, some populations must be sampled without replacement. The latter is necessary when the items of the sample are destroyed in the process of measurement. For example, since a fuse is destroyed in measuring the maximum blowing current, it cannot be used for further measurement.

The main object in taking a sample is to draw some conclusion about the population from which it is obtained. The relation of sample to population is one of the most important problems in statistical theory and practice, since good estimates concerning a population necessitate good samples. Securing good samples is not always easy, but generally it can be done. A precise definition of a good sample, a so-called *random sample*, will not be given here, but the following will suffice.

**DEFINITION 8-3.** A *random sample* is a sample in which any one individual measurement in the population is as likely to be included as any other.

**DEFINITION 8-4.** A *biased* sample is a sample in which certain individual measurements have a greater chance to be included than others.

Since from now on frequent reference will be made to samples and populations, it is necessary to distinguish between the mean of a sample and the mean of a population, also between the standard deviation of a sample and that of a population. Table 8-1 indicates the notation which will be used to distinguish between samples and populations.

TABLE 8-1.   Notation for Samples and Populations

| Characteristic | Sample | Population |
|---|---|---|
| Number of variates | $n$ | $N$ |
| Mean | $\overline{X}$ | $m$ |
| Standard deviation | $\hat{s}$ | $\sigma$ |

Thus, for example, for a sample of $n$ variates we have the following formulae for its mean and standard deviation

$$(8\text{-}1) \qquad \overline{X} = \frac{\sum\limits_{i=1}^{n} X_i}{n},$$

$$(8\text{-}2) \qquad \hat{s} = \sqrt{\frac{\sum\limits_{i=1}^{n} (X_i - \overline{X})^2}{n}}.$$

In preceding chapters $m$ and $\sigma$ were used, sometimes for samples, sometimes for populations. For simplicity we made no distinction. Usually, Roman letters are used for measurements obtained from samples, and the corresponding Greek letters are used for population measurements. We shall follow this convention in later chapters. If we were to follow it strictly, we should of course have denoted by Greek letters the number of variates and the mean of a population, as is done in some texts ($\mu$ being used for the mean). However, since by tradition $N$ and $m$ are so generally used for number of variates and mean of a population, we shall adhere to this widely accepted practice.

**DEFINITION 8-5.** A numerical characteristic of a population, such as its mean or standard deviation, is called a *population parameter* or simply a *parameter*.

**DEFINITION 8-6.** A quantity calculated from a sample, such as its mean or standard deviation, is called a *sample statistic* or simply a *statistic*.

Since parameters of a given population are based upon all its variates, they are fixed for that population. On the other hand, since statistics are based upon only a part of a population, they usually vary from sample to sample. In order to develop valid statistical procedures we must first know something about the distribution of certain statistics.

Throughout the rest of this book we shall assume that populations consist of finitely many variates in order to simplify many of the discussions. Actually, all of the results which are derived will, with occasional slight changes in wording, be true also for infinite populations. The assumption that the size $N$ of a population must be finite should not cause any concern, since there is no restriction on how large $N$ can be. Indeed, in most of the discussions $N$ is assumed to be a very large (although finite) number.

## 8.2.   Distribution of the Sample Mean

Consider a population of $N$ variates with mean $m$ and standard deviation $\sigma$, and draw all possible samples of $n$ variates from this population, denoting their means by $\overline{X}_1, \overline{X}_2, \cdots, \overline{X}_M$. (See Figure 8-1.) Assume here that the samples are replaced, so that the total number of samples $(M)$ which can be drawn is equal to the number of combinations of $N$ things taken $n$ at a time, i.e., $M = C_{N,n}$. The mean of all these sample means is denoted by $m_{\overline{x}}$, and

Fig. 8-1. Relation between sample means and population parameters.

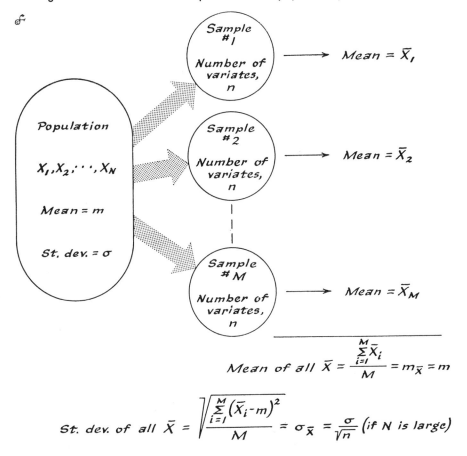

$$\text{Mean of all } \overline{X} = \frac{\sum\limits_{i=1}^{M} \overline{X}_i}{M} = m_{\overline{x}} = m$$

$$\text{St. dev. of all } \overline{X} = \sqrt{\frac{\sum\limits_{i=1}^{M}(\overline{X}_i - m)^2}{M}} = \sigma_{\overline{x}} = \frac{\sigma}{\sqrt{n}} \ (\text{if } N \text{ is large})$$

the standard deviation of these sample means by $\sigma_{\bar{x}}$. Strictly speaking, $m_{\bar{x}}$ and $\sigma_{\bar{x}}$ should be used, but from here on, where no confusion is possible, small letters will be used as subscripts. Then we can prove that

(8-3)                                              $$m_{\bar{x}} = m,$$

(8-4)                                              $$\sigma_{\bar{x}} = \sigma\sqrt{\frac{N - n}{n(N - 1)}}.$$

Since in general $N$ is very large when compared with $n$, a simpler relationship can be obtained for a **very** large value of $N$. The expression under the square root of (8-4) may be written

$$\frac{N - n}{n(N - 1)} = \frac{N}{n(N - 1)} - \frac{1}{N - 1} = \frac{1}{n\left(1 - \frac{1}{N}\right)} - \frac{1}{N - 1},$$

which for very large $N$ is close to $1/n$. Therefore, for large $N$ formula (8-4) becomes

(8-5)                                              $$\sigma_{\bar{x}} = \frac{\sigma}{\sqrt{n}}.$$

Formula (8-3) does not seem surprising, since we would expect the mean of all the sample means of a population to be about the same as the mean of all the variates of the population, although it may seem surprising that this mean should always be precisely equal to the population mean.

Formula (8-5) is reasonable, since we would expect the sample means to vary less than the variates of the population, and to vary less and less as $n$ becomes larger and larger (i.e., have a much smaller standard deviation than the variates of the population).

The proofs of (8-3) and (8-4) will not be included here. It can be shown in a simple case, where $N = 3$ and $n = 2$, how easy it is to verify these formulae.

If $N = 3$, there are 3 variates in the population—call them $X_1$, $X_2$, $X_3$. Since $n = 2$, all possible samples of 2 variates from this population are: $X_1$, $X_2$, and $X_1$, $X_3$, and $X_2$, $X_3$. Let the mean of the first sample be denoted by $\bar{X}_1$, that of the second sample by $\bar{X}_2$, and so on. Then

$$\bar{X}_1 = \frac{X_1 + X_2}{2}, \quad \bar{X}_2 = \frac{X_1 + X_3}{2}, \quad \bar{X}_3 = \frac{X_2 + X_3}{2}.$$

To verify (8-3) we must show that $m_{\bar{x}}$, the mean of $\bar{X}_1$, $\bar{X}_2$, $\bar{X}_3$, i.e., $(\bar{X}_1 + \bar{X}_2 + \bar{X}_3)/3$, is equal to $m$, the mean of $X_1$, $X_2$, $X_3$, i.e., $(X_1 + X_2 + X_3)/3$. Now

$$m_{\bar{x}} = \tfrac{1}{3}(\bar{X}_1 + \bar{X}_2 + \bar{X}_3) = \tfrac{1}{3}\left(\frac{X_1 + X_2}{2} + \frac{X_1 + X_3}{2} + \frac{X_2 + X_3}{2}\right)$$

$$= \tfrac{1}{3}\frac{2X_1 + 2X_2 + 2X_3}{2} = \tfrac{1}{3}(X_1 + X_2 + X_3) = m.$$

To verify (8-4) for $N = 3$ and $n = 2$, it is necessary to show that $\sigma_{\bar{x}} = \sigma\sqrt{1/4}$ or $\sigma_{\bar{x}}^2 = \frac{1}{4}\sigma^2$. The variance $\sigma^2$ is obtained as

$$\sigma^2 = \frac{\sum\limits_{i=1}^{3}(X_i - m)^2}{3} = \frac{2}{9}\left[\sum_{i=1}^{3}X_i^2 - (X_1X_2 + X_1X_3 + X_2X_3)\right],$$

where the latter step is easily verified as required in exercise 5, and

$$\sigma_{\bar{x}}^2 = \frac{\sum\limits_{i=1}^{3}(\bar{X}_i - m)^2}{3} = \frac{1}{18}\left[\sum_{i=1}^{3}X_i^2 - (X_1X_2 + X_1X_3 + X_2X_3)\right],$$

which can also be easily checked as required in exercise 6. Therefore,

$$\sigma_{\bar{x}}^2 = \frac{1}{18}\left(\frac{9}{2}\sigma^2\right)$$
$$= \frac{1}{4}\sigma^2.$$

**THEOREM 8-1.** If $X$ is normally distributed with mean $m$ and stand-ard deviation $\sigma$ and if all possible samples of $n$ variates are drawn from the population (as shown in Figure 8-1), then the sample mean $\overline{X}$ will be normally distributed with mean $m$ and standard deviation $\sigma/\sqrt{n}$.

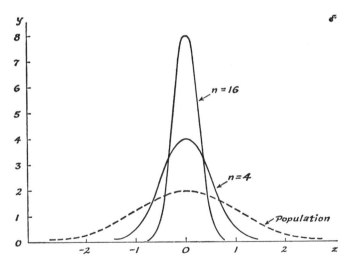

Fig. 8-2. Distribution of the means of samples of 4 and 16 variates from a normally distributed population.

In other words, if we graph on the horizontal axis the sample means $\overline{X}$, instead of $X$ as we did in Chapter 7, the $y$-values will satisfy equation (7-5) with

$$z = \frac{\overline{X} - m_{\bar{x}}}{\sigma_{\bar{x}}}$$

where

$$\sigma_{\overline{x}} = \frac{\sigma}{\sqrt{n}}.$$

The distributions of sample means for samples of 4 and 16 variates together with the population distribution as shown in Figure 8-2 clearly indicate the way in which the type of resulting normal distribution varies with a change in size of sample. As we might expect, with increasing values of the sample size ($n$) the normal probability curve becomes narrower and taller, since the means of large samples will obviously vary less than those of small samples, and the area under all probability curves will always be equal to unity.

Although Theorem 8-1 is applicable only if the population has a normal distribution, Theorem 8-2 is applicable for the much more general case where the distribution of the population is unknown.

> **THEOREM 8-2.** If $X$ has a distribution with mean $m$ and standard deviation $\sigma$ and if all possible samples of $n$ variates are drawn, then the sample mean $\overline{X}$ will have a distribution which for larger and larger $n$ approaches the normal distribution with mean $m$ and standard deviation $\sigma/\sqrt{n}$.

Theorem 8-2 states therefore that for "large $n$" (which is assumed to mean that $n$ is greater than 30) $\overline{X}$ will be approximately normally distributed, even if the population does not satisfy a normal distribution.

The proofs of Theorems 8-1 and 8-2 are dependent on more advanced mathematical procedures than are assumed here, and will not be given.

*Example 8-1.* The mean height of a group of 1000 college students is 68.20 inches, and the standard deviation is 2.50 inches. Find the probability that in a sample of 100 students the mean will be greater than 68.90 inches.

*Solution.* Since by Theorem 8-2 the mean of the samples is approximately normally distributed with

$$m_{\overline{x}} = m = 68.20$$

and

$$\sigma_{\overline{x}} = \frac{\sigma}{\sqrt{n}} = \frac{2.50}{10} = 0.25,$$

we must find the area under the normal probability curve to the right of $\overline{X} = 68.90$, i.e., to the right of

$$z = \frac{\overline{X} - m}{\sigma_{\overline{x}}} = \frac{68.90 - 68.20}{0.25} = 2.80.$$

From Appendix Table I this area is found to be 0.0026; therefore in a sample of 100 students the probability that the mean will be greater than 68.90 inches is 0.0026.

## 8.3. Distribution of the Sample Standard Deviation

Consider a population of $N$ variates with mean $m$ and standard deviation $\sigma$, and draw all possible samples of $n$ variates from this population. Suppose there are $M$ such samples having standard deviations $\hat{s}_1, \hat{s}_2, \cdots, \hat{s}_M$. We shall denote the mean of all these standard deviations by $m_{\hat{s}}$, and the standard deviation of all these standard deviations by $\sigma_{\hat{s}}$. Then for large $n$ it can be proved that

(8-6) $$m_{\hat{s}} = \sigma,$$

and

(8-7) $$\sigma_{\hat{s}} = \frac{\sigma}{\sqrt{2n}}.$$

Since these formulae as well as theorems describing the distribution of the standard deviation have little practical application, we consider it sufficient to state these formulae without further discussion. They are given merely for reasons of completeness.

## 8.4. Distribution of the Difference between Two Sample Means

Consider two populations with means $m_x$ and $m_y$, and standard deviations $\sigma_x$ and $\sigma_y$, respectively. Let $N$ denote the number of all possible pairs of samples which can be taken from these populations such that the first of each pair is from the first population and has $n_1$ variates and the other is from the second population and has $n_2$ variates. Let the means of the samples from the first population be denoted by $\overline{X}_1, \overline{X}_2, \cdots, \overline{X}_N$, and those from the second by $\overline{Y}_1, \overline{Y}_2, \cdots, \overline{Y}_N$. Then consider for each pair the difference between the mean of the first sample and that of the second; thereby $N$ such differences are obtained, as shown in Figure 8-3.

In many practical problems it is of great importance to know what the mean and standard deviation of these $N$ differences are in terms of the means and the standard deviations of the two populations. Denoting by $m_{\overline{x}-\overline{y}}$ the mean and by $\sigma_{\overline{x}-\overline{y}}$ the standard deviation of these $N$ differences, it can be proved that

(8-8) $$m_{\overline{x}-\overline{y}} = m_x - m_y,$$

Fig. 8-3. Relation between differences of sample means and population parameters.

Mean of all $\bar{X}-\bar{Y} = \dfrac{\sum\limits_{i=1}^{N}(\bar{X}_i - \bar{Y}_i)}{N} = m_{\bar{x}-\bar{y}} = m_x - m_y$

St. dev. of all $\bar{X}-\bar{Y} = \sqrt{\dfrac{\sum\limits_{i=1}^{N}[(\bar{X}_i - \bar{Y}_i) - m_{\bar{x}-\bar{y}}]^2}{N}} = \sigma_{\bar{x}-\bar{y}} = \sqrt{\sigma_{\bar{x}}^2 + \sigma_{\bar{y}}^2}$

*(if the populations are independent)*

and that if the populations are independent (i.e., there is no relationship whatsoever between specific variates of the two populations),

(8-9)
$$\sigma_{\bar{x}-\bar{y}} = \sqrt{\sigma_{\bar{x}}^2 + \sigma_{\bar{y}}^2},$$

where

$$\sigma_{\bar{x}} = \frac{\sigma_x}{\sqrt{n_1}}, \quad \sigma_{\bar{y}} = \frac{\sigma_y}{\sqrt{n_2}}.$$

The proof of (8-8) should be carried out as an exercise. The proof of (8-9) will be given in Chapter 12 [see formula (12-26)].

**THEOREM 8-3.** If $X$ and $Y$ are normally and independently distributed with means $m_x$ and $m_y$ and standard deviations $\sigma_x$ and $\sigma_y$, respectively, and if all possible pairs of samples are drawn from these populations (as shown in Figure 8-3), then the difference between sample means $\bar{X} - \bar{Y}$ is normally distributed with mean $m_x - m_y$ and standard deviation

$$\sigma_{\bar{x}-\bar{y}} = \sqrt{\sigma_{\bar{x}}^2 + \sigma_{\bar{y}}^2}.$$

In other words, if we graph the differences of the sample means, $\bar{X} - \bar{Y}$, on the horizontal axis, and the relative frequency, $y$, with which each difference $\bar{X} - \bar{Y}$ occurs on the vertical axis, the curve will satisfy equation (7-5) with

$$z = \frac{(\bar{X} - \bar{Y}) - m_{\bar{x}-\bar{y}}}{\sigma_{\bar{x}-\bar{y}}},$$

where

$$\sigma_{\bar{x}-\bar{y}} = \sqrt{\sigma_{\bar{x}}^2 + \sigma_{\bar{y}}^2}, \quad \sigma_{\bar{x}} = \frac{\sigma_x}{\sqrt{n_1}}, \quad \text{and} \quad \sigma_{\bar{y}} = \frac{\sigma_y}{\sqrt{n_2}}.$$

Again, since the proof of this theorem depends on more advanced mathematics, it will be omitted.

*Example 8-2.* From two normal and independent populations, where the mean of the second population is 0.50 less than that of the first, pairs of samples are drawn such that each pair contains one sample from each population. If the samples from the first population contain 90 variates, and those from the second 120 variates, and if the standard deviation of the first population is 10, and that of the second is 8, find the probability that in a pair of samples the difference between the first and second sample means exceeds 1.00 in absolute value.

*Solution.* Denoting by $X$ the variable of the first population, by $Y$ that of the second, we have

$$m_x - m_y = 0.50.$$

Now, since

$$\sigma_x = 10, \quad \sigma_y = 8, \quad n_1 = 90, \quad n_2 = 120,$$

we have

$$\sigma_{\bar{x}} = \frac{10}{\sqrt{90}}, \quad \sigma_{\bar{y}} = \frac{8}{\sqrt{120}}.$$

The calculations for $\sigma_{\bar{x}}$ and $\sigma_{\bar{y}}$ should not be carried any further since the computations from here on become simpler if these quantities are left in this form; in particular, since in the next step the squares of $\sigma_{\bar{x}}$ and $\sigma_{\bar{y}}$ are required, the square-roots appearing in the denominators of $\sigma_{\bar{x}}$ and $\sigma_{\bar{y}}$ should not be computed. Using the values of $\sigma_{\bar{x}}$ and $\sigma_{\bar{y}}$ in the above form, we then obtain

$$\sigma_{\bar{x}-\bar{y}} = \sqrt{\frac{10^2}{90} + \frac{8^2}{120}} = \sqrt{\frac{100}{90} + \frac{64}{120}} = \sqrt{1.1111 + 0.5333}$$

$$= \sqrt{1.6444} = 1.28.$$

From Theorem 8-3 we know that the difference between means for all pairs of samples of sizes 90 and 120 is normally distributed with mean $m_{\bar{x}-\bar{y}} = m_x - m_y = 0.50$ and standard deviation $\sigma_{\bar{x}-\bar{y}} = 1.28$. We wish to find the probability that this difference exceeds 1.00 in absolute value, i.e., that the difference is either greater than 1.00 or less than $-1.00$. Now, we have for

$$\bar{X} - \bar{Y} = 1.00: \qquad z_1 = \frac{1.00 - 0.50}{1.28} = \frac{0.50}{1.28} = 0.39,$$

and for

$$\bar{X} - \bar{Y} = -1.00: \qquad z_2 = \frac{-1.00 - 0.50}{1.28} = \frac{-1.50}{1.28} = -1.17,$$

so we need the area under the normal probability curve to the right of 0.39 and to the left of $-1.17$, which is found from Appendix Table I to be

$$P = (0.5000 - 0.1517) + (0.5000 - 0.3790) = 0.3483 + 0.1210 = 0.4693.$$

Important applications of Theorem 8-3 will be given in Chapter 9.

## 8.5.  Standard Error

DEFINITION 8-7. The *standard error* of a statistic is the standard deviation of the sampling distribution of that statistic.

For example, the standard error of the mean is another designation for the standard deviation of the mean. From the previous discussion in this chapter we can therefore say: the standard error of the mean is $\sigma/\sqrt{n}$; the standard error of the standard deviation is $\sigma/\sqrt{2n}$; and the standard error of the difference between the means of samples from two independent populations is

$$\sqrt{\sigma_{\bar{x}}^2 + \sigma_{\bar{y}}^2}.$$

## Exercises

1. Verify formula (8-3) for $N = 4$ and $n = 2$.

2. Verify formula (8-3) for $N = 4$ and $n = 3$.

3. Verify formula (8-3) for $N = 5$ and $n = 4$.

4. Verify formula (8-3) for $N = 5$ and $n = 3$.

5. For the case where $N = 3$ and $n = 2$, show that

$$\sum_{i=1}^{3} (X_i - m)^2 = \tfrac{2}{3} \left[ \sum_{i=1}^{3} X_i^2 - (X_1X_2 + X_1X_3 + X_2X_3) \right].$$

6. For the case where $N = 3$ and $n = 2$, show that

$$\sum_{i=1}^{3} (\overline{X}_i - m)^2 = \tfrac{1}{6} \left[ \sum_{i=1}^{3} X_i^2 - (X_1X_2 + X_1X_3 + X_2X_3) \right].$$

7. Verify formula (8-4) for $N = 4$ and $n = 3$.

8. In a normal population with mean 72.10 and standard deviation 3.10, find the probability that in a sample of 90 variates the mean will be less than 71.70.

9. In a savings bank the average account is $159.32 with a standard deviation of $18.00. What is the probability that a group of 400 accounts taken at random shows an average deposit of $160.00 or more?

10. In a particular area the daily wages of coal miners are normally distributed with a mean of $16.50 and a standard deviation of $1.50. What is the probability that a representative sample of 25 miners will have an average daily wage below $15.75?

11. The heights of a certain group of adults have a mean of 67.42 inches and a standard deviation of 2.58 inches. If these heights are normally distributed, and if 25 people are taken at random from the group, what is the probability that their mean will be 68.00 inches or more?

12. A random sample of 100 variates is drawn from a normal population with mean 50 and standard deviation 8, and a random sample of 400 variates is drawn from a normal population with mean 40 and standard deviation 12. Find the probability that
    (a) the mean of the first sample exceeds the mean of the second sample by 8 or more;
    (b) the two means differ in absolute value by 12 or more.

13. From each of two normal and independent populations with identical means and with standard deviations of 6.40 and 7.20, a sample of 64 variates is drawn. Find the probability that the difference between the means of the samples exceeds 0.60 in absolute value.

14. If a random sample of 36 variates is taken from a population, how many variates should be taken in another sample from the same population to make the standard error of the mean of the second sample $\tfrac{2}{3}$ of the standard error of the mean of the first sample?

15. If two random samples are taken from a population, and if the standard error of the mean of one of them is $k$ times the standard error of the mean of the other, how are the sizes of the samples related?

16. In one restaurant the average amount spent for breakfast is 98.3 cents with a standard deviation of 15.0 cents, and in a second restaurant the corresponding figures are 92.4 and 12.0 cents. If a random sample of 80 breakfast charges is taken from the first restaurant and a random sample of 60 from the second, what is the probability that the difference between the average amounts of these two samples is less than 1 cent in absolute value?

17. It is known that in a certain large city persons eating in a restaurant spend, on the average, 98.3 cents for breakfast with a standard deviation of 15.0 cents. If each of 50 restaurants is asked to select at random the breakfast bills of 100 persons and to report the average amount spent by these 100 persons, how many restaurants may be expected to report the average bill as $1.00 or more?

18. The average gasoline mileage for cars of make $A$ is 20 miles per gallon with a standard deviation of 6 miles per gallon. Comparable figures for cars of make $B$ are 25 and 5.5 miles per gallon. Assume that the gasoline mileage for each of the two makes is normally distributed. What is the probability in a gasoline mileage contest that the average gasoline mileage for 10 cars of make $A$ is greater than that for 9 cars of make $B$?

19. On the average, students from university $A$ get up 50 minutes after sunrise with a standard deviation of 15 minutes; students from university $B$ get up 60 minutes after sunrise with a standard deviation of 18 minutes. A group of 25 students from university $A$ takes a trip with a group of 20 students from university $B$. Find the probability that the average time of rising for the group from university $B$ is earlier than that for the group from university $A$.

20. Past experience shows that, on the average, men and women students perform equally well in tests on statistics. The standard deviation of the men students, however, is found to be 15; that of the women students 12. What is the probability that, in an examination in statistics taken by 120 students of which 69 are men, the average of the women students will exceed that of the men by more than 3.0 points?

21. If all possible samples of size 25 are drawn from a normally distributed population with mean equal to 20 and standard deviation equal to 4, within what range will the middle 90% of the sample means fall?

22. The daily wages in a particular industry are normally distributed with a mean of $13.20. If 9% of the mean daily wages of samples of 25 workers fall below $12.53, what is the standard deviation of daily wages in this industry?

23. From a normal distribution all possible samples of size 10 are selected. If 2% of these samples have means which differ from the mean of the population by more than 4.00 in absolute value, find the standard deviation of the population.

24. In a normal distribution of a continuous variable with mean 9.00 the probability that the mean of a random sample of 25 variates exceeds 10.00 is 0.33. What is the probability that a single variate selected at random from this distribution is greater than 10.00?

25. If it is assumed that the heights of men are normally distributed with a standard deviation of 2.5 inches, how large a sample should be taken in order to be fairly sure (probability 0.95) that the sample mean does not differ from the true mean (population mean) by more than 0.50 in absolute value?

26. Referring to the data of exercise 25, how large a sample should be taken if we want to be 99% sure that the sample mean does not differ from the true mean by more than 0.50 in absolute value?

27. A normal population has a standard deviation of 2.0. How large a sample should be taken in order to be 99% sure that the sample mean differs from the population mean by less than 0.8?

28. In measuring reaction time, a psychologist estimates that the standard deviation of the population is 0.05 seconds. How large a sample of measurements must he take in order to be 99% sure that he will estimate the mean of the population with an error not exceeding 0.01 seconds?

# 9 Testing Hypotheses, Significance Levels, Confidence Limits. Large Sample Methods

## 9.1. Testing Hypotheses

We shall now consider one of the most important problems, that of testing statistical hypotheses.

> **DEFINITION 9-1.** A *statistical hypothesis* is an assumption made about some parameter, i.e., about a statistical measure of a population.

From this definition it follows that not every hypothesis is a statistical hypothesis. The following hypotheses are not statistical hypotheses:

(a) Mars is inhabited by human beings.

(b) Mr. E. is the candidate who would be the best president for the United States.

Neither of these statements is an assumption about a parameter. On the other hand, only a slight change in wording of statement (b) would result in the following statistical hypothesis:

(c) Mr. E. is the candidate most favored for the presidency of the United States.

The last statement is a statistical hypothesis, since it states an assumption about a parameter, the percentage of all people favoring Mr. E.

In order to establish the truth or falsity of a statistical hypothesis with complete certainty it may be necessary to examine the entire population. Since this is frequently impossible or impractical, we are forced to take a sample from the population and use the sample in deciding whether the hypothesis is true or false. Example 9-1 will serve as an illustration.

*Example 9-1.*   Suppose we wish to test the "honesty" of a coin. This is a statistical hypothesis, since the assumption of "honesty" is equivalent to the assumption that for the population of a very large number of tosses of this coin, the probability $p$ of obtaining heads is $\frac{1}{2}$. Suppose now in tossing this coin 100 times we obtain 60 heads, and from this information we are forced to reach a decision regarding the honesty of the coin.

*Solution.*   If we had obtained 50 or close to 50 heads we would not have doubted the honesty of the coin. The obtained number, 60, however, is sufficiently far from 50 to cause some doubt. Consequently, it seems reasonable to calculate—on the assumption that the coin is honest—the probability of obtaining 60 or more heads in 100 throws.

Using the normal curve approximation to the binomial distribution, we find:

Hypothesis:     $p = \frac{1}{2}$.

$$q = \tfrac{1}{2},$$
$$n = 100,$$
$$m = \tfrac{1}{2} \cdot 100 = 50,$$
$$\sigma = \sqrt{100 \cdot \tfrac{1}{2} \cdot \tfrac{1}{2}} = \sqrt{25} = 5,$$
$$z = \frac{59.5 - 50}{5} = \frac{9.5}{5} = 1.90,$$
$$P = 0.5000 - 0.4713 = 0.0287.$$

Therefore, if an honest coin is tossed 100 times, the probability of obtaining 60 or more heads is 0.0287, certainly not a high probability. From this result we are justified in drawing one of two conclusions:

1. The hypothesis is correct, but a rare event has occurred.

2. The hypothesis is not correct.

In statistics it is customary to choose the second of these two alternatives whenever the probability is less than a given value $\alpha$, called the significance level.

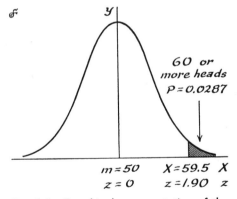

Fig. 9-1. Graphical representation of the probability involved in Example 9-1.

**DEFINITION 9-2.**   In testing a statistical hypothesis, the hypothesis is declared to be true if the calculated probability exceeds a given value $\alpha$, called the *significance level;* and it is considered false if the calculated probability is less than $\alpha$.

**DEFINITION 9-3.** If the calculated probability is less than $\alpha$, indicating that the hypothesis is false, the result is termed *significant*.

It is a commonly accepted convention to consider a result significant if the calculated probability is less than $\alpha = 0.05$, and to term it *highly significant* if the calculated probability is less than $\alpha = 0.01$.

In Example 9-1 we conclude that, since 0.0287 is less than 0.05, the result is significant (although not highly significant), and consequently on the basis of the 5% level of significance ($\alpha = 0.05$) we reject the hypothesis that the coin is honest. It should be noted that, if the hypothesis is assumed to be correct, by chance alone once in 20 trials the calculated probability will be less than $\alpha = 0.05$, and once in 100 trials it will be less than $\alpha = 0.01$. Therefore, in using the 5% level of significance we will be in error on the average once in 20 trials, and at the 1% level once in 100 trials. If we are not willing to draw the wrong conclusion that frequently we must select a smaller level of significance, but no matter how small the level selected, we still run the risk of being in error in our conclusion.

Why, in Example 9-1, did we calculate the probability of obtaining 60 or more heads and not the probability of obtaining a deviation of 10 or more from the expected number of heads (i.e., 60 or more or 40 or less heads)? The answer is that the appropriate method depends on what is considered to be the unusual or noteworthy situation. If we wish to consider the large number of heads as the remarkable event, we calculate the probability of obtaining 60 or more heads; on the other hand, if we find the deviation from the expected result the noteworthy feature, the probability of obtaining 60 or more or 40 or less heads is the appropriate probability to calculate. The latter probability is twice the former, i.e., $2(0.0287) = 0.0574$, so in this case, using $\alpha = 0.05$ as the significance level, we do not call this result significant.

**DEFINITION 9-4.** If only one tail of a curve is used in testing a statistical hypothesis, we speak of a *one-tailed test;* if both tails are used, we refer to the test as *two-tailed*.

The decision to apply a one-tailed test or a two-tailed test must be reached by a careful consideration of the question to be answered in the analysis. If the interest in the problem is restricted to the fact that either a very low or a very high result was obtained (but not both), a one-tailed test is called for; otherwise, a two-tailed test should be applied. In case of doubt, a two-tailed test is recommended.

When $\alpha = 0.05$ is used, a result in a two-tailed test is significant if $z$ falls in the shaded part of Figure 9-2, i.e., if $z > 1.96$ or $z < -1.96$, where 1.96 is

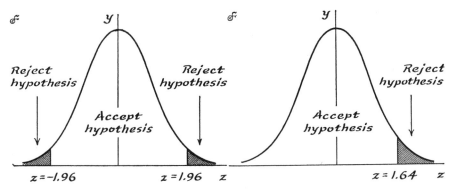

Fig. 9-2. Two-tailed test for $\alpha = 0.05$.  Fig. 9-3. One-tailed test for $\alpha = 0.05$.

the value of $z$ obtained from Appendix Table I for which each of the shaded areas is 0.0250; similarly, a result in a one-tailed test is significant if $z$ falls in the shaded part of Figure 9-3, i.e., if $|z| > 1.64$, where 1.64 is the $z$-value for which the shaded area is 0.0500. These values of $z$ are called critical values.

Why, in Example 9-1, in testing the honesty of the coin, did we not calculate the probability of obtaining exactly 60 heads in 100 throws? This probability obviously is very small. Indeed, even the probability of obtaining the most likely event (50 heads) for an honest coin is quite small (0.0796). Therefore, in testing hypotheses it is never proper to use the probability of obtaining precisely the event which occurred, but rather the probability of the occurrence of that event or one which deviates even more from the hypothesis.

*Example 9-2.* From Mendelian inheritance theory, we know that certain crosses of peas should give yellow and green peas in the ratio 3:1. In a particular experiment, 179 yellow and 49 green peas are obtained. Is this a significant deviation from the theory on the basis of the 5% level of significance?

*Solution.* Here we are testing the statistical hypothesis that the probability $p$ of obtaining yellow peas is $p = \frac{3}{4}$. Since the sample contains 228 peas, we would expect, according to the hypothesis, $\frac{3}{4} \cdot 228 = 171$ yellow peas. Consequently, we calculate the probability of obtaining in a sample of 228 peas a deviation of 8 or more from the expected result (i.e., 179 or more or 163 or less yellow peas). Since the question concerns a deviation from theory, and a deviation can occur on either side of the expected result, a two-tailed test is applicable. If the question had been "Is this a significantly large number of yellow peas?" we would have used a one-tailed test.

The calculations for the normal curve approximation of the binomial distribution involved are shown below.

Hypothesis:     $p = \frac{3}{4}$.

$$q = \frac{1}{4},$$
$$n = 228,$$
$$m = \frac{3}{4} \cdot 228 = 171,$$
$$\sigma = \sqrt{228 \cdot \frac{3}{4} \cdot \frac{1}{4}} = \sqrt{42.75} = 6.54,$$
$$z = \frac{178.5 - 171}{6.54} = 1.15,$$
$$P = (0.5000 - 0.3749) \cdot 2 = (0.1251) \cdot 2 = 0.2502.$$

Since $P > 0.05$, the result does not represent a significant deviation from the theory. The same conclusion also follows from the fact that $1.15 < 1.96$, the critical value of $z$.

It should be emphasized that the testing of statistical hypotheses does not constitute a mathematical proof of the truth or falsity of the hypothesis. Unfortunately, there is no absolute certainty that the conclusion reached will be correct. In fact, in testing statistical hypotheses, two types of incorrect conclusions are possible.

**DEFINITION 9-5.** If it happens that the hypothesis being tested is actually true, and if from the sample we reach the conclusion that it is false, we say that a *type 1 error* has been committed.

In Example 9-1, where 60 heads were obtained in 100 throws of a coin, a one-tailed test resulted in the conclusion that the hypothesis should be rejected, which meant that the coin was not honest. If now it happens that this coin actually is honest, we have committed a type 1 error. The probability of committing a type 1 error is the relative frequency with which we reject a correct hypothesis, and this is precisely equal to the significance level $\alpha$. The smaller the value of $\alpha$, the smaller the chance of committing a type 1 error.

**DEFINITION 9-6.** If it happens that the hypothesis being tested is actually false, and if from the sample we reach the conclusion that it is true, we say that a *type 2 error* has been committed.

In Example 9-2 we concluded that the hypothesis of a $3:1$ ratio was correct. If now it happens that this hypothesis actually is not true, and some other segregation ratio is applicable, we have committed a type 2 error.

The probability of committing a type 2 error is usually denoted by $\beta$. For a given number of observations it can be shown that if $\alpha$ is given $\beta$ can be determined, and that if $\alpha$ is decreased $\beta$ is increased. This means that, for a fixed sample size, if the probability of committing a type 1 error is decreased, the probability of committing a type 2 error is increased, and vice versa. If we wish to decrease the chances of both types of error at the same time, it can be accomplished only by increasing the size of the sample.

**TABLE 9-1.    Hypotheses and Conclusions Reached from Sample**

| Conclusion | | Hypothesis Stated Is | |
|---|---|---|---|
| | | True | False |
| Sample indicates | reject hypothesis | Type 1 error | Correct con-clusion |
| | accept hypothesis | Correct con-clusion | Type 2 error |

Depending upon whether the stated hypothesis is true or false, and depending upon the conclusion reached from the sample, there are four different possibilities as summarized in Table 9-1.

*Example 9-3.*    The mean breaking strength of a certain type of cord has been established from considerable experience at 18.3 ounces with a standard deviation of 1.2 ounces. A new machine is purchased to manufacture this type of cord. A sample of 100 pieces obtained from the new machine shows a mean breaking strength of 17.0 ounces. Would you say that this sample is inferior on the basis of the 1% level of significance?

*Solution.*    Here we are testing the statistical hypothesis that the population from which the sample of 100 pieces is taken has a mean equal to or greater than that of the population of breaking strengths established from long experience (18.3 ounces). If the mean of the population from which the sample of 100 pieces is drawn exceeds 18.3 ounces, the new machine is not producing an inferior product, and the hypothesis would not be rejected. Therefore we can confine our attention to testing the hypothesis that $m = 18.3$ ounces.

We calculate the probability of obtaining from a population with a mean of 18.3 and standard deviation of 1.2 a sample of 100 pieces with a mean of 17.0 or less. A one-tailed test is applicable, since inferiority can occur only on the left side of the distribution. If this probability is less than 1%, we reject the hypothesis; otherwise, we accept it.

Recalling Theorem 8-2 concerning the distribution of the means of samples, the necessary calculations can be made:

Hypothesis:    $m = 18.3$.

$$\sigma = 1.2,$$
$$\overline{X} = 17.0,$$
$$n = 100,$$

$$\sigma_{\overline{x}} = \frac{1.2}{\sqrt{100}} = \frac{1.2}{10} = 0.12,$$

$$z = \frac{17.0 - 18.3}{0.12} = \frac{-1.3}{0.12} = -10.83.$$

Since $|z| = 10.83$ is larger than any value of $z$ listed in Appendix Table I, the corresponding tail area is much less than 0.01 and, consequently, the result is highly significant. We therefore conclude that the sample is indeed inferior. Since the probability found here is so small, we are almost certain that our conclusion is correct, and the chance of having committed a type 1 error is almost negligible.

A frequently tested hypothesis in statistics is the assumption that the means of two populations are identical. Suppose we are given two samples of sizes $n_1$ and $n_2$, and that we have calculated the means of these samples ($\overline{X}$ and $\overline{Y}$, respectively). We then wish to test the hypothesis that the two populations from which these samples were selected have identical means. This is determined by calculating the probability of selecting from two populations with identical means two samples for which the means differ by $|\overline{X} - \overline{Y}|$ or more. A two-tailed test is normally used in testing the hypothesis that two means are equal (or that the difference between means is zero) although there are rare occasions when a one-tailed test may be preferable. Since in this case we are dealing with the distribution of differences between sample means, Theorem 8-3 is applicable.

*Example 9-4.* The gasoline mileage for 50 cars of make $A$ has a mean of 17.0 miles per gallon with a standard deviation of 2.5 miles per gallon, while that for 70 cars of make $B$ has a mean of 18.6 miles per gallon with a standard deviation of 3.0 miles per gallon. If this is the only information available on the gasoline consumption of these two makes of cars, can we conclude that cars of make $B$ consume less gasoline than those of make $A$ (5% level)?

*Solution.* Here we are testing the statistical hypothesis that the means of the two populations (distances traveled per gallon of gasoline for makes $A$ and $B$, denoted by $X$ and $Y$, respectively) are identical, or $m_x = m_y$. We then calculate the probability of selecting from these two populations two samples of sizes 50 and 70, for which the difference in sample means exceeds in absolute value $|17.0 - 18.6| = 1.6$.

As is almost always true in problems of this type, the standard deviations, $\sigma_x$ and $\sigma_y$, of the two populations are unknown. Since, however, both samples are quite large, no serious error is committed by assuming that the standard deviation of each population is identical with the standard deviation of the sample taken from that population. Such an assumption is generally permissible if the numbers of observations in each of the samples exceed 30. For smaller samples, this assumption is not valid; the appropriate procedure for small samples will be discussed in Chapter 10.

The calculations for this example follow.

Hypothesis:      $m_x = m_y$,   or   $m_x - m_y = 0$.

$$\overline{X} = 17, \quad \overline{Y} = 18.6,$$
$$\hat{s}_x = \sigma_x = 2.5, \quad \hat{s}_y = \sigma_y = 3.0,$$
$$n_1 = 50, \quad n_2 = 70,$$

$$\sigma_{\overline{x}} = \frac{\sigma_x}{\sqrt{n_1}} = \frac{2.5}{\sqrt{50}}, \quad \sigma_{\overline{y}} = \frac{\sigma_y}{\sqrt{n_2}} = \frac{3.0}{\sqrt{70}},$$

$$\sigma_{\overline{x}-\overline{y}} = \sqrt{\sigma_{\overline{x}}^2 + \sigma_{\overline{y}}^2} = \sqrt{\frac{(2.5)^2}{50} + \frac{(3.0)^2}{70}} = \sqrt{\frac{6.25}{50} + \frac{9.00}{70}}$$

$$= \sqrt{0.1250 + 0.1286} = \sqrt{0.2536} = 0.50,$$

$$z = \frac{(\overline{X} - \overline{Y}) - (m_x - m_y)}{\sigma_{\overline{x}-\overline{y}}} = \frac{(17.0 - 18.6) - 0}{0.50}$$

$$= \frac{-1.60}{0.50} = -3.20.$$

Since $|z| = 3.20 > 1.96$, the result is significant. If the populations actually have identical means, the probability of obtaining a difference of 1.60 miles per gallon or more (in absolute value) between the two sample means is very small, in fact 0.0014, and this is an excellent indication that cars of make $B$ consume less gasoline than those of make $A$.

## 9.2.   Confidence Limits

Suppose we are given a sample of $n$ variates having mean $\overline{X}$ and standard deviation $\hat{s}$. We shall now consider the problem of estimating the mean of the population from which the sample was selected.

To illustrate, suppose a random sample of 100 variates is taken from a normal population and is found to have a mean of 40 and a standard deviation of 11. It will not be possible to determine precisely the mean of the population, since this sample of 100 variates with mean 40 could have been taken from any population with mean at or near 40. Consequently, the best we can hope for is to establish limits within which the mean of the population will fall with a specified probability or confidence (usually taken as 95%).

DEFINITION 9-7.   The limits which will contain a parameter with a probability of 95% (or some other given per cent) are called the 95% (or that other per cent) *confidence limits* for the parameter.

DEFINITION 9-8.   The interval between the confidence limits is called the *confidence interval*.

The larger the specified confidence, the longer the confidence interval.

Let us now calculate the 95% confidence limits for the mean of the population from which the sample of 100 variates was selected.

From Theorem 8-1 we know that $\overline{X}$ is normally distributed with mean $m$ and standard deviation $\sigma_{\overline{x}}$. To calculate $\sigma_{\overline{x}}$ we shall assume that, since the sample is large, the standard deviation of the population can be well approximated by the standard deviation of the sample, i.e., $\sigma = \hat{s}$. Then we find

$$\sigma_{\overline{x}} = \frac{\sigma}{\sqrt{n}} = \frac{11}{10} = 1.10.$$

Therefore, 95% of the sample means lie between the values of $\overline{X}$ obtained by solving for $\overline{X}$ the two equations

$$\frac{\overline{X} - m}{1.10} = \pm 1.96.$$

The value of 1.96 is obtained from Appendix Table I as the value of $z$ corresponding to an area of $\frac{1}{2}(0.95) = 0.475$. The solutions are

$$\overline{X}_1 = m - 2.16, \quad \text{and} \quad \overline{X}_2 = m + 2.16.$$

However, since in the illustration we are given $\overline{X}$ and wish to determine $m$, we must solve the above equations for $m$, which gives

$$m_1 = \overline{X} - 2.16 = 40 - 2.16 = 37.84,$$

and

$$m_2 = \overline{X} + 2.16 = 40 + 2.16 = 42.16.$$

Fig. 9-4. The distributions corresponding to the two extreme values of the mean.

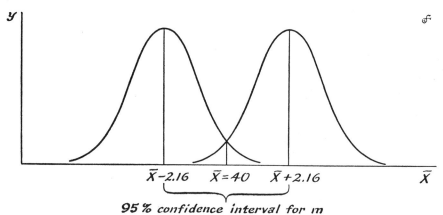

$\overline{X}-2.16$     $\overline{X}=40$     $\overline{X}+2.16$

95% confidence interval for $m$

These values, $m_1$ and $m_2$, constitute the lower and upper 95% confidence limits for the mean of the population. Frequently they are written more briefly as

$$m = 40 \pm 2.16.$$

These limits, then, define an interval which would contain the mean of the population with a probability of 95%. Figure 9-4 shows the distribution of the populations with these two extreme values of the mean.

Note that this method of obtaining confidence limits is applicable only to large samples, where it is permissible to assume that the standard deviation of a sample can be taken as an approximation of the standard deviation of the population. The procedure to be followed for small samples (30 or fewer variates) will be discussed in Chapter 10.

*Example 9-5.* A sample of 70 variates has a mean of 65 with a standard deviation of 4.2. Find the 98% confidence limits for the mean of the population.

*Solution.* Here we are given $\overline{X} = 65$, $\hat{s} = 4.2$, $n = 70$.
Assuming $\sigma = \hat{s}$, we find

$$\sigma_{\overline{x}} = \frac{\sigma}{\sqrt{n}} = \frac{4.2}{\sqrt{70}} = \frac{4.2}{8.37} = 0.50.$$

From Appendix Table I, the value of $z$ corresponding to an area of $\frac{1}{2}(0.98) = 0.49$ is 2.33; thus

$$\frac{\overline{X} - m}{0.50} = \pm 2.33.$$

Therefore

$$\overline{X} - m = \pm 1.16,$$

and

$$m = \overline{X} \pm 1.16 = 65 \pm 1.16,$$

which are the 98% confidence limits for the mean of the population.

# Exercises

Unless otherwise specified, use the 5% level of significance. Answer each question exactly in the form in which it is asked (i.e., do not merely state that a result is significant or not significant).

1. A die is rolled 120 times. If 25 times a 3 is obtained, does this cause us to doubt that this is an honest die?

2. A coin is tossed 600 times.
    (a) If 325 heads are obtained, is this considered a significantly large deviation from the expected number of heads?
    (b) Is this considered a significantly large number of heads?

3. From experience it is known that 20% of a certain kind of seed germinate. If in an experiment 60 out of 400 seeds germinate, is this considered a significantly poor germination on the basis of the 1% level of significance?

4. It is known from long experience that 5% of certain articles produced are defective and have to be discarded. A new man who has produced 600 of these articles has made 42 defective articles. Does this cast doubt on the man's ability to perform the job?

5. At a university, student records kept over a period of many years indicate that 64% pass the entrance examination in mathematics. During the fall of 1959, of 400 freshmen taking the test, 70% passed. Was this a significant improvement in the students' aptitude in mathematics?

6. If experience shows that 4% of all-white males of exact age 65 die within a year, and it is found that 55 such males of a group of 1000 actually die within a year, should the group be regarded as being essentially different from the general mass, using the 1% level of significance?

7. Of 64 offspring of a certain cross between guinea pigs, 8 are black and the others are not black. According to the genetic model, these numbers (black and not black) should be in the ratio 3:13. Are the observed data consistent with the model at the 5% level of significance?

8. A standard medication reduces reports of post-operative pains in 80% of the patients treated. A new medication for the same purpose is tested. In at least how many patients out of 100 tested must the medication be effective so that it can be considered a superior medication at the 1% level of significance?

9. The height of adults in a certain town has a mean of 65.42 inches with a standard deviation of 2.32 inches. A sample of 144 adults living in the slum district is found to have a mean height of 64.82 inches. Does this indicate that the residents of the slums are significantly retarded in growth on the basis of the 1% level of significance?

10. A manufacturer of string has established from several years' experience that the string he manufactures has a mean breaking strength of 15.9 pounds with a standard deviation of 2.3 pounds. A change is made in the manufacturing process, after which a sample of 64 pieces is taken,

whose mean breaking strength is found to be 15.0 pounds with a standard deviation of 2.2 pounds. Does this mean that the new process has a significantly damaging effect on the strength of the string?

11. A car manufacturer claims that its cars use on the average 5.50 gallons of gasoline for each 100 miles. A salesman selling cars for this company tests 35 cars for gasoline mileage and finds that the average consumption of gasoline for these 35 cars is 5.65 gallons for each 100 miles with a standard deviation of 0.35 gallons. Do these results cast doubt on the claim of the company (1% level)?

12. The daily wages in a particular industry are normally distributed with a mean of $13.20 and a standard deviation of $2.50. If a company in this industry employing 40 workers pays these workers on the average $12.20, can this company be accused of paying inferior wages at the 1% level of significance?

13. Two types of electric bulbs are observed as to length of life, and the following data are obtained:

|  | Type I | Type II |
|---|---|---|
| Number in sample | 46 | 64 |
| Mean of sample | 1070 hours | 1041 hours |
| Sum of squares of deviations from mean | $\Sigma(X - \overline{X})^2 = 21,000$ | $\Sigma(Y - \overline{Y})^2 = 23,200$ |

Are the mean lives of the two types of electric bulbs significantly different on the basis of the 1% level of significance?

14. The following data pertain to growth of wheat under two treatments, A and B:

|  | Treatment A | Treatment B |
|---|---|---|
| Number of stalks | 44 | 36 |
| Mean height | 15.6 | 14.1 |
| Sum of squares of deviations from mean | $\Sigma(X - \overline{X})^2 = 167.52$ | $\Sigma(Y - \overline{Y})^2 = 159.89$ |

Is there a significant difference between these two means?

15. Two manufacturing processes are to be compared. A sample of size 100 of the first process is found to have a mean of 107 and a standard deviation of 17. For the second process a sample of size 90 has a mean of 103 and a standard deviation of 16. Is there a significant difference between the means of the two processes?

16. Two brands of frozen food are compared. A sample of 40 items of the first brand has mean 77 and variance 80, while a sample of 50 items of the second brand has mean 73 and variance 100. The means of the two samples are judged to be significantly different. What is the smallest level of significance (an integer) at which this judgment is correct?

17. It has been claimed that 50% of the people have exactly two colds per year. If we decide to reject this claim if among 400 people 216 or more say that they have had two colds per year,
    (a) what is the probability that we have committed a type 1 error;
    (b) is it possible in this investigation to commit a type 2 error? Explain.

18. A sample of 36 variates has a mean of 40 and a standard deviation of 2.1. Find the 95% confidence limits for the mean of the population.

19. In a sample of 60 variates the mean is found to be 35 and the standard deviation 4.2. Find limits within which the population mean is expected to lie with a probability of 98%.

20. Suppose the standard deviation of stature in males is 2.48 inches. One hundred male students chosen at random in a large university are measured, and their average height is found to be 68.52 inches. Determine the 99% confidence limits for the mean height of the men in this university.

21. From two samples the following data are calculated:
$$\overline{X} = 75, \quad n_1 = 36, \quad \Sigma(X - \overline{X})^2 = 1482;$$
$$\overline{Y} = 60, \quad n_2 = 64, \quad \Sigma(Y - \overline{Y})^2 = 1830.$$
Find the 98% confidence limits for the difference between the means of the populations from which these samples were selected.

22. Two different samples from the same population are used to find confidence limits for the mean of the population. The first sample gives confidence limits of 11 and 21, the second 13 and 25. If the same level of significance is used, what is the ratio of the size of the first sample to the size of the second sample?

23. The average monthly income of families in a certain city is to be estimated from a random sample selected from a directory. If the average income is to be estimated within $100.00 with a probability of 90% (that is, if we desire to be 90% confident that the sample mean and the mean income of all families do not differ by more than $100.00), find the least size of the sample required for such an estimate. Assume it is known that the standard deviation of the incomes of the families in the city is $200.00.

24. In a plant-breeding experiment in which two types of flowers (types $A$ and $B$) can occur, the expected probability of occurrence of type $A$ is $\frac{7}{16}$. A worker carrying out an experiment yielding these two types of flowers finds that exactly one-half of his flowers are of type $A$ and, therefore, rejects, at the 1% level of significance, the hypothesis that $\frac{7}{16}$ of the flowers are of type $A$. What is the least number of flowers the experimenter could have investigated for the rejection of the hypothesis to be justified?

25. From a sample of size 10, taken from a normal distribution, the 99% confidence limits for the mean of the population are calculated to be $\overline{X} \pm 5.2$. Determine the standard deviation of the population.

# 10 Student's *t*-Distribution. Small Sample Methods

## 10.1. The Best Estimate of the Standard Deviation of the Population

In the preceding chapter it was pointed out that if a sample is small ($n$ equal to 30 or less), its standard deviation $\hat{s}$ can no longer be used as an approximation of the standard deviation of the population $\sigma$. Since in general a population will contain more extreme data than a sample, it is to be expected that usually $\sigma$ will be somewhat larger than $\hat{s}$. Of course, it is impossible to write a precise formula for $\sigma$ in terms of $\hat{s}$, since different samples from the same population may have rather widely differing standard deviations. In most cases, however, the quantity

$$\sqrt{\frac{n}{n-1}}\,\hat{s}$$

will give an excellent approximation for $\sigma$, although it rarely will be precisely equal to $\sigma$. This quantity we shall denote by $s$; thus

(10-1)
$$s = \sqrt{\frac{n}{n-1}}\,\hat{s}$$

is the "best estimate of the standard deviation of the population" as obtained from a sample. Keep in mind that $s$ may not always approximate $\sigma$ very well. Indeed, it may happen, in a particular case that $\hat{s}$ is closer to $\sigma$ than to $s$.

We note from (10-1) that, if $n$ is large, the expression under the radical is close to 1; thus, as indicated before, $\hat{s}$ for large $n$ affords a good approximation of $\sigma$.

Formula (10-1) can be justified as follows: Consider a population with a large number of variates; then the mean of all the sample variances $\hat{s}^2$ can be shown to equal

$$m_{\hat{s}^2} = \frac{n-1}{n}\,\sigma^2.$$

Now since most of the $\hat{s}^2$ do not differ much from $m_s^2$, let us replace $m_s^2$ by $\hat{s}^2$ and $\sigma$ by $s$, the estimate of the standard deviation; thus

$$\hat{s}^2 = \frac{n-1}{n} s^2,$$

from which formula (10-1) follows.

Suppose a sample of $n$ variates $X_1, X_2, \cdots, X_n$ is given; then the best estimate of the standard deviation of the population is given by

$$s = \sqrt{\frac{n}{n-1}}\,\hat{s} = \sqrt{\frac{n}{n-1}}\sqrt{\frac{\Sigma(X-\overline{X})^2}{n}} = \sqrt{\frac{\Sigma(X-\overline{X})^2}{n-1}},$$

and the formula

(10-2)
$$s = \sqrt{\frac{\Sigma(X-\overline{X})^2}{n-1}}$$

gives the best estimate of the standard deviation of the population when the $n$ variates of a sample are known. It should be noted that the formulae for $s$ and $\hat{s}$ differ only in that the former has $n-1$ in the denominator whereas the latter has $n$.

Many textbooks in statistics refer to the expression given in formula (10-2) as the "standard deviation of the sample." This is merely a matter of terminology, which in no way affects any of the theorems which follow. The authors of this book prefer to denote the standard deviation of the sample by $\hat{s}$. The use of this terminology seems more appropriate, since if the mean of a set of data is the same whether the data are considered as a sample or as a population, the same should be true for the standard deviation; i.e., the standard deviation of a set of data should not depend on whether the data are considered as a sample or a population.

We shall now introduce a notation which is universally accepted; that is, whenever the standard deviation of a population is unknown and statistics have to be calculated from the best estimate of the standard deviation, $\sigma$ is replaced by $s$ in the corresponding formulae. Thus, the best estimate of the standard deviation of the mean of samples of $n$ variates is denoted by $s_{\overline{x}}$ and is equal to

(10-3)
$$s_{\overline{x}} = \frac{s}{\sqrt{n}}.$$

## 10.2.   Student's *t*-Distribution

Consider the case where the standard deviation of the population is unknown and its estimate $s$, obtained from a sample, has to be used. We must first determine what effect the substitution of $s$ for $\sigma$ has on the theorems of Chapter 8. This problem was first studied by W. S. Gosset, a statistician at Guinness' Brewery in Dublin who wrote under the pseudonym "Student." He noted that the quantities resulting from this substitution no longer satisfied a normal distribution, but satisfy a different type of distribution which has since been called Student's *t*-distribution.

**DEFINITION 10-1.** If the probability of occurrence of a quantity $t$ is given by

$$(10\text{-}4) \qquad\qquad y = c\left(1 + \frac{t^2}{\nu}\right)^{-\frac{\nu+1}{2}},$$

the distribution is called a *Student's t-distribution*, where $\nu$ is called the number of degrees of freedom, and $c$ is a constant depending on $\nu$ and is chosen in such a way that the total area under the probability curve (10-4) is equal to 1.

Number of degrees of freedom is a term frequently used in statistics, and it is defined below.

**DEFINITION 10-2.** For a given set of conditions, the *number of degrees of freedom* (frequently denoted by *df* or *D.F.*) is the maximum number of variates which can freely be assigned (i.e., calculated or assumed) before the rest of the variates are completely determined; that is, it is the total number of variates minus the number of independent relationships existing among them.

To graph the curves given by (10-4) for various values of $\nu$, we note that for all values of $\nu$ the curve reaches its maximum value at $t = 0$ and is symmetric about a line drawn at $t = 0$ perpendicular to the horizontal axis.

Figure 10-1 shows the graphs of (10-4) for $\nu = 3$ and $\nu = 7$, and also the normal probability curve.

The curves given by (10-4) approach the horizontal axis at a less rapid rate than does the normal curve, but it can be proved that as $\nu$ becomes larger and larger the curves given by (10-4) approach the normal curve.

To determine probabilities from Student's *t*-distribution, we determine the appropriate areas under the curves given by (10-4). These can be found by use of Appendix Table II, which gives for various $\nu$-values (listed in the first column) the values of $t$ corresponding to various two-tail areas. For example, for $\nu = 20$, we find the *t*-value corresponding to a value of 0.05 for the two tail areas to be $t = 2.086$. This means that the probability of obtaining in a Student's *t*-distribution a value of $t > 2.086$ or $t < -2.086$ for $\nu = 20$ is equal to 0.05.

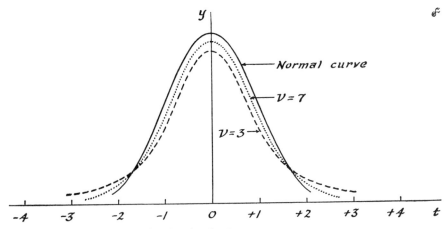
Fig. 10-1. Typical Student's t-distributions.

## 10.3. The Distribution of the Mean

We may now state the theorem which results from the substitution of $s$ for $\sigma$ in Theorem 8-1.

**THEOREM 10-1.** If a variable $X$ satisfies a normal distribution and has mean $m$, and if all possible samples of $n$ variates are taken from this population and their means denoted by $\overline{X}$, then the quantity

$$(10\text{-}5) \qquad\qquad t = \frac{\overline{X} - m}{s_{\overline{x}}}$$

satisfies a Student's t-distribution with $n - 1$ degrees of freedom, where

$$s_{\overline{x}} = \frac{s}{\sqrt{n}}.$$

Note that the difference between this theorem and Theorem 8-1 is that $\sigma_{\overline{x}}$ is replaced by $s_{\overline{x}}$ and that the resultant quantity $t$ satisfies a Student's t-distribution whereas the quantity $z$ satisfies a normal distribution.

*Example 10-1.* A sample of 16 variates is found to have a mean of 28.0 and a standard deviation of 3.0. On the basis of the 5% level of significance, is there reason to reject the hypothesis that the mean of the population is 30.0?

*Solution.* To test the hypothesis that $m = 30.0$ we calculate the probability of selecting from a population with $m = 30.0$ a sample of 16 variates whose mean is 28.0 or less or 32.0 or more (assuming a two-tailed test). Actually, since we are using the 5% level, it is sufficient to determine whether this probability is more or less than 0.05. The calculations follow.

Hypothesis:    $m = 30.0$.

$$\hat{s} = 3.0,$$

$$s = \sqrt{\frac{16}{15}}\,(3.0) = \frac{12}{\sqrt{15}},$$

$$s_{\bar{x}} = \frac{s}{\sqrt{16}} = \frac{1}{\sqrt{16}}\frac{12}{\sqrt{15}} = \frac{3}{\sqrt{15}} = 0.78,$$

$$t = \frac{28.0 - 30.0}{0.78} = \frac{-2.0}{0.78} = -2.56.$$

For $\nu = 15$, $t_{.05} = 2.131$.

Since $|t| = 2.56 > 2.131$, the probability mentioned above is less than 0.05, so we conclude that the result is significant, which causes us to reject the hypothesis.

By linear interpolation, the probability of obtaining a mean of 28 or less or 32 or more is found to be 0.0226, a result which, however, is not precise due to the inaccuracy inherent in linear interpolation.

It might be interesting to determine the probability which would have been obtained if we had mistakenly used large sample methods, i.e., if we had approximated $\sigma$ by $\hat{s}$ and used the normal curve. In that case we would have found

$$\sigma = \hat{s} = 3.0,$$

$$\sigma_{\bar{x}} = \frac{3}{\sqrt{16}} = 0.75,$$

$$z = \frac{28.0 - 30.0}{0.75} = \frac{-2.0}{0.75} = -2.67,$$

$$P = (0.5000 - 0.4962)2 = (0.0038)2 = 0.0076,$$

a value considerably smaller than 0.0226.

This demonstrates that the mistaken use of large sample methods, when, properly, Student's t-distribution should be applied, will cause us to underestimate the probability involved, and therefore will frequently cause us to call a result significant even though it may not actually be so. That the use of large sample methods (normal curve) will result in too small a probability can also be seen from Figure 10-1, which shows that for a given value of $t$ (or $z$) the two tail areas are considerably smaller for the normal probability curve than for the Student's t-curves.

*Example 10-2.*  A company claims that the average life of batteries of a certain type is 21.5 hours. A laboratory tests 6 batteries manufactured by this company and obtains the following lives in hours: 19, 18, 22, 20, 16, 25. Do these results indicate that batteries of this type have a shorter life than that claimed by the company (5% level)?

*Solution.* To test the hypothesis that $m \geq 21.5$, we calculate the probability of selecting from a population with $m = 21.5$ a sample of 6 variates whose mean is less than that obtained in the experiment. A one-tailed test is applicable here.

Hypothesis:     $m = 21.5$.

| $X$ | $X - \overline{X}$ | $(X - \overline{X})^2$ |
|-----|-----|-----|
| 19 | $-1$ | 1 |
| 18 | $-2$ | 4 |
| 22 | 2 | 4 |
| 20 | 0 | 0 |
| 16 | $-4$ | 16 |
| 25 | 5 | 25 |
| 120 | 0 | 50 |

$$\overline{X} = \frac{120}{6} = 20.0,$$

$$s = \sqrt{\frac{50}{5}} = \sqrt{10},$$

$$s_{\overline{x}} = \frac{\sqrt{10}}{\sqrt{6}} = \sqrt{1.67} = 1.29,$$

$$t = \frac{20.0 - 21.5}{1.29} = \frac{-1.5}{1.29} = -1.16.$$

Since we are using a one-tailed test, we need to find the value of $t$ such that the area to its left is equal to 0.05, which is the same as finding the value of $t$ for which both tail areas total 0.10. Thus, we find for $\nu = 5$, $t_{.10} = 2.015$.

Now since $|t| = 1.16 < 2.015$, the probability mentioned above exceeds 5%, so the result is not significant. Consequently, the results do not indicate that batteries of this type have a shorter life than that claimed by the company.

It should be recalled from Chapter 4 that for purposes of machine calculation it is very convenient to use the fact that

(10-6)     $$\Sigma(X - \overline{X})^2 = \Sigma X^2 - \frac{(\Sigma X)^2}{n},$$

whenever sums of squares of deviations have to be calculated. Formula (10-6) was not used in Example (10-2), since we were dealing with a very small sample and simple numbers. Since, however, such a situation ordinarily will not prevail, the use of (10-6) is encouraged.

*Example 10-3.* A sample of 25 variates is found to have a mean of 38.5 and a standard deviation of 2.3. Find the 95% confidence limits for the mean of the population.

*Solution.* In this case we find

$$s = \sqrt{\frac{25}{24}} (2.3) = \frac{11.5}{\sqrt{24}},$$

$$s_{\bar{x}} = \frac{1}{\sqrt{25}} \frac{11.5}{\sqrt{24}} = \frac{2.3}{\sqrt{24}} = \frac{2.3}{4.90} = 0.47.$$

To determine the 95% confidence limits for $m$, we find from Appendix Table II, for 24 degrees of freedom, the value of $t$ for which the two tail areas total 0.05 to be $t_{.05} = 2.064$. Therefore

$$\frac{\bar{X} - m}{0.47} = \pm 2.064,$$

which we solve for $m$:

$$m = \bar{X} \pm 0.970 = 38.5 \pm 0.970.$$

A mistaken use of large sample methods would have resulted in our obtaining the confidence limits $m = 38.5 \pm 0.902$, which does not differ appreciably from the above result, owing to the relatively large size of the sample.

## 10.4. The Distribution of the Difference between Means

We shall now study the changes which result in Theorem 8-3 if the standard deviations of the two populations are unknown, as is frequently the case. Before introducing the appropriate estimates, we shall make the additional assumption that the two populations have identical standard deviations. The reader may be inclined to believe that this is a rather severe restriction. It will be shown, however, that in most applications this assumption is satisfied. If we are given two samples with variates $X_1, X_2, \cdots, X_{n_1}$ and $Y_1, Y_2, \cdots, Y_{n_2}$, from two different populations with identical standard deviations, it would seem natural to make use of all these variates to arrive at an estimate of this common standard deviation. This is done by replacing the numerator of formula (10-2) by the total of the sums of the squares of the deviations of the variates of each sample from its mean, and the denominator by the total of the degrees of freedom of the two samples. The standard deviation evaluated in this way is not affected by any difference which may exist between the means of the populations. This substitution results in the formula

$$(10\text{-}7) \qquad s = \sqrt{\frac{\Sigma(X - \overline{X})^2 + \Sigma(Y - \overline{Y})^2}{n_1 + n_2 - 2}},$$

which is frequently referred to as a "pooled estimate of the standard deviation," since we have pooled the information available from two samples.

We can now state the theorem which results from the substitution of the estimate $s$ as given by (10-7) for both $\sigma_x$ and $\sigma_y$ in Theorem 8-3.

**THEOREM 10-2.**  Let $X$ and $Y$ be the variables of two normally and independently distributed populations having means $m_x$ and $m_y$, respectively, and identical standard deviations. Take all possible pairs of samples of sizes $n_1$ and $n_2$, respectively, from these populations, and denote their means by $\overline{X}$ and $\overline{Y}$, respectively, and consider for each pair the difference between sample means $\overline{X} - \overline{Y}$. Then the quantity

$$(10\text{-}8) \qquad t = \frac{(\overline{X} - \overline{Y}) - m_{\overline{x}-\overline{y}}}{s_{\overline{x}-\overline{y}}}$$

satisfies a Student's $t$-distribution with $n_1 + n_2 - 2$ degrees of freedom, where

$$(10\text{-}9) \qquad s_{\overline{x}-\overline{y}} = \sqrt{s_{\overline{x}}^2 + s_{\overline{y}}^2}, \quad s_{\overline{x}} = \frac{s}{\sqrt{n_1}}, \quad s_{\overline{y}} = \frac{s}{\sqrt{n_2}},$$

and $s$ is given by (10-7).

This theorem now makes it possible to solve the very practical problem of determining from two given samples whether or not the respective populations have the same or different means.

*Example 10-4.*  Strength tests on two types of wool fabric give the following results (in pounds per square inch):

Type I:   138, 127, 134, 125
Type II:   134, 137, 135, 140, 130, 134

Is the difference in means of the two types sufficient to warrant the conclusion that one is better than the other (5% level)?

*Solution.*  Denoting by $X$ the variates of the sample of type I, by $Y$ those of the sample of type II, and assuming that the populations from which these two samples were taken have identical standard deviations, estimated by $s$, we find

| X | Y | $X - \bar{X}$ | $(X - \bar{X})^2$ | $Y - \bar{Y}$ | $(Y - \bar{Y})^2$ |
|---|---|---|---|---|---|
| 138 | 134 | 7 | 49 | −1 | 1 |
| 127 | 137 | −4 | 16 | 2 | 4 |
| 134 | 135 | 3 | 9 | 0 | 0 |
| 125 | 140 | −6 | 36 | 5 | 25 |
|  | 130 |  |  | −5 | 25 |
|  | 134 |  |  | −1 | 1 |
| 524 | 810 | 0 | 110 | 0 | 56 |

Hypothesis:     $m_x = m_y$,  or   $m_x - m_y = 0$.

$$\bar{X} = \frac{524}{4} = 131,$$

$$\bar{Y} = \frac{810}{6} = 135,$$

$$s = \sqrt{\frac{110 + 56}{8}} = \sqrt{\frac{166}{8}} = \sqrt{20.75},$$

$$s_{\bar{x}} = \frac{\sqrt{20.75}}{\sqrt{4}} = \sqrt{5.19},$$

$$s_{\bar{y}} = \frac{\sqrt{20.75}}{\sqrt{6}} = \sqrt{3.46},$$

$$s_{\bar{x}-\bar{y}} = \sqrt{5.19 + 3.46} = \sqrt{8.65} = 2.94,$$

$$t = \frac{(131 - 135) - 0}{2.94} = \frac{-4}{2.94} = -1.36.$$

For $\nu = 8$, $t_{.05} = 2.306$.

Since $|t| = 1.36 < 2.306$, we conclude that the probability of selecting from two populations with identical means and identical standard deviations two samples whose means differ by more than 4 (in absolute value) is considerably more than 5%, which indicates that this result is not significant. Therefore, the difference between means of the two types is not sufficient to warrant the conclusion that one is better than the other.

The assumption of identical standard deviations of the two populations in problems of this type needs justification. Let us assume a population whose variates are $X_1, X_2, \cdots, X_N$; furthermore, let us assume that the effect of a treatment upon these variates is such that it raises each of them by a fixed amount $d$ resulting in a new population $Y_1, Y_2, \cdots, Y_N$. The mean of the population of $Y$'s is

$$m_y = \frac{\Sigma(X + d)}{N} = \frac{\Sigma X + Nd}{N} = \frac{\Sigma X}{N} + d = m_x + d;$$

thus the mean has been changed by the amount $d$. Let us now compare the standard deviations of these populations:

$$\sigma_y^2 = \frac{1}{N}\left\{\Sigma(Y - m_y)^2\right\} = \frac{1}{N}\left\{\Sigma[(X + d) - (m_x + d)]^2\right\}$$

$$= \frac{1}{N}\left\{\Sigma(X - m_x)^2\right\} = \sigma_x^2;$$

thus there has been no change in the standard deviations. This demonstrates that if treatments have purely additive effects they change the means but not the standard deviations.

On the other hand, there are treatments which have other than additive effects and consequently may influence the standard deviations. In the rare situations where this occurs, Theorem 10-2 is, of course, not applicable. The procedure applicable in such a case will not be discussed, although it requires only a relatively minor modification of Theorem 10-2.

The question of deciding from two given samples whether or not the assumption of identical standard deviations of the two populations is valid is answered by use of the so-called $F$-distribution, which is discussed in Chapter 16.

## 10.5.   The Case of Paired Variates

Many experiments are performed in such a way that each variate of one sample is paired with a particular variate of another sample. If, for example, the effectiveness of a fertilizer is to be determined, the experimenter might select 10 plots, treat half of each plot with the fertilizer, and leave the other half untreated to serve as a control. In this case, the yields from the treated and untreated halves of each plot constitute a set of paired variates. Such a procedure of carrying out the experiment is superior to selecting 20 plots, fertilizing half of them, and not fertilizing the other half. In the paired experiment, the chance that a possible significant difference between means is due to the treatments which were applied rather than some extraneous source such as soil or weather conditions is greatly increased. Consequently, wherever possible a paired experiment should be applied.

However, for paired experiments Theorem 10-2 is not applicable, since it requires that the populations be independent, which is not the case with pairing.

To analyze paired experiments, we consider for each pair the difference between the variates $X$ and $Y$, and denote this difference by $D$,

$$D = X - Y.$$

We now consider the population of differences so obtained. Select all possible samples of size $n$ from this population, denoting their means by $\bar{D}_1$, $\bar{D}_2$, $\cdots$ , and consider the distribution of these sample means. This situation is completely analogous to that of Theorem 10-1, the difference $D$ now playing the role of the variable $X$ of Theorem 10-1. Consequently, a mere change of notation in Theorem 10-1 gives us the distribution of $\bar{D}$ and results in Theorem 10-3.

> **THEOREM 10-3.** Let $X$ and $Y$ be the variables of two normally distributed populations in which the variates are paired, and for each pair let the difference between the variates be denoted by $D$. Now if all possible samples of $n$ variates are taken from this population of $D$ values, and the sample mean is denoted by $\bar{D}$, then the quantity
>
> (10-10) $$t = \frac{\bar{D} - m_{\bar{d}}}{s_{\bar{d}}}$$
>
> satisfies a Student's $t$-distribution with $n - 1$ degrees of freedom, where
>
> (10-11) $$s_{\bar{d}} = \frac{s_d}{\sqrt{n}}, \quad s_d = \sqrt{\frac{\Sigma(D - \bar{D})^2}{n - 1}}.$$

The subscript $d$ in $s_d$ indicates that we are dealing with a population of differences.

To determine whether two sample means from paired populations differ significantly, we set up the hypothesis that the two populations have identical means, in which case

$$m_d = \frac{\Sigma D}{N} = \frac{\Sigma(X - Y)}{N} = \frac{\Sigma X}{N} - \frac{\Sigma Y}{N} = 0,$$

and calculate the probability of obtaining from two such populations a pair of samples for which the value of $\bar{D}$ exceeds (in absolute value) that obtained in the experiment.

*Example 10-5.* In a certain school, 16 girl beginners in the first grade were selected and paired on the basis of IQ, socio-economic rating of family, general health, and family size. One member of each pair had attended 1 year of kindergarten and the other had not. On a certain first grade readiness test given to all 16 pupils the scores were as follows:

| Pair | Kindergarten | No Kindergarten |
|------|--------------|-----------------|
| 1 | 83 | 78 |
| 2 | 74 | 74 |
| 3 | 67 | 63 |
| 4 | 64 | 66 |
| 5 | 70 | 68 |
| 6 | 67 | 63 |
| 7 | 81 | 77 |
| 8 | 64 | 65 |

Using the 5% level of significance, is there evidence from this investigation that kindergarten is of benefit in preparing for the first grade?

*Solution.* Denoting the variates of the first sample by $X$ and those of the second sample by $Y$, we find

| $X$ | $Y$ | $D = X - Y$ | $D - \bar{D}$ | $(D - \bar{D})^2$ |
|-----|-----|-------------|---------------|-------------------|
| 83 | 78 | 5 | 3 | 9 |
| 74 | 74 | 0 | $-2$ | 4 |
| 67 | 63 | 4 | 2 | 4 |
| 64 | 66 | $-2$ | $-4$ | 16 |
| 70 | 68 | 2 | 0 | 0 |
| 67 | 63 | 4 | 2 | 4 |
| 81 | 77 | 4 | 2 | 4 |
| 64 | 65 | $-1$ | $-3$ | 9 |
|    |    | 16 | 0 | 50 |

Hypothesis:     $m_d = 0$.

$$\bar{D} = \frac{16}{8} = 2.0,$$

$$s_d = \sqrt{\frac{50}{7}} = \sqrt{7.14},$$

$$s_{\bar{d}} = \frac{\sqrt{7.14}}{\sqrt{8}} = \sqrt{0.892} = 0.94,$$

$$t = \frac{2.0 - 0}{0.94} = 2.13.$$

For $\nu = 7$, $t_{.05} = 2.365$.

Since $t = 2.13 < 2.365$, the result is not significant, and we cannot conclude from these data that kindergarten is of benefit in preparing for the first grade.

It should be understood that Theorem 10-3 is applicable only when variates are paired. When variates are not paired, Theorem 10-2 applies. Consequently, in order to use the proper statistical analysis of a test for a significant difference between means, we must know whether or not pairing was employed in the experiment.

*Example 10-6.* In a wheat variety test conducted on 16 pairs of plots, the mean difference in yields between the two varieties is found to be 3.0 bushel per acre. The standard error of this mean difference is 1.1 bushels per acre.
  (a) Determine the 98% confidence limits for the mean difference in yields between the two varieties.
  (b) Use the answer to part (a) to decide whether there is a significant difference in yields between the two varieties (2% level).

*Solution.* (a) $n = 16$, $\bar{D} = 3.0$, $s_{\bar{d}} = 1.1$.
We are asked to estimate the mean $m_d$ of the population of differences in yields between the two variates. Since this is a paired experiment, Theorem 10-3 is applicable. The *t*-value for 15 degrees of freedom for which the two tail areas add up to 0.02 is found from Appendix Table II to be $t_{.02} = 2.602$; thus

$$\frac{\bar{D} - m_d}{1.1} = \pm 2.602$$

and

$$m_d = \bar{D} \pm 2.862 = 3.0 \pm 2.862$$

or

$$0.138 \quad \text{and} \quad 5.862,$$

which are the 98% confidence limits.

  (b) If there is no significant difference between the varieties at the 2% level, the 98% confidence limits for $m_d$ must include 0, the mean difference between the two varieties. Since, however, from part (a) $m_d$ is between 0.138 and 5.862, 0 is not included, and a significant difference in yields is indicated.

# Exercises

Unless otherwise specified, use the 5% level of significance. Answer each question exactly in the form in which it is asked. Also, in each case list the number of degrees of freedom and the appropriate tabular *t*-value.

1. A sample of 14 variates has a mean of 34.86 and a standard deviation of 4.23. Find limits within which 99% of the time we would be correct in saying that the population mean lies.

2. In a sample of 23 variates the mean is 26.3 and the standard deviation 1.9. Find the 98% confidence limits for the mean of the population.

3. (a) Find the 90% confidence limits for the mean of a normally distributed population with standard deviation 3.83, if a sample taken from that population has the following variates: 18.5, 20.6, 12.9, 14.6, 19.8, 15.0.

   (b) What 90% confidence limits would have been found if in part (a) the standard deviation of the population had been unknown?

4. A sample of 10 observations has a mean of 45 and a standard deviation of 12.

   (a) Find the 98% confidence limits for the mean of the population.

   (b) Do the same for a sample of 15 observations, everything else being the same.

   (c) Do the same for a sample of 20 observations, everything else being the same.

   (d) What is the implication regarding the relation between the size of the sample and the length of the confidence interval, other things being the same?

5. The drained weights, in ounces, of a random sample of 8 cans of cherries are as follows: 12.1, 11.9, 12.4, 12.3, 11.9, 12.1, 12.4, 12.1.

   (a) Find the 99% confidence limits for the mean drained weight per can of cherries for the population from which the sample is taken.

   (b) Using the result of part (a), does this sample indicate (1% level) that the production standard of 12.35 ounces average drained weight per can of cherries is being maintained? Explain your answer.

6. A test of the breaking strengths of 10 safety belts manufactured by a company showed a mean breaking strength of 7910 lbs. and a standard deviation of 90 lbs., whereas the manufacturer claimed a mean breaking strength of 8000 lbs. In view of the lower mean breaking strength of the sample, can we still support the manufacturer's claim (1% level)?

7. Assume that on the average students are the individual owners of 25 paperback books. A sample of 9 students is found to possess an average of 30 such books. This sample mean is found to be just barely significant at the 10% level. What is the standard deviation of the sample of 9 students?

8. From a sample of five grapefruit the 95% confidence limits for the mean weight of all grapefruit in a shipment are calculated to be 12.89 and 17.11 ounces. Find the mean and standard deviation of this sample of five grapefruit.

9. From a sample of 26 variates, the 95% confidence limits for the mean of the population whose standard deviation is unknown are determined to be 21.50 and 26.50. Find the 98% confidence limits for the mean of the population.

10. The results of quality control tests on two manufacturing processes are as follows:

Process I:  1.5, 2.5, 3.5, 2.5
Process II:  2.5, 3.0, 3.0, 4.0, 3.5, 2.0

Do these results allow the conclusion that the processes yield different qualities (10% level)?

11. A new method for making concrete has been proposed. To test whether the new method has increased the compressive strength, five sample blocks are made by each method. The compressive strengths in pounds per square inch are as follows:

New Method:  154, 143, 132, 147, 139
Standard Method:  144, 131, 155, 126, 134

Would you say that the new method has increased the compressive strength?

12. The table below gives data on the gain in weight of two lots of rats:

| Diet | High Protein | Low Protein |
|---|---|---|
| Number of rats | 12 | 7 |
| Mean gain (in grams) | 120 | 101 |
| Sum of squares of deviations from mean | 5032 | 2552 |

Do these data indicate a significant difference between mean gains in weight for the two groups?

13. A cigarette manufacturer tests tobaccos of two different brands for nicotine content and obtains the following results (in milligrams):

Brand *A*:  24, 26, 25, 22, 23
Brand *B*:  27, 28, 25, 29, 26

Do these results indicate that there is a difference in the mean nicotine content of the two brands?

14. Below are figures for protein tests of the same variety of wheat grown in two districts. If these are the only figures available, test whether or not there is a significant difference between the average proteins for the two districts.

District 1:  12.6, 13.4, 11.9, 12.8, 13.0
District 2:  13.1, 13.4, 12.8, 13.5, 13.3, 12.7, 12.4

15. Solve Example 9-4 by the methods of this chapter, i.e., small sample methods.

16. Solve exercise 13, Chapter 9, by the methods of this chapter.

17. Solve exercise 14, Chapter 9, by the methods of this chapter.

18. Two samples of 15 specimens each of two types of wool fabric were subjected to strength tests. The mean of the first sample was 131 pounds per square inch, that of the second 136 pounds per square inch. The respective standard deviations of the two samples were 6.25 pounds per square inch and 4.65 pounds per square inch. Does this indicate that the second type of wool fabric is superior?

19. A certain test is given to a 45-student statistics class, in order to determine the difference in accomplishment of men and women. The 20 women students have an average score of 60 with a standard deviation of 19, and the 25 men students have an average score of 66 with a standard deviation of 16. What are the 98% confidence limits for the difference between the mean scores of men and women students?

20. Two analysts $A$ and $B$ study the melting point of a metal. Five readings by $A$ show a variance of 12 and 4 readings by $B$ a variance of 20. What is the least absolute value of the difference between the means of the readings that would be considered significant at the 5% level?

21. In an experiment involving 10 plots of wheat, half of each plot is sown with seed of a rust-resistant variety, and the other half is sown with ordinary seed. Do the results listed below (weight of grain in pounds) indicate that there is a significant difference between the two seeds?

| Plot | Rust-resistant | Ordinary | Plot | Rust-resistant | Ordinary |
|------|----------------|----------|------|----------------|----------|
| 1    | 49             | 47       | 6    | 49             | 44       |
| 2    | 58             | 57       | 7    | 66             | 67       |
| 3    | 53             | 49       | 8    | 55             | 52       |
| 4    | 60             | 57       | 9    | 44             | 42       |
| 5    | 45             | 44       | 10   | 52             | 53       |

22. In a paired feeding experiment, the gains in weight (in pounds) of hogs fed on two different diets are as listed below. Can either diet be considered superior?

| Pair | Diet A | Diet B |
|------|--------|--------|
| 1 | 25 | 19 |
| 2 | 30 | 32 |
| 3 | 28 | 21 |
| 4 | 34 | 34 |
| 5 | 23 | 19 |

23. A newly discovered apple is delicious in flavor. It is decided to test its yielding capacities by planting the apple adjacent to a standard apple in 8 orchards scattered about a region suitable for production of both varieties. When the trees are mature, the yields in bushels are measured. The data are as follows:

| Orchard | New Apple | Standard Apple |
|---------|-----------|----------------|
| 1 | 13 | 12 |
| 2 | 14 | 16 |
| 3 | 19 | 17 |
| 4 | 10 | 9 |
| 5 | 15 | 16 |
| 6 | 14 | 12 |
| 7 | 12 | 10 |
| 8 | 11 | 8 |

Do these results indicate a greater yield for the new apple than for the standard apple?

24. A company wishes to study the effectiveness of a coffee break on the productivity of its workers. It selects 6 workers and measures their productivity on a day without a coffee break, and later measures the productivity of the same 6 workers on a day when they are given a coffee break. The scores measuring the productivity are as follows:

| Worker | Without Coffee Break | With Coffee Break |
|--------|----------------------|-------------------|
| 1 | 23 | 28 |
| 2 | 35 | 38 |
| 3 | 29 | 29 |
| 4 | 33 | 37 |
| 5 | 43 | 42 |
| 6 | 32 | 30 |

Do these results indicate that a coffee break raises productivity?

25. Some believe that the ability of students to perform arithmetic improves after they have taken this course in statistics. A sample of 8 students is given an aptitude test on arithmetic before and after taking this course, with the following results, based on a scale of 10.

| Student | Before | After |
|---------|--------|-------|
| 1 | 7 | 8 |
| 2 | 6 | 5 |
| 3 | 7 | 9 |
| 4 | 8 | 8 |
| 5 | 6 | 3 |
| 6 | 8 | 9 |
| 7 | 5 | 8 |
| 8 | 2 | 9 |

Do these results confirm this belief ($2\frac{1}{2}\%$ level)?

26. To test two promising new corn hybrids under normal farming conditions, a seed company selects 8 farms at random in Iowa and plants both hybrids in experimental plots on each farm. The yields, in bushels per acre, for the 8 locations are:

| Farm | Hybrid A | Hybrid B |
|------|----------|----------|
| 1 | 86 | 80 |
| 2 | 87 | 79 |
| 3 | 56 | 58 |
| 4 | 93 | 91 |
| 5 | 84 | 77 |
| 6 | 93 | 82 |
| 7 | 73 | 74 |
| 8 | 79 | 66 |

Set up the 95% confidence limits for the mean difference in yield of the two hybrids.

27. In a study using identical twins, one twin is given a drug and then an intelligence test while under the influence of the drug; the other twin is given the same intelligence test under normal conditions. If this experiment is conducted on 6 pairs of twins and results in a mean difference in intelligence of 5 points with a standard deviation of 6.48, set up the 95% confidence limits for the mean difference in scores.

28. At the University of California in Davis an experiment was carried out to determine the effect of light on the time of day at which eggs are laid. A group of 8 hens was kept in total darkness, and the number of eggs laid each hour was recorded over a 29-day period. Another group of 8 hens was exposed to 1 minute of light every hour for a 29-day period, and again the number of eggs laid each hour was recorded. The results are listed in the table below.

*Number of Eggs Laid*

| Time | Total Darkness | One Minute of Light Per Hour |
|---|---|---|
| Midnight– 1 A.M. | 0 | 1 |
| 1– 2 | 0 | 1 |
| 2– 3 | 0 | 0 |
| 3– 4 | 6 | 2 |
| 4– 5 | 8 | 5 |
| 5– 6 | 5 | 2 |
| 6– 7 | 8 | 9 |
| 7– 8 | 5 | 9 |
| 8– 9 | 15 | 4 |
| 9–10 | 9 | 19 |
| 10–11 | 12 | 7 |
| 11–12 Noon | 9 | 9 |
| Noon– 1 P.M. | 8 | 10 |
| 1– 2 | 8 | 9 |
| 2– 3 | 6 | 3 |
| 3– 4 | 2 | 4 |
| 4– 5 | 1 | 5 |
| 5– 6 | 1 | 2 |
| 6– 7 | 0 | 2 |
| 7– 8 | 0 | 0 |
| 8– 9 | 0 | 0 |
| 9–10 | 0 | 0 |
| 10–11 | 0 | 2 |
| 11–Midnight | 0 | 0 |

Can we conclude from these data that the 1 minute of light each hour had an effect on the average time at which eggs were laid?

# 11   Nonparametric Statistics

## 11.1.   Introduction

The theorems of Chapters 8 and 10 are true only if the populations involved are normally distributed. For example, the sample mean satisfies a normal distribution only if the population is normally distributed, although for populations which are not normal the distribution of the sample mean approaches that of a normal distribution as the size of the sample increases. In general, the distributions of sample statistics depend upon the type of distribution which is satisfied by the population. Since in many cases little or no knowledge is available about the distribution of the population, it becomes desirable to employ methods which make no assumptions regarding the distribution and the parameters of the population.

> **DEFINITION 11-1.**  Statistical analyses which do not depend upon the knowledge of the distribution and parameters of the population are called *nonparametric* or *distribution-free methods*.

There was relatively little interest in nonparametric statistics until about 1945, when Frank Wilcoxon proposed a test, now referred to as the Wilcoxon two-sample test, which is distinguished by both its simplicity and the very excellent results it gives, even in the case where the distribution of the population is known to be normal. For these reasons, the use of nonparametric techniques has become widespread. As in the use of the Student's *t*-distribution, the case where the variates of the two samples are from two independent populations must be distinguished from the case where the variates are paired. For the first case, the Wilcoxon two-sample test will be discussed; for the second, the sign test and the Wilcoxon test for paired variates will be considered.

## 11.2.   The Wilcoxon Two-Sample Test for the Unpaired Case

Assume that two samples of $n_1$ and $n_2$ variates, respectively, are given and that we wish to test the hypothesis of equal population means. Then the two samples together have $n = n_1 + n_2$ variates. In Wilcoxon's test, these $n$ variates are graded (or ranked) according to increasing size, that is, we substitute the scores (or ranks) 1, 2, 3, $\cdots$, $n$ for the actual numerical data. If there is no significant difference between the two sample means, then the total of the ranks corresponding to the first and those corresponding to the second sample should be about the same. If, however, the total of the ranks for one sample is appreciably less than that of the other, we calculate—under the hypothesis of equal population means—the probability of obtaining by chance alone a sum of ranks less than or equal to that obtained in the given experiment. If this probability is less than the significance level, we reject the hypothesis; otherwise, we accept it.

The procedure can be better understood in terms of an example.

*Example 11-1.* A new method for making concrete has been proposed. To test whether the new method has increased the compressive strength, five sample blocks are made by each method. The compressive strengths in pounds per square inch are as follows:

New Method:      148, 143, 138, 145, 141
Standard Method:   139, 136, 142, 133, 140

Does this indicate that the new method has increased the compressive strength (5% level)?

*Solution.* The combined data of the two samples should be arranged in increasing order of magnitude with corresponding ranks indicated, and in order to distinguish between the two samples, the variates belonging to the sample with the smaller mean are underlined. For this example, this is the sample made by the standard method.

Original data:   133, 136, 138, 139, 140, 141, 142, 143, 145, 148
Ranks:            1,   2,   3,   4,   5,   6,   7,   8,   9,   10

We now calculate the sum of the ranks corresponding to the standard method and find

$$W_1 = 1 + 2 + 4 + 5 + 7 = 19,$$

while the sum of the ranks corresponding to the new method is

$$W_2 = 3 + 6 + 8 + 9 + 10 = 36.$$

The total of all ranks is

$$W_1 + W_2 = 19 + 36 = 55.$$

This sum, 55, is, of course, independent of the outcome of this experiment, since it represents the sum of the 10 ranks, that is, $1 + 2 + 3 + \cdots + 10$. If there is no effect of the new method of making concrete, then the total of the ranks for the standard method, $W_1$, should be about the same as that for the new method, $W_2$. Indeed, under the hypothesis of no difference in the two methods, any sum of 5 ranks, such as $3 + 4 + 6 + 8 + 9$ would be just as likely to occur for a value of $W_1$ as some other sum of 5 ranks, such as $2 + 4 + 5 + 6 + 8$.

Consequently, assuming a one-tailed test, we shall now determine the probability of obtaining among all possible sums of ranks one which is less than or equal to the value of $W_1 = 19$ obtained in this case. This calculation is easily made: the total number of possible ways of selecting 5 ranks from 10 is the number of combinations of 10 objects taken 5 at a time, that is, $C_{10,5} = 252$. Of these, the following have a sum less than or equal to 19 (note that we start by listing first the sum of ranks giving the smallest total and then proceed in a systematic way):

$$1 + 2 + 3 + 4 + 5 = 15 \qquad 1 + 2 + 3 + 5 + 8 = 19$$
$$1 + 2 + 3 + 4 + 6 = 16$$
$$1 + 2 + 3 + 4 + 7 = 17 \qquad 1 + 2 + 3 + 6 + 7 = 19$$
$$1 + 2 + 3 + 4 + 8 = 18 \qquad 1 + 2 + 4 + 5 + 6 = 18$$
$$1 + 2 + 3 + 4 + 9 = 19 \qquad 1 + 2 + 4 + 5 + 7 = 19$$
$$1 + 2 + 3 + 5 + 6 = 17 \qquad 1 + 3 + 4 + 5 + 6 = 19$$
$$1 + 2 + 3 + 5 + 7 = 18$$

Consequently, since there are 12 cases, the probability of obtaining a sum of ranks less than or equal to 19 is given by

$$P = \tfrac{12}{252} = 0.0477.$$

Calculation of probabilities is facilitated by use of Appendix Table VI, giving, for various sample sizes $n_1$ and $n_2$ listed in the first two columns, the corresponding values of $C_{n,n_1}$, where $n = n_1 + n_2$, and the number of cases for which the sum of the ranks is less than or equal to that obtained in the experiment. The column headings $0, 1, 2, \cdots, 20$ of Table VI represent values of the quantity

$$U = W_1 - \tfrac{1}{2}n_1(n_1 + 1).$$

Thus, if Table VI is used in the solution of Example 11-1, we calculate

$$U = 19 - \tfrac{1}{2} \cdot 5 \cdot 6 = 4.$$

Then $C_{10,5} = 252$, and the number of cases for which the sum of the ranks is less than or equal to 19 is 12, the entry in the column headed 4.

It might be of interest to note that, if Example 11-1 had been solved by use of Student's $t$-distribution, using a one-tailed test, the probability would have been found to be $P = 0.033$. This would be the correct probability if the distribution of the population were normal; if it were not, the probability obtained by the Wilcoxon test might well be more accurate.

In the data of Example 11-1, none of the 10 given variates occurred more than once, that is, there were no ties. The question arises: how do we apply Wilcoxon's test to data with ties? The answer is supplied by Wilcoxon himself, who, when introducing his test in 1945 for the first time, gave an example in which there were several ties. This example is reproduced here as Example 11-2. In case of ties, the procedure is the same as in the case without ties, except for the assignment of ranks.

*Example 11-2.* The following data give the results of fly spray tests on two preparations in terms of percentage mortality.

$$\text{Sample A: } 68, 68, 59, 72, 64, 67, 70, 74$$
$$\text{Sample B: } 60, 67, 61, 62, 67, 63, 56, 58$$

Is there a significant difference (5% level) between the two preparations?

*Solution.* As before, the data are arranged in increasing order of magnitude, underlining those corresponding to the sample with the smaller mean, in this case, sample B. Three of the variates are 67; these variates correspond to ranks 9, 10, and 11. It seems reasonable, therefore, to assign to all three of these values the mean of these ranks, namely, $\frac{1}{3}$ of 30, or 10. The same procedure is followed for the two variates which are 68, corresponding to ranks 12 and 13. Again, since $12 + 13 = 25$, we assign to both variates the rank $\frac{1}{2}(25) = 12.5$. This, then, is the procedure generally followed in cases with tied data: equal ranks are assigned to tied data.

For this example, then, the ranks are determined as follows:

Original data:  $\underline{56}, \underline{58}, 59, \underline{60}, \underline{61}, \underline{62}, \underline{63}, 64, \underline{67}, \underline{67}, 67, 68, \quad 68, \quad 70, 72, 74$

Ranks:           $\underline{1}, \quad \underline{2}, \quad 3, \quad \underline{4}, \quad \underline{5}, \quad \underline{6}, \quad \underline{7}, \quad 8, \underline{10}, \underline{10}, 10, 12.5, 12.5, 14, 15, 16$

Now, since

$$W_1 = 1 + 2 + 4 + 5 + 6 + 7 + 10 + 10 = 45,$$
$$U = 45 - \frac{1}{2} \cdot 8 \cdot 9 = 9,$$

from Table VI, $C_{16,8} = 12{,}870$, and the number of cases for which the sum of the ranks is less than or equal to 45 is 95, so that

$$P = \frac{95}{12{,}870} = 0.00738,$$

or, since a two-tailed test is needed here, the probability of obtaining a difference as great as or greater than that found between the means of the given two samples would equal

$$2P = 0.01476,$$

from which we conclude that there is a significant difference between the two preparations.

It should be noted that Table VI was constructed under the assumption that there are no ties. The reader may, therefore, question whether it is permissible to use Table VI also in the case in which there are ties, as was done in Example 11-2. It can be shown that, under appropriate assumptions concerning the probability of occurrence of ties, use of Table VI is justifiable also for that case. If ties occur, it is possible that the value of $W_1$ may not be an integer. In that case, the appropriate value to be taken from Table VI should be obtained by linear interpolation. Thus, if in Example 11-2 $U$ had been 11.5, we would have calculated

$$P = \frac{212.5}{12,870}.$$

Wilcoxon's test is also applicable when the two samples are not of the same size. The procedure is essentially the same. In Table VI, $n_1$ and $W_1$ refer to the sample with the fewer observations. If the sample with $n_1$ observations has the larger mean, the observations should be ranked in order of decreasing size since Table VI deals only with the left tail of the distribution of $U$.

*Example 11-3.* Solve exercise 14, Chapter 10, by use of Wilcoxon's test.

*Solution.* Since the sample for District 1 has the smaller mean, we have $n_1 = 5$, $n_2 = 7$, and we list the original data in increasing order of magnitude together with the ranks as follows:

Data: 11.9, 12.4, 12.6, 12.7, 12.8, 12.8, 13.0, 13.1, 13.3, 13.4, 13.4, 13.5

Ranks: 1, 2, 3, 4, 5.5, 5.5, 7, 8, 9, 10.5, 10.5, 12

Now, since

$$W_1 = 1 + 3 + 5.5 + 7 + 10.5 = 27,$$
$$U = 27 - \tfrac{1}{2} \cdot 5 \cdot 6 = 12,$$

from Table VI, $C_{12,5} = 792$, and the number of cases for which the sum of the ranks is less than or equal to 27 is 171, so that

$$P = \tfrac{171}{792} = 0.216$$

and

$$2P = 0.432.$$

Therefore, there is no significant difference between the average proteins for the two districts.

Table VI can, of course, only be used for values of $n = n_1 + n_2$ not exceeding those listed in the first two columns. Fortunately, it has been proved that as $n$ becomes larger and larger, the distribution of the sum of the ranks, $W_1$, approaches a normal distribution, so that we have the following theorem.

**THEOREM 11-1.** Consider two samples of sizes $n_1$ and $n_2$, respectively, from two identical populations, and let $n = n_1 + n_2$. If the sums of the ranks of the two samples are $W_1$ and $W_2$, respectively, and if there are no ties, then, for large $n$, $W_1$ satisfies an approximately normal distribution with

(11-1)
$$m_w = \frac{n_1(n + 1)}{2}$$

and standard deviation

(11-2)
$$\sigma_w = \sqrt{\frac{n_1 n_2(n + 1)}{12}}.$$

Theorem 11-1 will not be proved, but the formula for $m_w$ will be verified.

*Proof of Formula (11-1).* Before proving the formula for $m_w$ in general, let us consider the special case of $n_1 = 5$, $n_2 = 5$, so that $n = 10$. Then $m_w$ equals the mean of all possible sums of 5 ranks taken from the set of ranks $1, 2, 3, \cdots, 10$. The smallest possible such sum is $1 + 2 + 3 + 4 + 5 = 15$, the next larger, $1 + 2 + 3 + 4 + 6 = 16$, and so on. Listing these sums in a systematic way, as in the solution of Example 11-1, we find that the rank 1 occurs in $C_{9,4}$ of these sums, that is, in the number of ways we can select from the 9 numbers $2, 3, 4, \cdots, 10$ any 4 of them. By the same reasoning, the number 2 will also appear in $C_{9,4}$ of these sums. Thus the sum of all possible rank sums is equal to

$$S = C_{9,4}(1 + 2 + 3 + \cdots + 10) = C_{9,4} \tfrac{1}{2} \cdot 10 \cdot 11,$$

since

$$1 + 2 + 3 + \cdots + n = \tfrac{1}{2}n(n + 1).$$

The total number of possible ways of forming sums of 5 ranks from the 10 numbers $1, 2, 3, \cdots, 10$ is, of course, given by $C_{10,5}$, so that

$$m_w = \frac{S}{C_{10,5}} = \frac{C_{9,4} \tfrac{1}{2} \cdot 10 \cdot 11}{C_{10,5}} = \frac{\dfrac{9!}{4!5!} \tfrac{1}{2} \cdot 10 \cdot 11}{\dfrac{10!}{5!5!}}$$

$$= \frac{5}{10} \cdot \tfrac{1}{2} \cdot 10 \cdot 11 = \frac{5 \cdot 11}{2} = 27.5,$$

which agrees with the value found by substituting $n_1 = 5$ and $n = 10$ in the formula for $m_w$, given by (11-1).

To prove formula (11-1) in general, note that $m_w$ equals the mean of all possible sums of $n_1$ ranks taken from the set of ranks 1, 2, 3, $\cdots$ , $n$. The smallest possible such sum is $1 + 2 + 3 + \cdots + n_1$, the next larger is $1 + 2 + 3 + \cdots + (n_1 + 1)$, and so on. Listing these sums again in a systematic way, we find that the rank 1 appears in $C_{n-1,n_1-1}$ of the sums, that is, in the number of ways we can select from the $n - 1$ numbers 2, 3, 4, $\cdots$ , $n$ any $n_1 - 1$ of them. Similarly, the number 2 will also appear in $C_{n-1,n_1-1}$ of these sums. Thus, the sum of all possible rank sums is equal to

$$S = C_{n-1,n_1-1}(1 + 2 + 3 + \cdots + n) = C_{n-1,n_1-1} \tfrac{1}{2} n(n + 1).$$

The total number of possible ways of forming sums of $n_1$ ranks from the $n$ numbers 1, 2, 3, $\cdots$ , $n$ is given by $C_{n,n_1}$, so that

$$m_w = \frac{S}{C_{n,n_1}} = \frac{C_{n-1,n_1-1} \tfrac{1}{2} n(n + 1)}{C_{n,n_1}} = \frac{\dfrac{(n-1)!}{(n_1-1)!(n-n_1)!} \tfrac{1}{2} n(n+1)}{\dfrac{n!}{n_1!(n-n_1)!}}$$

$$= \frac{n_1}{n} \tfrac{1}{2} n(n+1) = \frac{n_1(n+1)}{2}.$$

By a similar procedure, formula (11-2) can be verified.

*Example 11-4.*   Solve Example 11-1 by use of Theorem 11-1.

*Solution.*   Although the sizes of the samples of Example 11-1 are sufficiently small to permit use of Table VI, the normal curve approximation will be used in order to compare the results obtained by the exact method (use of Table VI) and the approximate method furnished by the normal curve approximation. The sizes of the samples are so small in this case that, in practice, the normal curve approximation should not be used.

Since $n_1 = 5$, $n_2 = 5$, and $n = 10$,

$$m_w = \frac{5 \cdot 11}{2} = 27.5,$$

$$\sigma_w = \sqrt{\frac{5 \cdot 5 \cdot 11}{12}} = \sqrt{22.92} = 4.79,$$

so that the probability of finding a sum of ranks less than or equal to 19 is the area under the normal probability curve to the left of

$$z = \frac{19.5 - 27.5}{4.79} = -1.67,$$

which equals 0.0475. This compares with 0.0477 obtained in Example 11-1.

For the case of tied ranks, Theorem 11-1 needs to be modified as follows: for each group of tied observations, let $t_i$ be the number of tied observations in the $i$th group. Then let

$$T_i = (t_i - 1)t_i(t_i + 1)$$

for the $i$th group of ties. Now Theorem 11-1 is applicable with the formula for $m_w$ remaining unchanged, but the formula for $\sigma_w$ replaced by

(11-3)
$$\sigma_w = \sqrt{\frac{n_1 n_2 \left[ n(n^2 - 1) - \sum_{i=1}^{k} T_i \right]}{12n(n - 1)}},$$

where $k$ is the number of groups containing ties. Note that when there are no ties, that is,

$$\sum_{i=1}^{k} T_i = 0,$$

formula (11-3) reduces to (11-2), so that formula (11-3) may be regarded as the general expression for $\sigma_w$, whether or not there are ties. Consequently, Theorem 11-1 can be stated in the following, more general form:

**THEOREM 11-2.**  Consider two samples of sizes $n_1$ and $n_2$, respectively, from two identical populations, and let $n = n_1 + n_2$. If the sums of the ranks of the two samples are $W_1$ and $W_2$, respectively, then, for large $n$, $W_1$ satisfies an approximately normal distribution with $m_w$ and $\sigma_w$ given by (11-1) and (11-3), respectively.

*Example 11-5.*  Solve Example 11-2 by use of Theorem 11-2.
*Solution.*  Since $n_1 = 8$, $n_2 = 8$, and $n = 16$, we find

$$m_w = \frac{8 \cdot 17}{2} = 68,$$

and, since there are two groups of tied ranks (that is, those tied at 10 and those tied at 12.5), we have $t_1 = 3$, $t_2 = 2$, and $T_1 = 2 \cdot 3 \cdot 4 = 24$, $T_2 = 1 \cdot 2 \cdot 3 = 6$, and

$$\sum_{i=1}^{2} T_i = 24 + 6 = 30,$$

so that

$$\sigma_w = \sqrt{\frac{8 \cdot 8 \cdot [16 \cdot 255 - 30]}{12 \cdot 16 \cdot 15}} = \sqrt{90} = 9.49.$$

Therefore, the probability of finding a sum of ranks less than or equal to 45 is the area under the normal probability curve to the left of

$$z = \frac{45.5 - 68}{9.49} = -2.37,$$

which equals 0.0089, so that, for a two-tailed test, twice this area equals 0.0178, which compares with 0.01476 obtained in Example 11-2. That, in this case, there is not too close an agreement between the two values is not surprising in view of the relatively small value of $n$ and the fact that, at the tail end of the distribution, the approximation is obviously worse than near its center. For larger values of $n$, however, the approximation will be much better.

Intuitively it would appear that Wilcoxon's test should be inferior to tests which use the actual numerical values of the samples. It would seem that replacement of the observations by their ranks, which merely indicate the order relationship between the observations, would disregard so much information that the test would not be an appropriate one to use in many cases. It is no surprise, then, that Wilcoxon's test and other nonparametric tests were regarded rather skeptically at first. Recent results, however, have shown this skepticism to be unwarranted; the reasons follow.

In order to determine how good a particular statistical test is, a precise definition of what is meant by a "good" statistical test is required. Clearly, one desirable property of a test is that, when the hypothesis is false, there is a high probability that the test will give a significant result, or, to put it differently, in a given experiment, the investigator would like to use the statistical test which gives the highest probability of detecting a false hypothesis. This probability is referred to as the *power* of the test. For a given statistical test, for example, the Student's $t$-test, the power of the test can always be increased by increasing the sample size. Clearly, with larger sample sizes, and assuming the hypothesis of equal population means to be false, the probability of rejecting the hypothesis is increased as the sample size increases.

A common method of comparing various statistical tests is by use of the *efficiency* which, roughly speaking, compares the sample sizes for two tests having the same power, that is, which detect a false hypothesis with the same probability. If a certain nonparametric test (for example, Wilcoxon's test) is said to have efficiency 100% when compared to another test (for example, Student's $t$-test), this means that, if the hypothesis is false, it will be detected by both tests with equal probability for the same size samples. If, however, this efficiency is 90% for the Wilcoxon test, such a false hypothesis will be detected by means of the $t$-test with a sample only $\frac{9}{10}$ as large as that needed in the Wilcoxon test.

We would, of course, expect that the Wilcoxon test would have generally a much lower efficiency relative to Student's $t$-test. Surprisingly, however, it has recently been shown that the Wilcoxon test is about 95.5% efficient for large samples if the population is normally distributed and that it is more efficient (efficiency is more than 100%) if the distribution deviates considerably from a normal distribution. Most surprising, however, is the result proved in December, 1963, by E. L. Lehmann: the efficiency of the Wilcoxon test relative to the $t$-test is never less than 86.4%, and it can be arbitrarily high and even infinite. Lehmann furthermore proved that this lowest efficiency of 86.4% is true even for the case where the Wilcoxon test is used to compare the means of more than two samples; this, however, will not be discussed here.

Consequently, at the very best, Student's $t$-test requires a sample only 13.6% smaller than the Wilcoxon test to detect with the same probability a significant difference, but in many cases Student's $t$-test may actually require a larger sample.

For these reasons, use of Wilcoxon's test would appear nearly always to be preferable to the use of Student's $t$-test.

In many cases it is not possible to obtain actual measurements for the samples, as in taste tests, where it is desired to determine preferences for certain foods. Clearly, in such tests it is not always possible to assign a meaningful numerical score to an individual's like or dislike for a particular food, yet it is possible to rank the foods according to increasing order of preference. Consequently, in such cases use of a nonparametric test, such as the Wilcoxon test, is imperative.

Further improvement in the efficiency is possible by means of recently developed nonparametric tests; in particular, by the use of Normal Scores. In this method, the observations are again first replaced by ranks, for example, in the case of 2 samples of 5 variates each, by 1, 2, 3, $\cdots$, 10. In the Normal Scores test, the ranks are assumed to follow a normal distribution and are therefore replaced by Normal Scores fitted to a normal distribution. This test will not be discussed, since, in most situations, the Wilcoxon test is entirely adequate.

## 11.3. The Sign Test for the Paired Case

The simplest, by far, of all nonparametric methods is the sign test, which is used to test the significance of the difference between two means in a paired experiment. It is particularly suitable when the various pairs are observed under different conditions, a case in which the assumption of normality may not hold. However, because of its simplicity, the sign test is often used even though the populations are normally distributed. In this test, as is implied by its name, only the sign of the difference between the paired variates is used. The method of applying the test will now be described.

First we determine for each pair the sign of the difference $D$. Under the hypothesis that the two population means are identical, the number of plus signs should approximately equal the number of minus signs. If $p$ denotes the probability of a difference $D$ being positive and $q$ the probability of its being negative, we have as hypothesis $p = \frac{1}{2}$. Suppose we are given a sample from this population and wish to determine whether it differs significantly from this hypothesis. For this purpose, we count the number of plus signs (call it $S$) and the number of minus signs (pairs of observations for which $D = 0$ are disregarded) and calculate the probability of obtaining, from a population for which $p = \frac{1}{2}$, a sample in which the number of plus signs differs as much as $S$ or more from the expected value.

*Example 11-6.* In a paired experiment, the gains in weight, in pounds, of hogs fed on two different diets are as given in Table 11-1. Is either diet superior at the 5% level of significance?

TABLE 11-1.  Gains in Weight (in pounds) of Hogs Fed on Two Different Diets

| Pair | Diet A | Diet B | Sign of $D = X - Y$ | Pair | Diet A | Diet B | Sign of $D = X - Y$ |
|------|--------|--------|---------------------|------|--------|--------|---------------------|
| 1 | 25 | 19 | + | 10 | 28 | 26 | + |
| 2 | 30 | 32 | − | 11 | 32 | 30 | + |
| 3 | 28 | 21 | + | 12 | 29 | 25 | + |
| 4 | 34 | 34 | 0 | 13 | 30 | 29 | + |
| 5 | 23 | 19 | + | 14 | 30 | 31 | − |
| 6 | 25 | 25 | 0 | 15 | 31 | 25 | + |
| 7 | 27 | 25 | + | 16 | 29 | 25 | + |
| 8 | 35 | 31 | + | 17 | 23 | 20 | + |
| 9 | 30 | 31 | − | 18 | 26 | 25 | + |

*Solution.* Disregarding the two cases where $D = 0$, we find that in the remaining sample of 16 differences 13 are positive. By means of the binomial distribution we can find the probability (under the hypothesis of equal chance for plus and minus signs) that 13 or more plus signs (or minus signs) are obtained. Since $n = 16$ is fairly large, it is convenient to use the normal curve approximation of the binomial distribution, for which

$$m = np = 8, \quad \sigma = \sqrt{npq} = \sqrt{4} = 2.$$

We need twice the area under the normal probability curve to the right of $X = 12.5$. Since

$$z = \frac{12.5 - 8}{2} = 2.25,$$

we find from Appendix Table I

$$P = 2(0.0122) = 0.0244,$$

which is less than 0.05. Thus the first diet can be considered superior.

It should be noted that the sign test is applicable only if $n$, the number of pairs, is not too small. For example, in an experiment where $n = 5$, the probability of the most extreme case, that of all signs being either plus or minus, is $2(\frac{1}{2})^5 = 0.0625$, which is more than 5%; thus, from a sample of 5 differences, it is never possible to conclude that the hypothesis of equal population means is incorrect. Clearly, then, use of the sign test at the 5% level of significance with a two-tailed test requires that $n$ be at least 6. It should preferably be larger, and must be so if the 1% level of significance is used.

Clearly, even for large $n$, we expect the sign test to have a lower efficiency than the $t$-test, which means that in many cases the sign test will not indicate a significant difference when the $t$-test applied to the same problem actually shows the result to be significant. Such a situation arises if the differences corresponding to the more frequently occurring sign are large in absolute value compared with those corresponding to the other sign. Another non-parametric test which does take into consideration the magnitude of the differences and, therefore, has a higher efficiency than the sign test, is given in Section 11.4. On the other hand, if the sign test gives a significant result, it is a valuable statistical technique requiring little calculation and, of course, no knowledge of the distribution of the population.

## 11.4. The Wilcoxon Test for the Paired Case

Assume that, as in Section 10.5, there are given two samples whose variates are paired. In Wilcoxon's test for this paired experiment, the differences, $D$, for each pair are calculated and their absolute values are ranked. If there is no significant difference between the means of the two samples, then the total of the ranks corresponding to positive values of $D$ and those corresponding to negative values of $D$ should be about the same. If, however, the total of the ranks corresponding to one sign is appreciably less than that corresponding to the other, then, under the hypothesis of equal population means, the probability of obtaining by chance alone a sum of ranks less than or equal to $W_1$ is calculated, $W_1$ being the smaller of the rank totals. If this probability is less than the significance level, the hypothesis is rejected; otherwise, it is accepted.

*Example 11-7.*   The data below represent the stands of wheat on eight pairs of plots, one of each pair planted to seed having received treatment A and the other treatment B.

| Pair | A | B |
|------|-----|-----|
| 1 | 209 | 151 |
| 2 | 200 | 168 |
| 3 | 177 | 147 |
| 4 | 169 | 164 |
| 5 | 159 | 166 |
| 6 | 169 | 163 |
| 7 | 187 | 176 |
| 8 | 198 | 188 |

Using the 5% level of significance, is there a significant difference between the two seed treatments?

*Solution.*   Denoting the variates of the first sample by $X$ and those of the second sample by $Y$, we find

| $X$ | $Y$ | $D = X - Y$ | Rank |
|-----|-----|-------------|------|
| 209 | 151 | 58 | 8 |
| 200 | 168 | 32 | 7 |
| 177 | 147 | 30 | 6 |
| 169 | 164 | 5 | 1 |
| 159 | 166 | -7 | 3 |
| 169 | 163 | 6 | 2 |
| 187 | 176 | 11 | 5 |
| 198 | 188 | 10 | 4 |

Note that ranks corresponding to a negative value of $D$ are underlined; in this case, there is only one such rank, namely the rank 3, so that $W_1 = 3$. Now, under the hypothesis that there is no difference between the two treatments A and B, the probability of each difference $D$ being positive is $\frac{1}{2}$. Consequently, the probability of obtaining any given sequence of signs for the eight differences (for example, the sequence $+ + - + - - - +$) is $(\frac{1}{2})^8 = \frac{1}{256}$, so that there are a total of 256 equally likely possibilities for the sequence of signs.

Assuming a two-tailed test, we determine the probability of obtaining among all possible sums of ranks (corresponding to negative $D$-values) one which is less than or equal to $W_1$ (in this case, 3) and then multiply this probability by 2. Now the following cases are the only ones for which the sum of the ranks (corresponding to negative $D$-values) is less than or equal to 3:

| | |
|---|---|
| no negative $D$-value: | 1 case |
| one negative $D$-value with rank either 1, 2, or 3: | 3 cases |
| two negative $D$-values with rank $1 + 2 = 3$: | 1 case |
| Total: | 5 cases |

Consequently, the probability of obtaining a sum of ranks less than or equal to 3 is given by

$$P = \tfrac{5}{256} = 0.0195$$

and the desired probability equals

$$2P = 0.0390,$$

which leads to the conclusion that the two treatments are significantly different.

Calculation of probabilities is facilitated by use of Appendix Tables VIIa and VIIb. Two tables are given for the following reason: if it is desired to find the number of cases for which the sum of ranks is less than or equal to a given value of $W_1$, where $W_1$ is less than or equal to $n$, then this number of cases is independent of $n$ and Table VIIa can be used. This was true in Example 11-7, where $W_1 = 3$ and $n = 8$. For this example, Table VIIa shows the number of cases for which $W_1$ is less than or equal to 3 to be 5.

If, however, it is desired to find the number of cases for which the sum of ranks is less than or equal to a given value of $W_1$, where $W_1$ is greater than $n$, then this number of cases depends on $n$ and Table VIIb must be used.

*Example 11-8.* Solve Example 11-7, assuming that in the data the values of 209 and 151 in pair 1 are interchanged, everything else remaining the same.

*Solution.* Interchanging the values of 209 and 151 in the first pair results in the value $D_1 = -58$, and the corresponding rank 8 must be underlined as corresponding to a negative $D$-value. Then $W_1 = 3 + 8 = 11$, and the number of cases for which the sum of the ranks is less than or equal to 11 (found in the row of Table VIIb for which $W_1 - n = 11 - 8 = 3$ and the column for which $n = 8$) is 49, and, for a two-tailed test,

$$P = 2(\tfrac{49}{256}) = 0.383,$$

so that this would then not be a significant result.

Although Tables VIIa and VIIb were constructed under the assumption that there are no ties, it can be shown that, under appropriate assumptions concerning the probability of occurrence of ties, use of these two tables is justifiable also for this case. If there are ties, we rank the differences which remain after disregarding those which are zero in the same way as we did in Section 11.2, that is, assign to differences which are the same in absolute value the mean of the ranks they would have been assigned if they had all been different. We underline the ranks corresponding to the sign for which the sum of the ranks is smaller and proceed as before, using linear interpolation in Tables VIIa and VIIb if the value of $W_1$ thus obtained is not an integer.

*Example 11-9.* Solve Example 10-5 by the use of Wilcoxon's test.

*Solution.* After disregarding the difference which is zero, we rank the remaining 7 differences as indicated below

| X | Y | $D = X - Y$ | Rank |
|---|---|---|---|
| 83 | 78 | 5 | 7 |
| 74 | 74 | 0 | — |
| 67 | 63 | 4 | 5 |
| 64 | 66 | -2 | 2.5 |
| 70 | 68 | 2 | 2.5 |
| 67 | 63 | 4 | 5 |
| 81 | 77 | 4 | 5 |
| 64 | 65 | -1 | 1 |

Since the sum of the ranks corresponding to negative values of $D$ is smaller than that corresponding to the positive ones, we underline them and find

$$W_1 = 1 + 2.5 = 3.5.$$

From Table VIIa, we find, by linear interpolation, the entry corresponding to $W_1 = 3.5$ to be 6, so that, for a one-tailed test

$$P = \tfrac{6}{128} = 0.0469.$$

Consequently, we conclude from these data that kindergarten is of benefit in preparing for the first grade, a result which agrees with the one obtained in the solution of Example 10-5.

Tables VIIa and VIIb can be used only for values of $n$ not exceeding those listed. As, however, $n$ becomes larger and larger, the distribution for $W_1$ approaches a normal distribution, so that we have the following theorem.

**THEOREM 11-3.** If, for a sample of $n$ differences $X - Y$, where $X$ and $Y$ are the variables of two identical populations, the sum of the ranks corresponding to the negative differences is $W_1$ and that corresponding to the positive differences is $W_2$, and if there are no ties, then, for large $n$, $W_1$ satisfies an approximately normal distribution with mean

(11-4)
$$m_w = \frac{n(n+1)}{4}$$

and standard deviation

(11-5)
$$\sigma_w = \sqrt{\frac{n(n+1)(2n+1)}{24}}.$$

No proof will be given for Theorem 11-3. The derivation of the formula for $m_w$ is analogous to that for formula (11-1) and is left as an exercise for the reader (see exercise 25).

*Example 11-10.* Solve Example 11-7 by use of Theorem 11-3.

*Solution.* Since the size of the sample of Example 11-7 is sufficiently small to permit use of Table VIIa, this example should, as a rule, not be solved by means of the normal distribution. This is, nevertheless, done here to compare the result obtained by the exact method (Table VII) with the approximation obtained by use of the normal curve.

Since $n = 8$,

$$m_w = \frac{8 \cdot 9}{4} = 18,$$

$$\sigma_w = \sqrt{\frac{8 \cdot 9 \cdot 17}{24}} = \sqrt{51} = 7.14,$$

so that the probability of finding a sum of ranks less than or equal to 3 is the area under the normal probability curve to the left of

$$z = \frac{3.5 - 18}{7.14} = -2.03,$$

which equals 0.0212. For a two-tailed test, the probability, therefore, is equal to

$$P = 2(0.0212) = 0.0424,$$

which compares with 0.0390 obtained in Example 11-7. The agreement is not too close, of course, because the value of $n$ was smaller than that which should be used in applying Theorem 11-3.

## Exercises

1. The measurements of the heights (in inches) of six adults of each of two different nationalities are given below:

> Nationality A:   64, 67, 68, 65, 62, 61
> Nationality B:   69, 70, 66, 63, 71, 72

Use Wilcoxon's two-sample test to determine whether there is a significant difference in mean heights for these two nationalities (5% level).

2. Wire cable is being manufactured by two processes. To determine if they have a different effect on the mean breaking strength of the cable, a laboratory test is performed, and six pieces of wire from one process are put under tension and the critical values of the load recorded for each piece. A similar process is followed for the seven pieces from the other process. The results are as follows:

> Process I:    9, 4, 10,  7,  8, 10
> Process II:   14, 9, 13, 12, 11,  8, 10

Use Wilcoxon's two-sample test to determine whether there is a significant difference (5% level) between the mean breaking strengths of cable manufactured by the two processes.

3. Solve Example 10-4 by the methods of this chapter.

4. Solve exercise 10, Chapter 10, by the methods of this chapter.

5. Solve exercise 13, Chapter 10, by the methods of this chapter.

6. Although in exercise 1 of this chapter the samples are small, solve this exercise by use of Theorem 11-1 to compare the result with the one obtained in exercise 1.

7. Solve exercise 2 of this chapter by use of Theorem 11-2.

8. Solve Example 11-3 by use of Theorem 11-2.

9. The following scores are obtained in a personality test in random samples of married and unmarried women:

> Unmarried:   85, 69, 76, 80, 61, 79
> Married:   73, 76, 66, 73, 73, 65

Use the appropriate nonparametric test to determine if these data indicate that married and unmarried women have the same average scores on this personality test (5% level).

10. Two manufacturing processes are compared by making six experiments for each of the two processes. If each of the results obtained under one process are lower than those of any of the other and if there are no ties, do these results indicate a significant difference between the two processes at the 1% level?

11. The yields of two inbred lines of corn obtained from several different experiments are listed below. Is there a significant difference between the two lines of corn on the basis of the 1% level of significance?

| Experiment | A Yield | B Yield | Experiment | A Yield | B Yield |
|---|---|---|---|---|---|
| 1 | 48.6 | 50.1 | 15 | 39.8 | 40.8 |
| 2 | 43.0 | 48.6 | 16 | 37.5 | 37.3 |
| 3 | 41.0 | 42.9 | 17 | 28.1 | 27.5 |
| 4 | 39.1 | 42.6 | 18 | 33.3 | 32.4 |
| 5 | 36.8 | 37.5 | 19 | 43.0 | 48.6 |
| 6 | 40.8 | 41.3 | 20 | 29.0 | 31.1 |
| 7 | 28.9 | 38.6 | 21 | 27.4 | 28.0 |
| 8 | 35.9 | 37.3 | 22 | 28.0 | 28.7 |
| 9 | 39.2 | 42.6 | 23 | 28.3 | 28.8 |
| 10 | 47.8 | 46.1 | 24 | 26.8 | 26.8 |
| 11 | 42.1 | 43.4 | 25 | 42.2 | 42.2 |
| 12 | 47.6 | 48.2 | 26 | 38.9 | 39.1 |
| 13 | 26.4 | 26.3 | 27 | 39.0 | 39.4 |
| 14 | 30.6 | 31.7 | 28 | 33.6 | 34.0 |

12. A paired feeding experiment is carried out with pigs to determine the relative value of limestone and bonemeal for bone development. For each pair the ash content in percentage of scapulas is recorded first for pigs fed limestone (X) and then for pigs fed bonemeal (Y). If 35 such experiments are carried out, and if in 27 of them X is greater than Y and in 3 of them X is equal to Y, does this indicate that limestone yields higher ash content than bonemeal (5% level)?

13. In an experiment consisting of 25 pairs, the number of plus signs exceeds the number of minus signs. If a two-tailed test is applied, how many minus signs can there be, at most, to allow us to consider the results significant on the basis of the 5% level of significance?

14. In an experiment consisting of 30 pairs, most of the signs are minus signs. If our interest is in minus signs only (so that a one-tailed test would be applied), what is the largest possible number of plus signs for which the results would be considered significant on the basis of the 5% level of significance?

15. If in an experiment consisting of $n$ pairs, 3 plus signs are obtained (all other signs being negative), no conclusions can be drawn if $n$ is small, since in that case, 3 or fewer plus signs in $n$ trials would by chance alone

occur with probability greater than 5% (assuming a population in which half the signs are positive). Find the largest value of $n$ for which, by chance alone, the probability of obtaining 3 or fewer plus signs in $n$ trials is still larger than 5%. Use a one-tailed test.

16. Find the largest value of $n$ such that, by chance alone, the probability of obtaining 4 or fewer plus signs (or minus signs) in $n$ paired experiments (where no differences equal zero) is larger than 1%.

17. In a paired feeding experiment, the gains in weight (in pounds) of hogs fed on two different diets are as listed below. Can either diet be considered superior at the 5% level of significance? (Use the Wilcoxon test.)

| Pair | Diet A | Diet B | Pair | Diet A | Diet B |
|------|--------|--------|------|--------|--------|
| 1 | 27 | 19 | 6 | 31 | 34 |
| 2 | 30 | 32 | 7 | 39 | 34 |
| 3 | 31 | 21 | 8 | 34 | 28 |
| 4 | 34 | 33 | 9 | 33 | 26 |
| 5 | 23 | 27 | 10 | 35 | 26 |

18. Solve exercise 17 of this chapter, assuming that in the data the values of 39 and 34 in pair 7 are interchanged, everything else remaining the same.

19. Solve exercise 24, Chapter 10, assuming that the numbers 29 and 37 for the third and fourth workers in the last column (with coffee break) are replaced by 33 and 39, everything else remaining the same. Use the Wilcoxon test.

20. The manufacturer of a suntan lotion wishes to know whether a new ingredient increases the protection his lotion gives against sunburn. Seven volunteers have their backs exposed to the sun with the old lotion on one side and the new lotion on the other side of the spine. The experimental data on the degree of sunburn (as measured on some scale) for the seven volunteers are as follows:

| Volunteer | Burn on Side with Old Lotion | Burn on Side with New Lotion |
|-----------|------------------------------|------------------------------|
| 1 | 42 | 38 |
| 2 | 51 | 53 |
| 3 | 31 | 36 |
| 4 | 61 | 52 |
| 5 | 44 | 33 |
| 6 | 55 | 49 |
| 7 | 48 | 36 |

Does this new ingredient improve the effectiveness of the lotion? (Use the Wilcoxon test.)

21. A random sample of six ladies agrees to be subjected to an experimental reducing diet. Their respective weights before and after the experiment are given as follows:

|             | Before | After |
|-------------|--------|-------|
| Mrs. Black  | 172    | 173   |
| Mrs. White  | 138    | 130   |
| Mrs. Brown  | 130    | 121   |
| Mrs. Blue   | 166    | 169   |
| Mrs. Green  | 139    | 132   |
| Mrs. Grey   | 124    | 126   |

Does this indicate that the diet is effective at the 5% level of significance? (Use the Wilcoxon test.)

22. Solve exercise 21, Chapter 10, by use of the Wilcoxon test.

23. Solve exercise 23, Chapter 10, by use of the Wilcoxon test.

24. Although in exercise 17 of this chapter the sample is small, solve this exercise by use of Theorem 11-3 to compare the result with the one obtained in exercise 17.

25. Prove formula (11-4).

# 12   Regression and Correlation

## 12.1.   Introduction

In the preceding chapters we have discussed only populations consisting of measurements of a single variable. We shall now consider populations made up of pairs of measurements.

> **DEFINITION 12-1.**   If for every measurement of a variable $X$ we know a corresponding value of a second variable $Y$, the resulting set of pairs of variates is called a *bivariate population*.

Two main questions will be discussed in this chapter:
1. Is there a relationship between the two variables of the bivariate population?
2. If such a relationship exists, how can it be expressed by means of an equation?

Let us consider the following example. The determination of the number of red blood cells by use of a microscope is time consuming and subject to considerable inaccuracies. On the other hand, the so-called packed cell volume of the blood is much easier to obtain. To find a possible relationship between these two variables, blood samples are taken from 10 dogs. For each of these samples the packed cell volume ($X$) and the corresponding red blood cell count ($Y$) are measured. The resultant data are presented in Table 12.1.

Here we wish to decide whether the red blood cell count is related to the packed cell volume and, if such is the case, to find an equation that will express the red blood cell count in terms of the packed cell volume. The value of such an equation is obvious: it will allow us to estimate (or predict) the number of red blood cells from measurements of the packed cell volume.

Unless otherwise designated, the variable from whose values predictions are to be made will be denoted by $X$, and the variable whose values are to be estimated (or predicted) will be denoted by $Y$. In other words, $X$ is considered the independent variable and $Y$ the dependent variable. In the following discussion we shall assume that $X$ can be measured exactly and that $Y$ may be subject to fluctuations for a given value of $X$. (This situation would cer-

**TABLE 12-1.   Packed Cell Volume and Red Blood Cell Count of 10 Dogs**

| Packed Cell Volume (mm) | Red Blood Cell Count (millions) |
|---|---|
| X | Y |
| 45 | 6.53 |
| 42 | 6.30 |
| 56 | 9.52 |
| 48 | 7.50 |
| 42 | 6.99 |
| 35 | 5.90 |
| 58 | 9.49 |
| 40 | 6.20 |
| 39 | 6.55 |
| 50 | 8.72 |

tainly obtain in the foregoing example, where for a given value of $X$—for example, 42—there may be several values of $Y$, owing to the inaccuracies inherent in a red blood cell count.) More precisely, we shall assume that the set of values of $Y$ which can be obtained by performing the experiment repeatedly for the same value of $X$ satisfies a normal distribution.

Let us suppose now that we are given a sample of $n$ pairs of values, the first variate of each pair being the $X$-value, the second the $Y$-value.

To begin the study of a possible relationship between $X$ and $Y$, let us represent the $n$ pairs of values as $n$ points on a graph.

**DEFINITION 12-2.** The graphical representation of a set of $n$ pairs of values of $X$ and $Y$ in a coordinate system is called a *scatter diagram*.

*Example 12-1.* Draw the scatter diagram for the data of Table 12-1.

*Solution.* The desired scatter diagram is shown in Figure 12-1.

Note that the 10 points of the above scatter diagram lie nearly on a straight line. How do we find the equation of such a line? We shall answer this question and discuss the case where the scatter diagram indicates a linear relationship.

Fig. 12-1. Scatter diagram for the data of Table 12-1.

## 12.2. The Linear Regression Equation

In order to find the equation of the line which is a "best fit" to a scatter diagram of $n$ points, we employ a theorem from elementary mathematics.

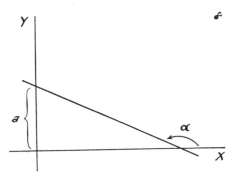

Fig. 12-2. Graph of straight line showing Y-intercept $a$ and angle of inclination $\alpha$.

**THEOREM 12-1.** The equation of any non-vertical line (Figure 12-2) can be written in the form $Y = a + bX$, where $a$ is the $Y$-intercept and $b$ the slope of the line. The slope is given by $b = \tan \alpha$, where $\alpha$ is the angle measured from the positive $X$-axis to the line, and is positive or negative as $\alpha$ is acute or obtuse.

*Proof of Theorem 12-1.* Let us suppose we are given a line, such as that in Figure 12-3, for which we know $a$, the $Y$-intercept, and $\alpha$, the angle of inclination. The equation of a line is the relationship which the coordinates

Fig. 12-3. The relations between the coordinates of an arbitrary point on a straight line and the Y-intercept and angle of inclination.

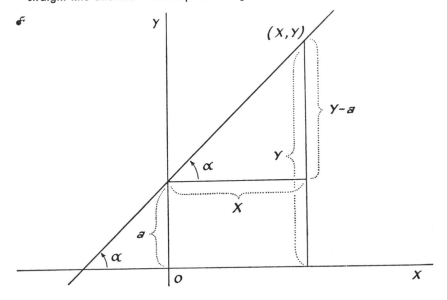

of any point must satisfy in order that the point lies on the line. Let the point $(X, Y)$ be a point on the line; then from the upper right triangle in Figure 12-3 we have $b = \tan \alpha = (Y - a)/X$ or $bX = Y - a$, from which we obtain

$$Y = a + bX.$$

It can be shown quite easily that the graph of an equation of the form $Y = a + bX$, for any values of the constants $a$ and $b$, will always represent a line with $a$ the $Y$-intercept and $b$ the slope. Thus, the graph of the equation $Y = -2 + X$ is a straight line, crossing the $Y$-axis 2 units below the $X$-axis and having a slope $b = \tan \alpha = 1$; since $\tan \alpha = 1$ when $\alpha = 45°$, the line forms an angle of $45°$ with the positive $X$-axis.

A particular line, therefore, is completely determined if the values of the constants $a$ and $b$ in its equation are given. Returning to the problem of finding the line of best fit to a scatter diagram of $n$ points, we must determine $a$ and $b$ in such a way that the $n$ points lie as close to the line as possible. Note that after the equation of the line of best fit has been determined, it will yield for each $X$-value a certain $Y$-value, which will be an estimate of the actual $Y$-value. To distinguish between these two $Y$-values, we shall denote the estimate, which is the value obtained from the line, by $Y_e$, and the actual $Y$-value, which is obtained by measurement, by $Y$. We can then write the equation of the line of best fit in the form

(12-1)                                $$Y_e = a + bX.$$

In order to determine the line of best fit we must decide what is meant by this term, or more precisely, we need a definition of the term. At first thought we might define such a line as being one for which half the points of the scatter diagram fall below the line, the other half above it. This, however, would not yield a single line, since there could be many such lines. A definition of the term, line of best fit, should give a unique line. Let us proceed by considering, for each value of $X$, the absolute value $|Y - Y_e|$ of the difference between the actual $Y$-value and the estimated $Y$-value (see Figure 12-4). This difference represents the error committed by using the estimated $Y$-value instead of the actual value. One way to determine the line of best fit might be to find that line for which the sum of these errors for all the given values of $X$, i.e., $\Sigma|Y - Y_e|$, has the smallest possible value. However, this procedure, while yielding a unique line, leads to the mathematical difficulties customarily associated with the occurrence of absolute values. A better method, and one which accomplishes the same aims, defines the line in such a way that $\Sigma(Y - Y_e)^2$ has the smallest value. This method, called the method of least squares, is the one most generally used in statistics for obtaining the line of best fit.

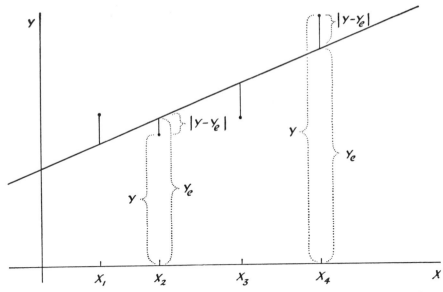

Fig. 12-4. The differences between observed values, $Y$, and estimated values, $Y_e$.

**DEFINITION 12-3.** The *method of least squares* is the method of fitting a line to a set of $n$ points in such a way that $\Sigma(Y - Y_e)^2$ has its smallest possible value, where the sum is calculated for the given $n$ pairs of values of $X$ and $Y$.

Our problem now has been reduced to finding, for a given sample of $n$ pairs of values of $X$ and $Y$, the constants $a$ and $b$ of the equation $Y_e = a + bX$ in such a way that $\Sigma(Y - Y_e)^2$ is minimized. By the methods of the differential calculus it is fairly easy to prove that $a$ and $b$ must be the solution of the following two linear equations. (The reader familiar with partial differentiation should prove this as an exercise.)

$$\begin{aligned} an + b\Sigma X &= \Sigma Y \\ a\Sigma X + b\Sigma X^2 &= \Sigma XY. \end{aligned}$$

(12-2)

**DEFINITION 12-4.** Equations (12-2) are called *normal equations*.

Observe that for a given sample of $n$ pairs of values of $X$ and $Y$, all of the quantities occurring in (12-2), except $a$ and $b$, will be known numbers (or numbers which can be calculated easily from the given data). The sums appearing in (12-2) extend over all pairs in that sample; thus $\Sigma XY$ is readily found by multiplying each $X$ by the corresponding $Y$ and totaling all the products.

We can solve equations (12-2) for $b$ by multiplying the first equation by

$\Sigma X$, the second by $n$, and subtracting the first equation from the second:

$$b = \frac{n\Sigma XY - \Sigma X\Sigma Y}{n\Sigma X^2 - (\Sigma X)^2}.$$

Dividing numerator and denominator by $n$, and recalling that $\overline{X} = \Sigma X/n$ and $\overline{Y} = \Sigma Y/n$, we can write

(12-3)
$$b = \frac{\Sigma XY - \dfrac{\Sigma X\Sigma Y}{n}}{\Sigma X^2 - \dfrac{(\Sigma X)^2}{n}} = \frac{\Sigma XY - n\overline{X}\,\overline{Y}}{\Sigma X^2 - n\overline{X}^2}.$$

Using this value of $b$ in the first of the two equations (12.2) and solving for $a$, we find

(12-4)
$$a = \overline{Y} - b\overline{X}.$$

**DEFINITION 12-5.** The line $Y_e = a + bX$ which has been fitted to a set of $n$ points $(X, Y)$ by the method of least squares is called the *line of regression of Y on X* or the *line of prediction for Y*.

*Example 12-2.* Find the line of regression of $Y$ on $X$ for the data of Table 12-1.

*Solution.* From formula (12-3) it is evident that, for the calculation of $b$, it is necessary to find the values of $XY$ and their sum, as well as the values of $X^2$ and their sum. These quantities are shown in the third and fourth columns, respectively, of Table 12-2. (The other columns of the table are not needed for the present calculations, but will be used later.)

TABLE 12-2.  Calculation of Regression Line and Related Quantities for the Data of Table 12-1

| X | Y | XY | X² | Y² | $Y_e$ | $Y - Y_e$ | $(Y - Y_e)^2$ |
|---|---|---|---|---|---|---|---|
| 45 | 6.53 | 293.85 | 2025 | 42.6409 | 7.28 | −0.75 | 0.5625 |
| 42 | 6.30 | 264.60 | 1764 | 39.6900 | 6.75 | −0.45 | 0.2025 |
| 56 | 9.52 | 533.12 | 3136 | 90.6304 | 9.22 | 0.30 | 0.0900 |
| 48 | 7.50 | 360.00 | 2304 | 56.2500 | 7.81 | −0.31 | 0.0961 |
| 42 | 6.99 | 293.58 | 1764 | 48.8601 | 6.75 | 0.24 | 0.0576 |
| 35 | 5.90 | 206.50 | 1225 | 34.8100 | 5.52 | 0.38 | 0.1444 |
| 58 | 9.49 | 550.42 | 3364 | 90.0601 | 9.57 | −0.08 | 0.0064 |
| 40 | 6.20 | 248.00 | 1600 | 38.4400 | 6.40 | −0.20 | 0.0400 |
| 39 | 6.55 | 255.45 | 1521 | 42.9025 | 6.22 | 0.33 | 0.1089 |
| 50 | 8.72 | 436.00 | 2500 | 76.0384 | 8.16 | 0.56 | 0.3136 |
| 455 | 73.70 | 3441.52 | 21203 | 560.3224 | | | 1.6220 |

Since

$$\bar{X} = \frac{455}{10} = 45.50 \quad \text{and} \quad \bar{Y} = \frac{73.70}{10} = 7.37,$$

using (12-3) we obtain

$$b = \frac{3441.52 - 10(45.50)(7.37)}{21203 - 10(45.50)^2} = \frac{88.17}{500.50} = 0.176,$$

and from (12-4)

$$a = 7.37 - (0.176)45.50 = 7.37 - 8.01 = -0.64;$$

thus the equation of the line of regression of $Y$ on $X$ takes the form

$$Y_e = -0.64 + 0.176X.$$

This equation can now be used in our original example to estimate the red blood cell count for various values of the packed cell volume. However, care should be taken to use the estimating equation only for such values of $X$ as lie within the range of the $X$-values of the given sample; in our original example the estimating equation could be safely applied only for values of $X$ between 35 and 58.

*Example 12-3.* From the data of Table 12-1 estimate the red blood cell count for a packed cell volume reading of 52 millimeters.

*Solution.* Using the estimating equation obtained in Example 12-2 for $X = 52$, we find

$$Y_e = -0.64 + (0.176)52 = 8.51.$$

In order to graph the line of regression we need determine only two points on the line. To facilitate the drawing, these two points should be fairly far apart.

*Example 12-4.* Draw the line of regression for the data of Table 12-1.

*Solution.* Using the equation of the line of regression obtained in Example 12-2, we find for the two extreme $X$-values:

$$X = 35: \quad Y_e = -0.64 + (0.176)35 = 5.52,$$
$$X = 58: \quad Y_e = -0.64 + (0.176)58 = 9.57.$$

Connecting these two points by a straight line, we obtain the graph shown in Figure 12-5.

In many cases the calculations required in finding the regression line can be greatly simplified by replacing the variable $X$ by $x$, where $x = X - \overline{X}$. Since $\Sigma x = \Sigma(X - \overline{X}) = 0$, the new variable $x$ has the property that its mean is equal to zero. This replacement is most convenient whenever all consecutive $X$-values of the given sample differ by the same amount, in which case the mean $\overline{X}$ may be found by inspection. In practice, this situation arises most frequently when the $X$'s are consecutive years, months, or other periods of time.

Fig. 12-5. Regression line fitted to the data of Table 12-1.

Since the mean of all $x$'s is zero, the values of $a$ and $b$ in the regression line

$$Y_e = a + bx$$

are given by

(12-5)
$$b = \frac{\Sigma x Y}{\Sigma x^2}, \quad a = \overline{Y}.$$

If, for example, the $X$-values are the years 1950, 1951, 1952, 1953, 1954, 1955, 1956, letting $x = X - 1953$ replaces these values by the much simpler numbers $-3, -2, -1, 0, 1, 2, 3$. In the corresponding regression line the $x$'s are measured with 1953 as origin. Whenever the $X$-values are an odd number of consecutive years (or other consecutive time periods), $x$ will be measured from the year in the center; for an even number of years, $x$ will be measured from the midpoint between the two years in the center. This procedure of replacing the $X$'s by $x$'s is advantageous only in the situations described above; in other types of problems such substitution frequently leads to unnecessary complications.

For many purposes it is convenient to write the slope of the regression line $b$ in the form

(12-6)
$$b = \frac{\Sigma x y}{\Sigma x^2},$$

where

$$x = X - \overline{X}, \quad y = Y - \overline{Y}.$$

*Proof of Formula (12-6).* To show that (12-6) is equivalent to (12-3), we rewrite the right-hand side of (12-6):

$$\frac{\Sigma xy}{\Sigma x^2} = \frac{\Sigma(X - \overline{X})(Y - \overline{Y})}{\Sigma(X - \overline{X})^2} = \frac{\Sigma(XY - X\overline{Y} - \overline{X}Y + \overline{X}\overline{Y})}{\Sigma(X^2 - 2X\overline{X} + \overline{X}^2)}$$

$$= \frac{\Sigma XY - \overline{Y}\Sigma X - \overline{X}\Sigma Y + n\overline{X}\overline{Y}}{\Sigma X^2 - 2\overline{X}\Sigma X + n\overline{X}^2}$$

$$= \frac{\Sigma XY - \overline{Y}n\overline{X} - \overline{X}n\overline{Y} + n\overline{X}\overline{Y}}{\Sigma X^2 - 2\overline{X}n\overline{X} + n\overline{X}^2} = \frac{\Sigma XY - n\overline{X}\overline{Y}}{\Sigma X^2 - n\overline{X}^2} = b.$$

For computing purposes the value of $b$ is obtained much faster by use of (12-3), since (12-3) does not require the calculation of deviations from the mean; on the other hand, (12-6) is useful in deriving relationships which exist between $b$ and certain other quantities which will be defined later.

One of the important properties of the line of regression is that it goes through the point for which $X = \overline{X}$ and $Y = \overline{Y}$. This is seen to be true for the line of regression obtained in Example 12-2, since for $X = \overline{X} = 45.50$, we find

$$Y_e = -0.64 + (0.176)45.50 = 7.37 = \overline{Y}.$$

We can easily prove that the point $(\overline{X}, \overline{Y})$ will always lie on the regression line. Substituting the value of $a$ from (12-4) into the equation of the line of regression (12-1), we can write

(12-7) $$Y_e = (\overline{Y} - b\overline{X}) + bX;$$

thus for $X = \overline{X}$ we obtain $Y_e = \overline{Y}$, which can also be seen directly from (12-4).

We shall now establish a formula which is of fundamental importance in regression analysis. To do this we need the following definition.

**DEFINITION 12-6.** The *sum of squares for regression* is defined as

(12-8) $$S.S.R. = \Sigma(Y_e - \overline{Y})^2.$$

It is a measure of the dispersion of the predicted $Y$-values (obtained from the regression line) about the mean of the $Y$-values of the given sample.

**DEFINITION 12-7.** The *sum of squares for error* for a regression line is defined as

(12-9) $$S.S.E. = \Sigma(Y - Y_e)^2.$$

It is a measure of the dispersion of the actual (or observed) $Y$-values about their corresponding values on the regression line.

Introducing now the additional notation,

(12-10) $$S.S. = \Sigma(Y - \overline{Y})^2,$$

which is a measure of the dispersion of the actual $Y$-values about their mean, we have the following formula:

$$(12\text{-}11) \qquad\qquad S.S. = S.S.R. + S.S.E.$$

This relationship shows that the dispersion of the $Y$-values about their mean is equal to the sum of the dispersion of the predicted $Y$-values about that mean and the dispersion of the actual $Y$-values about their corresponding values on the regression line.

*Proof of Formula (12-11).*

$$(12\text{-}12) \quad S.S. = \Sigma(Y - \overline{Y})^2 = \Sigma[(Y - Y_e) + (Y_e - \overline{Y})]^2$$
$$= \Sigma(Y - Y_e)^2 + 2\Sigma(Y - Y_e)(Y_e - \overline{Y}) + \Sigma(Y_e - \overline{Y})^2.$$

But from (12-7) it follows that the regression line can be written in the form

$$Y_e = \overline{Y} + b(X - \overline{X}) = \overline{Y} + bx,$$

and the sum appearing in the middle term of (12-12) can be written as

$$\Sigma(Y - Y_e)(Y_e - \overline{Y}) = \Sigma(Y - \overline{Y} - bx)bx = b\Sigma x(y - bx) = b[\Sigma xy - b\Sigma x^2].$$

Substituting in the bracketed expression the value of $b$ given by (12-6), we find

$$\Sigma(Y - Y_e)(Y_e - \overline{Y}) = b\left[\Sigma xy - \frac{\Sigma xy}{\Sigma x^2}\Sigma x^2\right] = 0;$$

thus the middle term in (12-12) equals 0, and

$$S.S. = \Sigma(Y - Y_e)^2 + \Sigma(Y_e - \overline{Y})^2 = S.S.E. + S.S.R.$$

## 12.3. The Standard Error of Estimate

We shall now determine whether or not a linear relationship can be said to exist between two variables. Sometimes, as we saw in Example 12-1, the scatter diagram shows fairly clearly the existence of a linear relationship; but if the points are widely scattered about the line of regression, there may be considerable doubt that the assumption of a linear relationship is warranted. We must therefore define a quantity which measures the spread of a set of points about the line of regression. Two such measures are in common use: the standard error of estimate, and the correlation coefficient. In practice, the latter is more widely employed.

For a population or a sample consisting of measurements of a single variable, the standard deviation is used in measuring the spread of the variates around the mean. A similar measure which indicates the spread of the given points around the fitted line of regression is called the standard error of estimate.

**DEFINITION 12-8.** The *standard error of estimate* for a regression line fitted to a sample of $n$ pairs of $X,Y$-values is defined as

(12-13)
$$\hat{s}_e = \sqrt{\frac{\Sigma(Y - Y_e)^2}{n}}.$$

It is evident that the nearer the points lie to a straight line, the smaller is the value of the standard error of estimate. A value of $\hat{s}_e = 0$ means that all points lie on a straight line. Although the standard error of estimate ordinarily is defined only for the regression line, i.e., the line obtained by the method of least squares, Definition 12-8 could be used to define the standard error of estimate for other lines fitting the given $n$ points. From equation (12-13) it is evident that the regression line is that line among all lines fitting the given $n$ points for which the standard error of estimate has its smallest possible value, since the regression line is determined by minimizing $\Sigma(Y - Y_e)^2$ and consequently $\hat{s}_e$.

*Example 12-5.* Find the standard error of estimate for the data of Table 12-1.

*Solution.* Using the equation of the line of regression obtained in Example 12-2, we calculate for each of the given $X$-values the corresponding value of $Y_e$; see the sixth column of Table 12-2. The values of $Y - Y_e$ and $(Y - Y_e)^2$ are listed in the seventh and eighth columns, respectively, of that table. Then

$$\hat{s}_e = \sqrt{\frac{1.6220}{10}} = \sqrt{0.162} = 0.40.$$

**Fig. 12-6.** Relation between regression line, points of scatter diagram, and standard error of estimate for large samples.

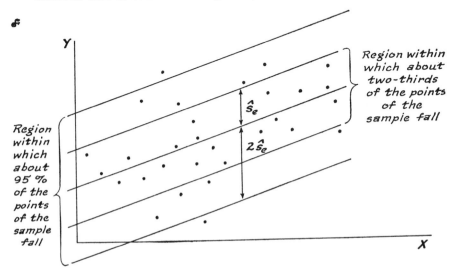

Since the standard error of estimate is the standard deviation of the errors of estimation, it has the property that, provided certain conditions (which we shall not state here) are satisfied, about two-thirds of the errors $|Y - Y_e|$ will be less than the standard error of estimate, and about one-third of the errors will exceed it. Thus two lines drawn parallel to the line of regression and at a vertical distance of $\hat{s}_e$ from it will define a region within which about two-thirds of the points of the given sample will fall. This statement is valid only if $n$ is fairly large. Furthermore, under the same conditions about 95% of the points will fall within a region bounded by two lines drawn parallel to the line of regression at a vertical distance of $2\hat{s}_e$ from it.

These regions are illustrated in Figure 12-6, the points representing a sample of 30 pairs of $X,Y$-values.

## 12.4.   The Correlation Coefficient

In studying the possibility of a relationship between $X$ and $Y$, if a sample of $n$ pairs is given, construction of the scatter diagram for the data is useful in suggesting the existence and nature of any such relationship. Such a scatter diagram is shown in Figure 12-7. If new axes are drawn through the point $O'(\overline{X}, \overline{Y})$ as origin, parallel to the original axes, the points of the scatter diagram will be distributed fairly uniformly below and above and to the right and left of the new origin. In Figure 12-7 we see that the coordinates $X$ and $Y$ of any point $P$, when related to the new axes, become $x$ and $y$, where $x = X - \overline{X}$ and $y = Y - \overline{Y}$.

Fig. 12-7. Scatter diagram with X, Y and x, y coordinate systems.

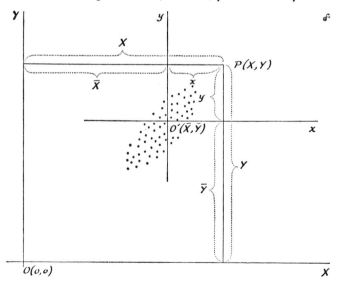

Figure 12-8 shows the signs of the product $xy$ in the four quadrants. If in each quadrant the number of points of the scatter diagram is approximately the same, no linear relationship is indicated, and the sum of the products $\Sigma xy$ will be numerically small. If, however, the points follow a linear trend and occur mostly in quadrants I and III, the positive products will predominate, and $\Sigma xy$ will be positive; if most of the points fall in quadrants II and IV, $\Sigma xy$ will be negative. It is evident therefore that $\Sigma xy$ and likewise the mean product $(1/n)\Sigma xy$ are indicators of a linear relationship between the values of $X$ and $Y$, and that the larger $\Sigma xy$ is in absolute value the closer the points lie to a straight line and the stronger is the evidence of a linear relationship. However, the quantities $\Sigma xy$ and $(1/n)\Sigma xy$ have units, and their magnitudes will depend upon the units in which $X$ and $Y$ are measured. If we want to use these quantities in making comparisons, we must free them of this disadvantage. To free them of units we shall proceed as we did for the $z$-value used in applications of the normal curve where deviations from the mean were expressed in terms of the standard deviation. If we take the unit of measurement in the $x$ direction as $\hat{s}_x$ and that in the $y$ direction as $\hat{s}_y$, the expression for the average product becomes

$$\frac{1}{n}\Sigma\frac{x}{\hat{s}_x}\cdot\frac{y}{\hat{s}_y} = \frac{\Sigma xy}{n\hat{s}_x\hat{s}_y} = \frac{\Sigma xy}{\sqrt{\Sigma x^2\Sigma y^2}},$$

which is called the coefficient of correlation. This is the most frequently used measure for determining the usefulness of a regression line for estimating purposes.

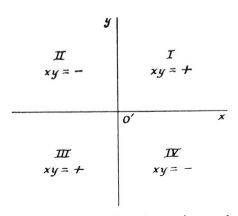

Fig. 12-8. Signs of $xy$ in quadrants of $x$, $y$ coordinate system.

DEFINITION 12-9. The *correlation coefficient* for a sample of $n$ pairs of $X,Y$-values is defined as

(12-14)
$$r = \frac{\Sigma xy}{\sqrt{\Sigma x^2\Sigma y^2}}.$$

An alternate form of the correlation coefficient shown above is given by

(12-15)
$$r = \frac{\Sigma xy}{n\hat{s}_x\hat{s}_y},$$

where

$$\hat{s}_x = \sqrt{\frac{\Sigma x^2}{n}}, \quad \hat{s}_y = \sqrt{\frac{\Sigma y^2}{n}}.$$

For purposes of computation (in order to avoid the use of deviations) it is best to write $r$ in either of the two forms:

(12-16)
$$r = \frac{\Sigma XY - \dfrac{\Sigma X \Sigma Y}{n}}{\sqrt{\left[\Sigma X^2 - \dfrac{(\Sigma X)^2}{n}\right]\left[\Sigma Y^2 - \dfrac{(\Sigma Y)^2}{n}\right]}}$$

$$r = \frac{\Sigma XY - n\bar{X}\bar{Y}}{\sqrt{(\Sigma X^2 - n\bar{X}^2)(\Sigma Y^2 - n\bar{Y}^2)}}.$$

The proof that both forms of (12-16) are equivalent to (12-14) is left as an exercise (see Exercise 2).

*Example 12-6.* Calculate the correlation coefficient for the data of Table 12-1.

*Solution.* Using the second of the two alternate forms of $r$ given by (12-16), we observe that the only values needed, in addition to those already calculated in finding the slope of the regression line $b$ (see Example 12-2), are the values of $Y^2$ and their sum, which are given in the fifth column of Table 12-2. Then

$$r = \frac{3441.52 - 10(45.50)(7.37)}{\sqrt{[21203 - 10(45.50)^2][560.3224 - 10(7.37)^2]}}$$

$$= \frac{88.17}{\sqrt{(500.50)(17.153)}} = \frac{88.17}{\sqrt{8585.08}} = \frac{88.17}{92.66} = 0.952.$$

In order to interpret the meaning of the correlation coefficient we shall first show that the following formula holds for $r$:

(12-17)
$$r^2 = \frac{S.S.R.}{S.S.}.$$

*Proof of Formula (12-17).* Recalling the definitions of $S.S.R.$ and $S.S.$, as given by (12-8) and (12-10), respectively, we have

$$\frac{S.S.R.}{S.S.} = \frac{\Sigma(Y_e - \bar{Y})^2}{\Sigma(Y - \bar{Y})^2} = \frac{\Sigma(\bar{Y} + bx - \bar{Y})^2}{\Sigma(Y - \bar{Y})^2} = \frac{\Sigma(bx)^2}{\Sigma y^2}$$

$$= b^2 \frac{\Sigma x^2}{\Sigma y^2} = \left(\frac{\Sigma xy}{\Sigma x^2}\right)^2 \frac{\Sigma x^2}{\Sigma y^2} = \frac{(\Sigma xy)^2}{\Sigma x^2 \Sigma y^2} = r^2.$$

Since $r^2$ appears in many other formulae, as well as in Formula (12-17), it is sometimes given a special name.

**DEFINITION 12-10.** The square of the correlation coefficient is defined as the *coefficient of determination*.

It can be seen from formula (12-17) that the coefficient of determination is the proportion of the total variation (or variance) in $Y$ which can be explained by the linear relationship existing between $X$ and $Y$. When multiplied by 100, the proportion is converted to per cent. Thus, the correlation coefficient of 0.952 found in Example 12-6 indicates that $(0.952)^2 \cdot 100 = 90.6\%$ of the variation in red blood cell counts is due to the linear relationship between the packed cell volume and the red blood cell count; the rest of the variation is due to unexplained factors, and is called the experimental error. Note that this interpretation in terms of percentages applies only to the variance of the $Y$'s, not to the standard deviation of the $Y$'s.

We can conclude that a correlation coefficient satisfies the following properties.

1. If all points of the scatter diagram lie on a line, then $r = +1$ or $-1$. This is evident, since in this case $S.S.E. = 0$ and consequently $S.S. = S.S.R.$; thus, from (12-17) $r^2 = 1$ and $r = +1$ or $-1$.
2. If no linear relationship exists between the $X$'s and $Y$'s, then $r = 0$, since, for no linear relationship, $S.S.R. = 0$; thus (12-17) becomes $r^2 = 0$.
3. Since the ratio given in (12-17) can never exceed 1 or ever be less than 0, $r^2$ is always between 0 and 1, and, consequently, $r$ is always between $-1$ and $+1$.

A relationship between the slope of the regression line and the correlation coefficient is given by the formula

$$(12\text{-}18) \qquad\qquad b = r \frac{\hat{s}_y}{\hat{s}_x}.$$

*Proof of Formula (12-18).*

$$r \frac{\hat{s}_y}{\hat{s}_x} = \frac{\Sigma xy}{n \hat{s}_x \hat{s}_y} \frac{\hat{s}_y}{\hat{s}_x} = \frac{\Sigma xy}{n \hat{s}_x^2} = \frac{\Sigma xy}{\Sigma x^2} = b.$$

From (12-18) it follows that $r$ is positive if and only if $b$ is positive, since $\hat{s}_x$ and $\hat{s}_y$, being standard deviations, are always nonnegative. Similarly, $r$ will be negative if and only if $b$ is negative. Thus, a positive $r$ indicates that, since $b = \tan \alpha$ (see Figure 12-2), the regression line forms an acute angle with the positive $X$-axis or that $Y$ increases with increasing $X$; a negative $r$ indicates that the regression line forms an obtuse angle with the positive $X$-axis or that $Y$ decreases with increasing $X$.

Figures 12-9, 12-10, and 12-11 show examples of $r = -1$, $r$ slightly less than 1, and $r \cong 0$.

Fig. 12-9. $r = -1$.          Fig. 12-10. $r$ slightly          Fig. 12-11. $r$ approxi-
                             less than 1.                     mately equal to 0.

A relationship between the correlation coefficient and the standard error of estimate of the sample is given by

$$(12\text{-}19) \qquad\qquad r^2 = 1 - \frac{\hat{s}_e^2}{\hat{s}_y^2}.$$

*Proof of Formula (12-19).*

$$r^2 = \frac{S.S.R.}{S.S.} \doteq \frac{S.S. - S.S.E.}{S.S.} = 1 - \frac{S.S.E.}{S.S.} = 1 - \frac{\dfrac{\Sigma(Y - Y_e)^2}{n}}{\dfrac{\Sigma(Y - \overline{Y})^2}{n}} = 1 - \frac{\hat{s}_e^2}{\hat{s}_y^2}.$$

## 12.5.  Significance of a Correlation Coefficient

For values of $r$ close to zero, there is no linear relationship; for values of $r$ near $\pm 1$, a very strong linear relationship exists. We must yet formulate precise conclusions for intermediate values of $r$. We may do this by considering the bivariate population from which the sample of $n$ pairs is taken. Let us denote the correlation coefficient of the population by $\rho$ and assume the population to be normal; i.e., for each $X$ all values of $Y$ which are obtained satisfy a normal distribution. If we take all possible samples of $n$ pairs from this population and consider the distribution of the correlation coefficients of these samples, we find that this distribution is not one of the well-known distributions we have studied. To illustrate this, the distributions of $r$ for various sample sizes when $\rho = 0$, 0.50, and 0.90 are shown in Figures 12-12, 12-13, and 12-14.

These figures show that the distribution of $r$ assumes widely different forms for various values of $\rho$ and $n$. As we shall see, the study of the case where $\rho = 0$ (Figure 12-12) is the most important study for practical purposes.

Fig. 12-12. The distribution of r for ρ = 0.

Fig. 12-13. The distribution of r for ρ = 0.50.

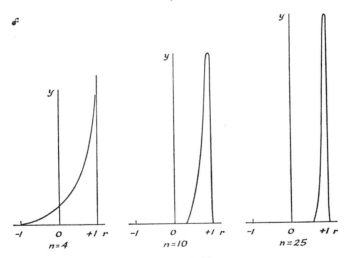

Fig. 12-14. The distribution of r for ρ = 0.90.

Figure 12-12 shows what at first might seem paradoxical: for $n = 3$ the curve is U-shaped. This shows that when a sample of size 3 is selected from a normal bivariate population in which there is no linear correlation the chance of obtaining a fairly high correlation coefficient for the sample is greater than the chance of obtaining a small correlation coefficient. For samples of size 4, the fact that the curve is a horizontal straight line shows that the chance of obtaining a particular correlation coefficient is equal to that of obtaining any other.

Considering now the special case where $\rho = 0$, it can be shown that, while $r$ itself does not satisfy one of the distributions studied so far, the quantity

$$\frac{r}{\sqrt{\dfrac{1 - r^2}{n - 2}}}$$

satisfies a Student's $t$-distribution. This results in the following theorem.

**THEOREM 12-2.** If from a normal bivariate population with correlation coefficient $\rho = 0$ all samples of size $n$ are taken and their correlation coefficients are denoted by $r$, then

(12-20) $$t = \frac{r}{\sqrt{\dfrac{1 - r^2}{n - 2}}}$$

satisfies a Student's $t$-distribution with $n - 2$ degrees of freedom.

The number of degrees of freedom is taken as $n - 2$, since for a regression line the constants $a$ and $b$ are fixed; i.e., there exist two independent relationships involving the $n$ pairs of values of $X$ and $Y$.

In order to decide whether, for a sample of size $n$, a given correlation coefficient indicates a linear relationship, we test the hypothesis that the sample is chosen from a population for which $\rho = 0$ and, therefore, determine the probability that from such a population a sample of size $n$ is taken for which the correlation coefficient equals or exceeds the absolute value of $r$ calculated for the given sample. Here, we use a two-tailed test. If the probability is less than 5% (or whatever other level of significance is chosen), we reject the hypothesis that the sample is taken from a population in which there is no linear relationship. The value of $r$ then indicates that the $X$- and $Y$-values can be assumed to be linearly related.

*Example 12-7.* In a sample of 42 pairs of $X, Y$-values the correlation coefficient is found to be 0.220. Does this indicate a significant correlation on the basis of the 5% level of significance?

*Solution.* We are testing here the hypothesis that $\rho = 0$. Using Theorem 12-2, we find

$$t = \frac{0.220}{\sqrt{\dfrac{1 - (0.220)^2}{40}}} = \frac{0.220}{0.154} = 1.43.$$

For $\nu = 40$, $t_{.05} = 2.021$.

Since $t = 1.43 < 2.021$, the correlation coefficient of 0.220 cannot be considered significant. This means that from a population with $\rho = 0$, samples of 42 pairs with a correlation coefficient of 0.220 or larger or $-0.220$ or less are obtained rather frequently—more than 5% of the time (actually, as we see from Appendix Table II, more than 10% of the time).

Since Theorem 12-2 is applicable only where $\rho = 0$, it can be used only to decide whether in a particular sample the correlation coefficient is significantly different from zero; it cannot be used to establish confidence limits for $\rho$.

Where $\rho$ does not equal zero, even for larger values of $n$ the distributions do not assume a bell-shaped form but are decidedly skewed, as shown in Figures 12-13 and 12-14. Indeed, the equation of the distribution curve of $r$ where $\rho$ is different from zero is so complicated it will not be given here. On the other hand, R. A. Fisher found that if instead of $r$ the quantity $Z$, defined in terms of $r$ as

(12-21)
$$Z = \tfrac{1}{2} \log_e \frac{1 + r}{1 - r},$$

is considered, its distribution will be approximately normal. Thus we have the following theorem.

THEOREM 12-3. If from a bivariate population with correlation coefficient $\rho$ all samples of size $n$ are taken, then

(12-22)
$$z = \frac{Z - m_Z}{\sigma_Z}$$

satisfies an approximately normal distribution with

(12-23)
$$m_Z = \tfrac{1}{2} \log_e \frac{1 + \rho}{1 - \rho}, \quad \sigma_Z = \frac{1}{\sqrt{n - 3}}.$$

The values of $Z$ corresponding to various positive values of $r$, as calculated from (12-21), are given in Appendix Table III. To find the values of $Z$ corresponding to negative values of $r$, we note that for $r = -|r|$, where $|r|$ is the absolute value of $r$ and, therefore, positive, we have

$$Z = \tfrac{1}{2} \log_e \frac{1 + r}{1 - r} = \tfrac{1}{2} \log_e \frac{1 - |r|}{1 + |r|} = \tfrac{1}{2}[\log_e (1 - |r|) - \log_e (1 + |r|)]$$

$$= -\tfrac{1}{2}[\log_e (1 + |r|) - \tfrac{1}{2} \log_e (1 - |r|)] = -\tfrac{1}{2} \log_e \frac{1 + |r|}{1 - |r|},$$

so that the value of $Z$ corresponding to $r = -|r|$ is the negative of the value of $Z$ corresponding to the absolute value of $r$.

*Example 12-8.* In a sample of 35 pairs the correlation coefficient is found to be 0.80. Use the 5% level of significance to test the hypothesis that $\rho = 0.90$.

*Solution.* In order to test this hypothesis, we determine the probability that from a population with $\rho = 0.90$ a sample with correlation coefficient $r = 0.80$ or less is taken (more precisely, we take twice this probability, since we apply a two-tailed test); if the probability exceeds 5%, we accept the hypothesis; otherwise, we reject it.

From Appendix Table III, we find $Z = 1.099$ for $r = 0.80$. Appendix Table III can also be used to find the value of $m_Z$, since the procedure for finding this value, as given by (12-23), is identical to that for finding $Z$ from $r$, as given by (12-21). From Appendix Table III, we find $m_Z = 1.472$ for $\rho = 0.90$. Furthermore,

$$\sigma_Z = \frac{1}{\sqrt{32}} = 0.177;$$

thus,

$$z = \frac{1.099 - 1.472}{0.177} = -2.11.$$

From Appendix Table I we find that the area under the normal probability curve to the left of $z = -2.11$ is

$$A = 0.0174;$$

hence, the desired probability has a value of

$$P = 2(0.0174) = 0.0348,$$

which is less than 5%. Therefore, at the 5% level of significance, we reject the hypothesis that the sample with correlation coefficient $r = 0.80$ is taken from a population with $\rho = 0.90$.

Note that the probability found here refers to the chance of obtaining a value of $z$ less than or equal to $-2.11$ or greater than or equal to 2.11. The value of $r$ corresponding to $z = -2.11$ is, of course, 0.80; however, the value of $r$ corresponding to $z = 2.11$ is not 1, as a superficial inspection might indicate, but is that value of $r$ for which the corresponding $Z$ satisfies the equation

$$\frac{Z - 1.472}{0.177} = 2.11,$$

from which we find $Z = 1.845$ and $r = 0.95$. Thus, the value of $P = 0.0348$ obtained above represents the probability that from a population with correlation coefficient 0.90 a sample of 35 pairs is taken for which the correlation coefficient is 0.80 or less or 0.95 or more.

Theorem 12-3 now enables us to set up confidence limits for $\rho$ when a sample correlation coefficient is known.

*Example 12-9.*   In a sample of 52 pairs the correlation coefficient is found to be 0.53. Find the 95% confidence limits for the correlation coefficient of the population.

*Solution.*   From Appendix Table III we find $Z = 0.590$ for $r = 0.53$. Furthermore,

$$\sigma_Z = \tfrac{1}{7} = 0.143.$$

Since, for the 95% confidence limits, $z = \pm 1.96$, we have

$$\frac{Z - m_Z}{0.143} = \pm 1.96.$$

Hence,

$$Z - m_Z = \pm 0.280,$$

and

$$m_Z = Z \pm 0.280 = 0.590 \pm 0.280.$$

Thus, $m_Z$ is between 0.31 and 0.87, and, correspondingly, $\rho$ is between 0.30 and 0.70, the latter two values being obtained from Appendix Table III for $Z$-values of 0.31 and 0.87, respectively.

Why are the confidence limits for $\rho$, 0.30 and 0.70, not symmetric with respect to the given value of $r = 0.53$? The answer is that the distribution of $r$, shown in Figures 12-13 and 12-14, is not symmetric but skewed, except when $\rho = 0$. Thus, whenever confidence limits for $\rho$ are determined from a given positive value of $r$, the upper confidence limit will be closer to $r$ than will be the lower one. If confidence limits are determined from a negative value of $r$, the lower confidence limit will be closer to $r$ than will be the upper one.

Clearly, Theorem 12-3 can be applied even when $\rho = 0$. But since Theorem 12-3 involves a distribution which is only approximately normal, whenever the hypothesis $\rho = 0$ is to be tested Theorem 12-2 should be used.

In Chapter 8 we stated without proof the formula for the standard deviation of the differences between sample means from two independent populations—see formula (8-9). We are now in a position to state a much more general formula.

The standard deviation of the differences between sample means from two populations, i.e., the differences shown in Figure 8-3, is given by

(12-24)                       $$\sigma_{\bar{x}-\bar{y}} = \sqrt{\sigma_{\bar{x}}^2 - 2\rho\sigma_{\bar{x}}\sigma_{\bar{y}} + \sigma_{\bar{y}}^2},$$

where $\rho$ is the correlation coefficient between the $\bar{X}$ and $\bar{Y}$; i.e.,

(12-25)                       $$\rho = \frac{\Sigma(\bar{X} - m_{\bar{x}})(\bar{Y} - m_{\bar{y}})}{N\sigma_{\bar{x}}\sigma_{\bar{y}}}.$$

*Proof of Formula (12-24).*

$$\sigma_{\bar{x}-\bar{y}}^2 = \frac{1}{N}\{\Sigma[(\bar{X}-\bar{Y})-m_{\bar{x}-\bar{y}}]^2\} = \frac{1}{N}\{\Sigma[(\bar{X}-\bar{Y})-(m_{\bar{x}}-m_{\bar{y}})]^2\}$$

$$= \frac{1}{N}\{\Sigma[(\bar{X}-m_{\bar{x}})-(\bar{Y}-m_{\bar{y}})]^2\}$$

$$= \frac{1}{N}\Sigma(\bar{X}-m_{\bar{x}})^2 - \frac{2}{N}\Sigma(\bar{X}-m_{\bar{x}})(\bar{Y}-m_{\bar{y}}) + \frac{1}{N}\Sigma(\bar{Y}-m_{\bar{y}})^2$$

$$= \sigma_{\bar{x}}^2 - 2\frac{\Sigma(\bar{X}-m_{\bar{x}})(\bar{Y}-m_{\bar{y}})}{N\sigma_{\bar{x}}\sigma_{\bar{y}}}\;\sigma_{\bar{x}}\sigma_{\bar{y}} + \sigma_{\bar{y}}^2 = \sigma_{\bar{x}}^2 - 2\rho\sigma_{\bar{x}}\sigma_{\bar{y}} + \sigma_{\bar{y}}^2.$$

Taking the square root of both sides of this equation results in formula (12-24).

If two populations are independent, there exists no relationship between $X$ and $Y$ and consequently none between $\bar{X}$ and $\bar{Y}$; thus $\rho = 0$, and (12-24) becomes

(12-26)                            $\sigma_{\bar{x}-\bar{y}} = \sqrt{\sigma_{\bar{x}}^2 + \sigma_{\bar{y}}^2},$

which is identical to formula (8-9).

## 12.6.  Comparison of Regression Line of Y on X with that of X on Y

If a sample of $n$ pairs of $X,Y$-values is given, there are occasions when either $X$ or $Y$ can be considered the independent variable. For example, from the data of Table 12-1 we may wish to determine a regression line from which to predict packed cell volumes from given red blood cell counts—in Example 12-2 we estimated red blood cell counts from given packed cell volumes. Also, it would be of interest to compare these two regression lines. When $Y$ is considered the independent variable, the regression line can be written in the form

(12-27)                            $X_e = c + dY,$

where $c$ and $d$ play the roles of $a$ and $b$ in the original line and are obtained by interchanging the $X$'s and $Y$'s in the formulae previously given for $a$ and $b$. Formula (12-27), then, is the result of minimizing $\Sigma(X - X_e)^2$ rather than $\Sigma(Y - Y_e)^2$.

When the two lines of regressions of $Y$ on $X$ and $X$ on $Y$ are graphed, will the graphs of these two lines ever coincide? This question is answered by Theorem 12-4.

**THEOREM 12-4.** The graphs of the regression lines of $Y$ on $X$ and $X$ on $Y$ are identical if and only if all points of the given sample lie on a straight line.

*Proof of Theorem 12-4.* If the graphs of the two lines are identical, the equations of the regression lines given by formulae (12-27) and (12-1) must be the same. Solving $Y_e = a + bX$ for $X$, we obtain

$$X = -\frac{a}{b} + \frac{1}{b} Y_e.$$

This equation will be identical to $X_e = c + dY$ if corresponding coefficients are the same; thus

$$\frac{1}{b} = d = \frac{\Sigma xy}{\Sigma y^2},$$

which can be written

$$b\Sigma xy = \Sigma y^2.$$

Then

$$b\frac{\Sigma xy}{\Sigma y^2} = 1, \quad \frac{\Sigma xy}{\Sigma x^2}\frac{\Sigma xy}{\Sigma y^2} = 1, \quad \frac{(\Sigma xy)^2}{\Sigma x^2 \Sigma y^2} = 1,$$

and

$$r^2 = 1,$$

which shows that all points lie on a straight line, and the graphs of the two lines are identical.

## 12.7.   Lines of Regression Through the Origin

Often the conditions of a practical problem require that the line of regression go through the origin. For example, if $X$ represents time measured from the germination of a plant, and $Y$ its height, then the value of $Y$ for $X = 0$ must equal zero. This is true also for the data of Table 12-1, since we know that for a packed cell volume of zero the red blood cell count must equal zero.

If, then, the hypothesis is made that the line of regression goes through the origin, the normal equations reduce to a single equation which is identical to the second of the equations (12-2) with $a = 0$. Thus we obtain immediately

(12-28)                                 $$b = \frac{\Sigma XY}{\Sigma X^2}.$$

The line of regression then takes the form

$$(12\text{-}29) \qquad\qquad Y_e = bX.$$

*Example 12-10.* Find the line of regression for the data of Table 12-1, assuming that the line goes through the origin.

*Solution.* Using the results of Table 12-2 we find

$$b = \frac{3441.52}{21203} = 0.162;$$

hence the regression line takes the form

$$Y_e = 0.162X.$$

In order to establish a possibly more accurate formula for the relationship between packed cell volume and red blood cell count, 562 pairs of observations on canine blood were made at the clinic of the School of Veterinary Medicine at the University of California at Davis, and the corresponding regression line was calculated. Its equation was precisely the same as that calculated above.

## 12.8. Polynomial Regression

If the value of $r$ indicates that no linear relationship exists between the variables $X$ and $Y$, the possibility remains that some other type of relationship exists. The scatter diagram might, for example, show the existence of a polynomial relationship—i.e., a relationship which, for the case of a polynomial of degree 3, would be of the form

$$(12\text{-}30) \qquad\qquad Y_e = a + bX + cX^2 + dX^3.$$

Here our problem is that of determining from a given sample of $n$ pairs of $X,Y$-values the constants $a$, $b$, $c$, and $d$ by the method of least squares so that again $\Sigma(Y - Y_e)^2$ has its smallest possible value. Using the differential calculus it is fairly easy to show that $a$, $b$, $c$, and $d$ must be the solution of the following system of four linear equations.

$$(12\text{-}31) \qquad \begin{aligned} an \quad\;\; + b\Sigma X \;\; + c\Sigma X^2 + d\Sigma X^3 &= \Sigma Y \\ a\Sigma X \;\; + b\Sigma X^2 + c\Sigma X^3 + d\Sigma X^4 &= \Sigma XY \\ a\Sigma X^2 + b\Sigma X^3 + c\Sigma X^4 + d\Sigma X^5 &= \Sigma X^2 Y \\ a\Sigma X^3 + b\Sigma X^4 + c\Sigma X^5 + d\Sigma X^6 &= \Sigma X^3 Y \end{aligned}$$

These equations are rather obvious generalizations of the corresponding equations (12-2) found for the linear case, i.e., for a polynomial of degree 1, and are also called normal equations.

The "polynomial of best fit," as obtained by the method of least squares, then would be found by solving equations (12-31) for $a$, $b$, $c$, and $d$ and substituting these values into (12-30).

## 12.9. Multiple Regression

We have confined our attention to the case of one independent variable. Now let us assume that a variable $Z$ is dependent upon the two independent variables $X$ and $Y$, and, to take the simplest possible case, let us suppose that there exists a linear relationship relating $Z$ to $X$ and $Y$ such as

(12-32) $$Z_e = a + bX + cY.$$

The reader familiar with solid analytic geometry will recall that, graphically, equation (12-32) represents a plane in three-dimensional space.

If we are now given $n$ sets of values for $X$, $Y$, $Z$, our problem is that of determining the constants $a$, $b$, and $c$ in such a way that the sum of squares $\Sigma(Z - Z_e)^2$ has its smallest possible value. It can be shown, again by use of the differential calculus, that $a$, $b$, and $c$ must be the solution of the following system of three linear equations.

(12-33)
$$
\begin{aligned}
an &+ b\Sigma X &+ c\Sigma Y &= \Sigma Z \\
a\Sigma X &+ b\Sigma X^2 &+ c\Sigma XY &= \Sigma XZ \\
a\Sigma Y &+ b\Sigma XY &+ c\Sigma Y^2 &= \Sigma YZ
\end{aligned}
$$

The "plane of best fit," as obtained by the method of least squares, then would be the result of substituting into (12-32) the values of $a$, $b$, and $c$ obtained by solving (12-33).

## Exercises

1. Given the following values of $X$ and $Y$:

| $X$ | $Y$ |
|---|---|
| 0 | 6 |
| 2 | −1 |
| 3 | −3 |
| 5 | −10 |
| 6 | −16 |

(a) Find the equation of the regression line of $Y$ on $X$.

(b) Draw the scatter diagram, and graph the line.

(c) Use the line to estimate $Y$ when $X = 4$.

(d) Calculate the standard error of estimate.

(e) Calculate the correlation coefficient.

2. Derive formula (12-16) from (12-14).

3. In the table below, $S$ is the weight of potassium bromide which will dissolve in 100 grams of water at $T°C$.

| $T$ | $S$ |
|-----|-----|
| 0   | 54  |
| 20  | 65  |
| 40  | 75  |
| 60  | 85  |
| 80  | 96  |

(a) Find the regression line for predicting $S$.

(b) Use this equation to estimate $S$ when $T = 50°$.

(c) Find the standard error of estimate.

(d) Find the correlation coefficient.

4. A manufacturer of optical equipment has the following data on the unit cost (in dollars) of certain custom-made lenses and the number of units made in each order.

| Number of Units (X) | Cost per Unit (Y) |
|---------------------|-------------------|
| 1                   | 58                |
| 3                   | 55                |
| 5                   | 40                |
| 10                  | 37                |
| 12                  | 22                |

(a) Use the regression equation to predict the unit cost in an order of 8 of these lenses.

(b) Find the correlation coefficient.

5. A study is made relating aptitude test scores to productivity in a factory after three months of personnel training. The 6 pairs of scores shown below are obtained by testing 6 randomly selected applicants and later measuring their productivity.

| Applicant | Aptitude Score (X) | Productivity (Y) |
|---|---|---|
| 1 | 9 | 23 |
| 2 | 17 | 35 |
| 3 | 20 | 29 |
| 4 | 19 | 33 |
| 5 | 20 | 43 |
| 6 | 23 | 32 |

(a) Find the equation of the line which can be used to predict the productivity from the aptitude score.

(b) What is the expected productivity of a worker who has an aptitude
score of 16?

(c) Find the line of regression that will permit prediction of aptitude
scores from productivity.

(d) Find the correlation coefficient.

(e) What per cent of the variance in $Y$ is explained by the linear relationship existing between $X$ and $Y$?

6. Given the following data on age in weeks, $X$, and mean height in centi-
meters, $Y$, of soybean plants:

| X | Y |
|---|---|
| 1 | 5 |
| 2 | 17 |
| 3 | 24 |
| 4 | 33 |
| 5 | 41 |

Find the equation of the line of regression of $Y$ on $X$. (Note: this line
must go through the origin.)

7. The regression line of wormy fruits, $Y$, on the size of crop on the tree in
hundreds of fruits, $X$, is

$$Y_e = 64 - 1.4X.$$

If it is known that

$$\bar{Y} = 45, \quad \hat{s}_x = 7.2, \quad \hat{s}_y = 10.5$$

find

(a) $\bar{X}$;

(b) the correlation coefficient;

(c) the regression line of $X$ on $Y$.

8. A correlation coefficient of 0.50 is found in a sample of 27 pairs. Can it be regarded as significantly different from zero on the basis of the 5% level of significance?

9. Suppose that a sample of 11 pairs taken from an approximately normal bivariate population yields a correlation coefficient of $-0.65$. Can this be considered a significant correlation at the 1% level?

10. How large a correlation coefficient is needed for a sample of size 25 in order to justify the claim that the variables are linearly related? Use the 5% level of significance.

11. How large a correlation coefficient is needed for a sample of size 11 so that the variables can be considered linearly correlated at the 1% level of significance?

12. Determine the complete range of values of the correlation coefficient for a sample of size 30 for which the correlation coefficient would be considered significantly different from zero at the 5% level.

13. Test at the 5% level the hypothesis that $\rho = 0.60$, if in a sample of 103 pairs the correlation coefficient is found to be equal to 0.90.

14. A machine, which can be run at different speeds, produces articles of which a certain number are defective. The number of defective items produced per hour seems to depend on machine speed, as indicated in the following results of an experimental run.

| Speed in r.p.s. | Number of Defectives per Hour |
|---|---|
| 8 | 5 |
| 12 | 8 |
| 14 | 9 |
| 16 | 11 |

   (a) Find the regression line of the number of defectives per hour on the machine speed in r.p.s.
   (b) Find the correlation coefficient.
   (c) Would you use the line obtained in part (a) to estimate machine speed for a given number of defectives per hour? Explain.
   (d) Which of the following two hypotheses is more reasonable? (i) The population correlation coefficient is 0. (ii) It is 0.7.

15. In a sample of 63 pairs the correlation coefficient is found to be 0.31. Find the 95% confidence limits for the correlation coefficient of the population.

16. Find the 98% confidence limits for the correlation coefficient of a popu-

lation from which a sample of 50 pairs with correlation coefficient $-0.48$ is taken.

17. In a sample of 45 pairs the correlation coefficient is found to be $-0.18$.
    (a) Find the 99% confidence limits for the correlation coefficient of the population.
    (b) Use the result of part (a) to determine whether there is a significant correlation in this sample at the 1% level of significance.

18. In a sample of 25 pairs of parent and child the correlation in a certain character is found to be 0.60. Is this value consistent with the view that the true correlation in that character is 0.46, using the 5% level of significance?

19. A correlation coefficient of 0.56 is said to be highly significant. Assuming that this refers to the 1% level of significance, what is the least number of observations that must have been made in order to warrant this statement?

20. At most, how many observations could have been made in a sample for which a correlation coefficient of 0.25 was not considered significant at the 5% level?

21. A sample of size 52 is taken from a population in which the correlation coefficient is 0.59. Find the probability that the correlation coefficient of the sample is 0.40 or less.

22. Find the probability that a sample of size 67 taken from a population with correlation coefficient 0.45 has a correlation coefficient between 0.55 and 0.65.

23. From a population with correlation coefficient 0.65, a large number of samples of equal size is taken. If 15% of these samples have correlation coefficients of 0.75 or more, what is the expected size of the sample?

24. The 98% confidence limits for the correlation coefficient of a normal bivariate population, as determined from a sample, are 0.29 and 0.71. What is the expected size of the sample?

25. In a bivariate population, the correlation coefficient is 0.60. If 3,000 samples of 39 pairs are taken from this population, how many would you expect to have a correlation coefficient of at most 0.55?

26. A sample is found to have a correlation coefficient of 0.69. If the hypothesis that this sample was taken from a population with a correlation coefficient of 0.57 is rejected at the 5% level, find the smallest possible size of the sample.

27. From a population with correlation coefficient 0.80, an experimenter selects 500 samples, all of equal size. If 115 of these samples show a correlation coefficient greater than 0.85, what is the expected sample size?

28. The 95% confidence limits for the correlation coefficient of a bivariate population are found to be 0.20 and 0.58. What would be the 99% confidence limits for the correlation coefficient of this population?

29. The 99% confidence limits for the correlation coefficient of a bivariate population are found to be $-0.22$ and 0.51. Find the number of pairs in the sample from which these confidence limits were calculated.

30. For a set of $n$ pairs of values of $X$, $Y$, the correlation coefficient is found to be 0.80. If, for this sample, $\Sigma(Y - Y_e)^2 = 9$, find $\Sigma(Y - \bar{Y})^2$.

31. If $b$ is the slope of the regression line of $Y$ on $X$, and $d$ the slope of the regression line of $X$ on $Y$, prove that

$$bd = r^2,$$

where $r$ is the correlation coefficient between $X$ and $Y$.

32. If, from a sample, the regression line of $Y$ on $X$ is found to be

$$Y_e = 10 - \tfrac{4}{3}X$$

and the one of $X$ on $Y$

$$X_e = 5 - \tfrac{1}{3}Y,$$

find

(a) the correlation coefficient;
(b) the values of $\bar{X}$ and $\bar{Y}$ for the sample.

33. Prove that the formula for the sum of squares for regression—Formula (12-8)—can be rewritten as

$$S.S.R. = b\Sigma xy,$$

where $b$ is the slope of the regression line.

34. Prove that for a bivariate population of $X,Y$-values the variance of the $X + Y$, i.e., $\sigma_{x+y}^2$, is given by

$$\sigma_{x+y}^2 = \sigma_x^2 + 2\rho\sigma_x\sigma_y + \sigma_y^2.$$

35. Prove that linear transformations of $X$ and $Y$ into $W$ and $Z$, respectively, i.e.,

$$W = aX + b$$
$$Z = cY + d,$$

where $a$, $b$, $c$, $d$ are constants, do not change the absolute value of the correlation coefficient. That is, if $r_{xy}$ is the correlation coefficient between the $X$-values and $Y$-values, and $r_{wz}$ is the correlation coefficient between the $W$-values and $Z$-values, then show that

$$|r_{wz}| = |r_{xy}|.$$

# 13 Chi-Square Distribution

## 13.1. Definition

If an experiment has only two possible outcomes, such as the appearance of a head or a tail in the tossing of a coin, the normal distribution can be used to determine whether the observed frequencies of these two events depart significantly from the expected frequencies. Whenever more than two events, say $k$ events, can occur, the normal distribution no longer can be applied to test for a possible significant difference between the observed and expected frequencies.

If we are considering more than two events, we must first define a quantity which measures the discrepancy between the $k$ observed frequencies $o_1, o_2, \cdots, o_k$ and their corresponding expected frequencies $e_1, e_2, \cdots, e_k$. This statistic, called chi-square, is defined as

$$(13\text{-}1) \qquad \chi^2 = \sum_{i=1}^{k} \frac{(o_i - e_i)^2}{e_i}.$$

Clearly, the closer the agreement between the expected and observed frequencies, the smaller will be the value of $\chi^2$. If $\chi^2 = 0$, each of the terms of the sum in (13-1) must be zero, and there is perfect agreement between observed and expected frequencies for all $k$ events.

TABLE 13-1. Observed and Expected Results of 120 Tosses of a Die and Calculation of Chi-Square

| Face | o | e | o − e | (o − e)² | $\frac{(o - e)^2}{e}$ |
|------|-----|-----|------|----------|----------------------|
| 1 | 13 | 20 | −7 | 49 | 2.45 |
| 2 | 28 | 20 | 8 | 64 | 3.20 |
| 3 | 16 | 20 | −4 | 16 | 0.80 |
| 4 | 10 | 20 | −10 | 100 | 5.00 |
| 5 | 32 | 20 | 12 | 144 | 7.20 |
| 6 | 21 | 20 | 1 | 1 | 0.05 |
| | 120 | 120 | 0 | | 18.70 |

*Example 13-1.* A die is tossed 120 times, and the results are listed in the second column of Table 13-1 (a 1 is obtained 13 times, a 2 is obtained 28 times, and so on). Assuming that the die is honest, find the value of $\chi^2$.

*Solution.* Since each face of an honest die is expected to show one sixth of the time, in this example each expected value equals 20 and $\chi^2$ is the sum of the numbers in the last column of Table 13-1. Consequently,

$$\chi^2 = 18.70.$$

## 13.2.  Distribution of Chi-Square

If an experiment, such as the preceding one, is repeated many times, always under the hypothesis that the expected values remain unchanged, and each time the value of $\chi^2$ is calculated, a set of values of $\chi^2$ is obtained for which the corresponding histogram can be drawn. It is important, for later discussion, to realize that $\chi^2$ is a discrete variable; that is, $\chi^2$ can only assume certain, but not all, nonnegative values. The reason for this may be clarified if we consider again the tossing of a die 120 times. For perfect agreement of observed and expected frequencies, $\chi^2$ equals 0; the next larger value of $\chi^2$ is obtained when one of the observed values is 21, another 19, and all the rest 20, in which case, as can be readily verified, $\chi^2 = 0.10$. Thus, in this example, $\chi^2$ cannot assume any value between 0 and 0.10.

Fortunately, as was true for the binomial distribution, there is a frequency curve which is an excellent approximation to the histogram of $\chi^2$, and, correspondingly, a probability curve which approximates the distribution of $\chi^2$.

**THEOREM 13-1.** The distribution of $\chi^2$ is well-approximated by the curve

(13-2) $$y = c(\chi^2)^{\frac{\nu-2}{2}} e^{-\frac{\chi^2}{2}},$$

where $\nu$ is the number of degrees of freedom, and $c$ is a constant depending on $\nu$ and determined in such a way that the total area under the probability curve (13-2) is equal to 1.

In graphing the curves given by (13-2) for various values of $\nu$ we note that for $\nu \geq 3$ the curve starts at the origin, reaches its highest point for $\chi^2 = \nu - 2$, and then decreases, approaching the horizontal axis asymptotically without, however, being symmetric about any vertical line. For $\nu = 2$, the curve has its highest point on the $y$-axis, and for $\nu = 1$, the curve has no maximum value for $\chi^2 \geq 0$; i.e., it is infinite for $\chi^2 = 0$, decreases continuously as $\chi^2$ increases, and approaches the horizontal axis. The graphs of (13-2) for $\nu = 1$, 3, 5, and 15 are shown in Figure 13-1.

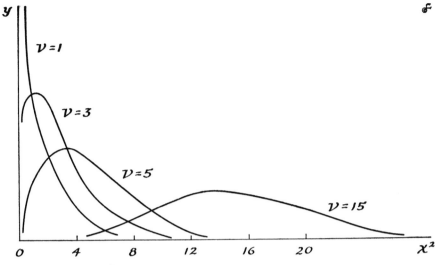

Fig. 13-1. The $\chi^2$-distributions for $\nu = 1, 3, 5, 15$.

Appendix Table IV gives for various $\nu$-values (first column) the values of $\chi^2$ for which the right-tail areas have the values listed at the heads of the other columns: e.g., for $\nu = 3$ the value of $\chi^2$ for a right-tail area of 0.30 is 3.66, which means that for 3 degrees of freedom the probability of obtaining a value of $\chi^2$ greater than or equal to 3.66 is 0.30.

*Example 13-2.*   On the basis of the 5% level of significance, do the results of Example 13-1 indicate that the die is dishonest?

*Solution.*   The hypothesis to be tested is that of the honesty of the die. This means we wish to test whether the expected frequencies are those given in the third column of Table 13-1. Under this hypothesis, the value of $\chi^2$ is the one already calculated in Example 13-1. Since the total of the observed values must equal 120, there is one relationship between them, and consequently the number of degrees of freedom is 1 less than the number of events, or $6 - 1 = 5$. At the 5% level the tabular value of $\chi^2$ corresponding to $\nu = 5$ is $\chi^2_{.05} = 11.07$. Inasmuch as the calculated $\chi^2$ of 18.70 exceeds this, the result is significant and the hypothesis of an honest die has to be rejected. Thus the indication is that the die is dishonest. Since $\chi^2 = 18.70$ falls between the values 15.09 and 20.52 (in Appendix Table IV) corresponding to $A = 0.01$ and $A = 0.001$, respectively, we can say that, for an honest die, the result obtained in Table 13-1, or one for which the observed values differ even more widely from the expected (i.e., one for which $\chi^2$ is equal to or larger than 18.70), can be expected by chance alone to occur with a probability of less than 0.01.

## 13.3.  Application to Genetics

The $\chi^2$ distribution is particularly useful in genetics, where in breeding experiments it is desired to determine whether observed results are consistent with expected segregations, the latter usually being given in the form of genetic ratios.

*Example 13-3.* According to Mendelian inheritance theory, in crossing two kinds of peas, four types of seeds, $A$, $B$, $C$, and $D$, are expected to occur in the ratio 9:3:3:1. In such an experiment an experimenter obtains 102 seeds of type $A$, 30 of type $B$, 42 of type $C$, and 15 of type $D$. Are these results consistent with the theory on the basis of the 5% level of significance?

*Solution.* Since a total of 189 seeds is involved in this experiment, the number of type $A$ seeds expected under the hypothesis of a 9:3:3:1 segregation ratio is $\frac{9}{16}$ of 189, or 106.3. (Although expressing expected values to one decimal place where numbers of seeds are involved may seem strange, it is considered advisable in order to assure greater precision in the results.) Expected frequencies of occurrence for the other types of seeds are calculated similarly, and they are listed in the second column of Table 13-2.

From Table 13-2, $\chi^2 = 3.09$, which has to be compared with $\chi^2_{.05} = 7.82$, the tabular value for $\nu = 3$ at the 5% level. This means that by chance alone we would expect to obtain more than 5% of the time (according to Appendix Table IV, about 37%) a value of $\chi^2$ as large as or larger than 3.09 when sampling from a population in which the 9:3:3:1 ratio holds. Therefore, the result is not significant, and there is good indication that observation agrees with expectation.

TABLE 13-2.  Observed Segregation in Four Types of Seeds with Calculation of Chi-Square

| o | e | o − e | (o − e)$^2$ | $\frac{(o - e)^2}{e}$ |
|---|---|---|---|---|
| 102 | 106.3 | −4.3 | 18.49 | 0.17 |
| 30 | 35.4 | −5.4 | 29.16 | 0.82 |
| 42 | 35.4 | 6.6 | 43.56 | 1.23 |
| 15 | 11.8 | 3.2 | 10.24 | 0.87 |
| 189 | 188.9 | 0 | | 3.09 |

## 13.4.  Application to Contingency Tables

DEFINITION 13-1.  A *contingency table* is an arrangement in which a set of objects is classified according to two criteria of classification, one criterion being entered in rows, the other in columns.

The number of rows of a contingency table is usually denoted by $j$, and the number of columns by $k$; such a table is also referred to as $j \times k$ table. Our main interest is in determining whether a relationship exists between the two criteria of classification or if they are independent. We are, therefore, testing the hypothesis of independence of the two criteria, and we calculate expected values in accordance with this hypothesis.

The application of $\chi^2$ to contingency tables is illustrated in Example 13-4 for a $2 \times 2$ table.

*Example 13-4.* Table 13-3 gives data on the number of men and women who became airsick on an airplane trip in rough weather. Do these data indicate that, in general, women are less susceptible to air sickness than are men (5% level)?

TABLE 13-3. Number of Men and Women Affected by Airsickness on an Airplane Trip

|  | Number of Cases of Airsickness | Number of Cases Free of Airsickness | Totals |
|---|---|---|---|
| Men | 24 | 31 | 55 |
| Women | 8 | 26 | 34 |
|  | 32 | 57 | 89 |

*Solution.* Since a quick examination of the table reveals that the percentage of women who became airsick is considerably smaller than the percentage of men, we might be led to conclude that this is also true for the population at large. This conclusion, however, would be completely unjustified without a statistical test.

As in any contingency table, we set up the hypothesis that the two criteria of classification (in this case, sex and susceptibility to airsickness) are independent. Under this hypothesis, we would expect the ratio of airsick men to all men on the plane to be the same as the ratio of airsick women to all women on the plane, and also the same as the ratio of all airsick people to the total number of people on the plane. Denoting by $x$ the expected number of airsick men on the plane, we have

$$x:55 = 32:89$$

and $x = 19.8$. The shortest way of finding the expected number of men free of airsickness is to subtract the expected number of airsick men from the total number of men on the plane, which in this case gives $55 - 19.8 = 35.2$. The other expected numbers are found similarly by subtraction, and are listed in the second column of Table 13-4.

**TABLE 13-4.** Calculation of Chi-Square for Data of Table 13-3

| o | e | o − e | (o − e)² | $\dfrac{(o - e)^2}{e}$ |
|---|---|---|---|---|
| 24 | 19.8 | 4.2 | 17.64 | 0.89 |
| 31 | 35.2 | −4.2 | 17.64 | 0.50 |
| 8 | 12.2 | −4.2 | 17.64 | 1.45 |
| 26 | 21.8 | 4.2 | 17.64 | 0.81 |
| 89 | 89.0 | 0 | | 3.65 |

Since for a 2 × 2 table the number of degrees of freedom $\nu$ is equal to 1 (for an explanation, see the end of this section), and since the tabular value at the 5% level for $\nu = 1$ is $\chi^2_{.05} = 3.84$, a value larger than the calculated value, we conclude that under the hypothesis of independence of sex and susceptibility to airsickness a deviation from expectation as large as or larger than that which occurred in this sample is found more than 5% of the time. Therefore, this result is not significant, and these data do not indicate that, in general, women are less susceptible to airsickness than men.

You may have noted that in Table 13-4 all of the absolute values of $o - e$ are the same. It is easy to prove that for any 2 × 2 table all the values of $|o - e|$ are identical; however, this is not true for a $j \times k$ table in general. The proof of this is left as an exercise (see Exercise 17).

Whenever the $\chi^2$-value in a contingency table gives a significant result, it indicates that the two criteria of classification are not independent but related. However, such a result does not indicate a causal relationship. For example, although a contingency table classifying a large number of people according to smoking habits and incidence of lung cancer might yield a significant $\chi^2$-value which would indicate that lung cancer occurs more frequently among smokers than among nonsmokers, this does not prove by any means that smoking increases the incidence of lung cancer. The relationship between lung cancer and smoking might be due to some factor which causes people to have a desire to smoke and also causes them to have lung cancer. Much misinterpretation of data is due to the erroneous assumption that a relationship between two criteria means that one causes the other.

Why is the number of degrees of freedom taken as 1 for a 2 × 2 table? Let us consider the general 2 × 2 arrangement shown in Table 13-5.

**TABLE 13-5.** General 2 × 2 Contingency Table

| | | | Totals |
|---|---|---|---|
| | a | b | A |
| | c | d | N − A |
| Totals | B | N − B | N |

For the observed frequencies $a$, $b$, $c$, $d$, the following relationships hold:

$$a + b = A$$
$$c + d = N - A$$
$$a + c = B$$
$$b + d = N - B.$$

But these four equations are not independent; indeed, the last equation can be obtained by subtracting the third from the sum of the first two. There are, therefore, only three independent relationships; thus, according to Definition 10-2, $\nu = 4 - 3 = 1$, since $\nu$ is the total number of variates minus the number of independent relationships existing between them. An alternative approach would be to note that for fixed totals only one of the numbers $a$, $b$, $c$, $d$ has to be given to fix the remaining numbers.

For a general $j \times k$ table $\nu = (j - 1)(k - 1)$, since if all entries except those in one row and one column are given, the rest can be determined from the marginal totals. The methods applied to $j \times k$ tables in general are completely analogous to those discussed for the special case of $2 \times 2$ tables and will not be considered further.

## 13.5.   Application to Testing for Normality

One of the important applications of $\chi^2$ is in determining whether or not a population satisfies a normal distribution. Here, we must have a fairly large sample from the population. First, we construct a frequency table for the data of the sample, and then calculate its mean $\overline{X}$ and standard deviation $\hat{s}$ which, since the sample is large, we use for the mean $m$ and standard deviation $\sigma$, respectively, of the population. Finally, we calculate, under the hypothesis that the population is normally distributed, the expected frequencies corresponding to each of the classes of the frequency table and compare them by means of a $\chi^2$-test with the observed frequencies.

This procedure requires that each of the expected frequencies be at least 5. If the expected frequencies of some classes at the beginning or end of the frequency table are less than 5, which they often are, such classes should be pooled with adjoining ones in order that the expected frequency of the pooled class will be at least 5.

In testing for normality, since for fixed total number, mean, and standard deviation three relationships exist between the variates of the sample, the number of degrees of freedom equals $\nu = h - 3$, where $h$ is the number of classes in the frequency table used in the calculation of $\chi^2$.

*Example 13-5.* Consider the data of Table 2-3 for the total seasonal rainfall at Sacramento, California, for the 90-year period 1854–1944. Using the 5% level of significance, is there reason to doubt that these data are normally distributed?

*Solution.* In Table 13-6 the data of Table 2-3 are listed in a frequency table which is similar to Table 2-4 except the last four classes are pooled into a single class in order that no expected frequency is below 5. Using the mean and standard deviation of this sample as estimates of their corresponding parameters, we have $m = 18.13$ and $\sigma = 6.28$ (see Examples 4-2 and 4-13). This allows us to calculate the expected frequencies for each of the classes of Table 13-6; thus, for the second class we find

$$z_1 = \frac{10.5 - 18.13}{6.28} = -1.21, \quad z_2 = \frac{13.5 - 18.13}{6.28} = -0.74.$$

From Appendix Table I we find the area between $z_1$ and $z_2$ to be

$$A = 0.3869 - 0.2704 = 0.1165,$$

and the expected frequency for that class is

$$e_2 = (0.1165)90 = 10.5.$$

In determining the expected frequency for the first class, we include the total area to the left of 10.5 under the normal probability curve, and for the last class we include the total area to the right of 25.5. This is done to make the total of all expected frequencies agree with the total of all observed frequencies (in this example the total is 90).

Since $\chi^2 = 2.95$ and the tabular value for $\nu = 7 - 3 = 4$ is $\chi^2_{.05} = 9.49$, there is no reason to doubt that the rainfall data as given in Table 2-3 are

TABLE 13-6. Observed and Expected Frequencies Under the Assumption of Normality and the Calculation of Chi-Square

| Class Boundaries | o | e | o − e | $(o-e)^2$ | $\dfrac{(o-e)^2}{e}$ |
|---|---|---|---|---|---|
| 7.5–10.5 | 12 | 10.2 | 1.8 | 3.24 | 0.32 |
| 10.5–13.5 | 10 | 10.5 | −0.5 | 0.25 | 0.02 |
| 13.5–16.5 | 15 | 15.1 | −0.1 | 0.01 | 0.00 |
| 16.5–19.5 | 19 | 17.1 | 1.9 | 3.61 | 0.21 |
| 19.5–22.5 | 12 | 15.4 | −3.4 | 11.56 | 0.75 |
| 22.5–25.5 | 14 | 10.9 | 3.1 | 9.61 | 0.88 |
| 25.5–37.5 | 8 | 10.9 | −2.9 | 8.41 | 0.77 |
| | 90 | 90.1 | −0.1 | | 2.95 |

normally distributed. Indeed, the very small value of $\chi^2$ indicates that the data of this sample are almost exactly normally distributed.

## 13.6.   Adjusted Chi-Square

The necessity for introducing adjusted chi-square can best be demonstrated by an example.

*Example 13-6.*   According to Mendelian inheritance theory, certain crosses of peas should give yellow and green peas in the ratio $3:1$. If an experimenter obtains 200 yellow peas and 48 green peas, are these results consistent with the theory on the basis of the 5% level of significance?

*Solution.*   Calculating $\chi^2$ in the usual fashion (which, as we shall see later, is not very accurate), we obtain, from Table 13-7, $\chi^2 = 4.21$.

**TABLE 13-7.   Calculation of Chi-Square for the Data of Example 13-6**

| o | e | o − e | $(o - e)^2$ | $\dfrac{(o - e)^2}{e}$ |
|---|---|---|---|---|
| 200 | 186 | 14 | 196 | 1.05 |
| 48 | 62 | −14 | 196 | 3.16 |
| 248 | 248 | 0 | | 4.21 |

Comparing this value of $\chi^2$ with the tabular value $\chi^2_{.05} = 3.84$ at the 5% level for $\nu = 1$, we conclude that these results deviate significantly from the theory. Indeed, by linear interpolation we find that, since for $\chi^2 = 3.84$, $A = 0.05$, and for $\chi^2 = 5.41$, $A = 0.02$, the probability of getting $\chi^2$ greater than or equal to 4.21, assuming that the Mendelian theory is valid, is 0.043. Note that this value represents the probability of obtaining 200 or more or 172 or less yellow peas, since also for 172 yellow peas and 76 green peas the value of $\chi^2$ is 4.21.

This probability can also be calculated using the normal distribution, approximating the binomial distribution involved, since in this example only two events can occur. Recalculating this probability, we find

$$m = 248 \cdot \tfrac{3}{4} = 186, \quad \sigma = \sqrt{248 \cdot \tfrac{3}{4} \cdot \tfrac{1}{4}} = 6.82.$$

Thus the probability of obtaining 200 or more or 172 or less yellow peas is equal to twice the area to the right of

$$z = \frac{199.5 - 186}{6.82} = 1.98$$

under the normal probability curve; i.e., $P = 0.048$, which is a larger value than 0.043 obtained by the $\chi^2$-method. The reason for this discrepancy immediately becomes evident if we recall that $\chi^2$ is a discrete variable. We can readily verify that the next lower value of $\chi^2$ which is obtainable here (when $o_1 = 199$, $o_2 = 49$) is 3.64 (see Figure 13-2, which also shows that the next higher value of $\chi^2$ is 4.84). By using the $\chi^2$-distribution we have found the area under the curve to the right of $\chi^2 = 4.21$ (shaded area in Figure 13-2). Actually, the probability that $\chi^2$ is greater than or equal to 4.21 includes the entire area of the rectangle of which 4.21 is the midpoint; thus we have omitted the dotted area. Therefore, in finding the desired probability, the area under the chi-square curve to the right of the left border of the rectangle with midpoint 4.21 should be taken. This left border is located at approximately

$$\tfrac{1}{2}(3.64 + 4.21) = 3.92.$$

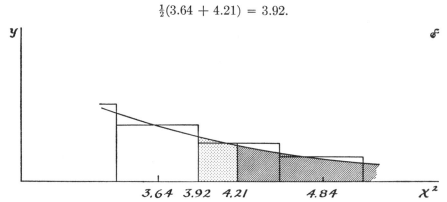

Fig. 13-2. Adjusted chi-square.

An alternate, and quicker, method of obtaining this smaller value of $\chi^2$, corresponding to the left boundary of the rectangle (instead of its midpoint), and called *adjusted chi-square*, was given for 1 degree of freedom by Yates:

$$(13\text{-}3) \qquad\qquad \text{adj. } \chi^2 = \sum_{i=1}^{k} \frac{(|o_i - e_i| - \tfrac{1}{2})^2}{e_i}.$$

Note that the absolute value of each of the differences of the observed and expected frequencies is reduced by $\tfrac{1}{2}$. If the number of degrees of freedom is greater than 1, the correction to be applied is more complicated, but also less important in that it will not alter the results materially; for these reasons, it will not be discussed.

**DEFINITION 13-2.** The adjustment made on $\chi^2$ and given by (13-3) is called *Yates' correction for continuity*.

From the preceding discussion it is clear that, for 1 degree of freedom, adjusted $\chi^2$ should always be used. If all expected values, however, are large, the difference between unadjusted and adjusted $\chi^2$ is small. This situation is analogous to that where the binomial distribution is approximated by the normal curve: when it is desired to find from the normal probability curve the probability that a variate taken at random will be greater than or equal to a given number $A$, the smaller the number of trials, the more important it becomes to subtract $\frac{1}{2}$ from $A$ (i.e., to find the area to the right of $X = A - \frac{1}{2}$). On the other hand, note that in Example 13-6, where certainly only large expected values are involved, the failure to adjust $\chi^2$ results in an error of about 10% in the probability. Such an error in a particular case (see exercise 4) may make a result appear significant whereas it really is not significant. Therefore, consistent use of adjusted $\chi^2$ for all cases involving 1 degree of freedom is recommended. The reader should note that adjusted $\chi^2$ should have been used in Example 13-4 if it had been discussed prior to Section 13.4.

*Example 13-7.* Solve Example 13-6 by using adjusted $\chi^2$, and find the probability of the event discussed in that example.

*Solution.* Using (13-3), we find from Table 13-8 adjusted $\chi^2 = 3.92$.

TABLE 13-8.  Calculation of Adjusted Chi-Square for the Data of Example 13-7

| o | e | $\|o - e\|$ | $\|o - e\| - \frac{1}{2}$ | $(\|o - e\| - \frac{1}{2})^2$ | $\dfrac{(\|o - e\| - \frac{1}{2})^2}{e}$ |
|---|---|---|---|---|---|
| 200 | 186 | 14 | 13.5 | 182.25 | 0.98 |
| 48 | 62 | 14 | 13.5 | 182.25 | 2.94 |
| 248 | 248 | | | | 3.92 |

Since adjusted $\chi^2 = 3.92$ (which agrees with the value found previously from Figure 13-2), we find by interpolation that the area under the chi-square curve to the right of $\chi^2 = 3.92$ equals 0.048, which agrees exactly with the value obtained by use of the normal curve.

# Exercises

In the following exercises, if no statement to the contrary is made, use the 5% level of significance. Also use one-decimal accuracy for expected values.

1. A die is tossed 100 times and the following results are obtained.

| Face | o |
|------|-----|
| 1 | 12 |
| 2 | 17 |
| 3 | 20 |
| 4 | 22 |
| 5 | 13 |
| 6 | 16 |

Determine whether this die could still be considered honest on the basis of the 1% level of significance.

2. In a cross between ivory and red snapdragons the following counts are observed in the $F_2$ generation.

| Phenotype | Number of Plants |
|-----------|------------------|
| Red | 20 |
| Pink | 55 |
| Ivory | 25 |

On the basis of these data, can segregation be assumed to occur in the simple Mendelian ratio 1:2:1?

3. In an experiment involving crossing two hybrids of a species of flower the results shown below are observed. Are these results consistent with the expected proportion 9:3:3:1?

| Magenta Flower, Green Stigma | Magenta Flower, Red Stigma | Red Flower, Green Stigma | Red Flower, Red Stigma |
|---------|---------|---------|---------|
| 120 | 49 | 36 | 12 |

4. In a certain cross of two varieties of peas genetic theory leads us to expect half the seeds to be wrinkled and half of them to be smooth. In a sample of 800 seeds we find 440 wrinkled.
   (a) Find the value of unadjusted $\chi^2$.
   (b) If in a sample of 400 seeds the count is 220 wrinkled, would unadjusted $\chi^2$ also be half of its original value?
   (c) Using unadjusted $\chi^2$, calculate the probability of obtaining in a total of 400 seeds a number of wrinkled seeds differing by 20 or more from the value expected by the theory (i.e., 220 or more or 180 or less).
   (d) Solve part (c), using the normal distribution.
   (e) Solve part (c), using adjusted $\chi^2$.

5. An honest coin is tossed 120 times.
   (a) Using adjusted $\chi^2$, find the probability of obtaining 68 or more or 52 or less heads.
   (b) Find the same probability, using the normal curve.

6. If 8% of certain articles produced are defective, calculate the probability that in a sample of 200 such articles more than 20 are defective,
   (a) using the normal distribution,
   (b) using adjusted $\chi^2$.

7. A manufacturer of automobile tires claims that 98% of his products are perfect. Assuming that this claim is correct, find the probability that in a sample of 500 tires he has 15 or more defective tires
   (a) using the normal distribution,
   (b) using adjusted $\chi^2$.

8. Of 64 offspring of a certain cross between guinea pigs, 34 are red, 10 are black, and 20 are white. According to the genetic model, these numbers should be in the ratio 9:3:4. Are the data consistent with the model?

9. According to the genetic model, offspring of a certain cross between guinea pigs are red, black, or white in the ratio 9:3:4. A worker wishing to disprove this theory for a particular experiment has reason to believe that the offspring will occur in the ratio 8:5:3. If in this experiment the results occur precisely in the ratio 8:5:3, how many offspring must there be in the sample in order that the worker can be 95% confident he has disproved the hypothesis of a 9:3:4 ratio?

10. In a random sample of 1000 housewives 55% state a preference for brand $A$ and 45% for brand $B$. Is this result compatible with the hypothesis that 50% of all housewives prefer brand $A$?

11. During an epidemic of cholera the following data on the effectiveness of inoculation as a means of preventing the disease were obtained.

|                | Not Attacked | Attacked |
|----------------|--------------|----------|
| Inoculated     | 192          | 4        |
| Not Inoculated | 113          | 34       |

   Do these data indicate the effectiveness of the inoculation on the basis of the 1% level of significance?

12. Fifty individuals are classified according to eye color and shade of hair. Can we conclude from the data shown below that for these individuals there is a significant connection between eye color and hair shade?

|            | Light Hair | Dark Hair |
|------------|------------|-----------|
| Blue Eyes  | 23         | 7         |
| Brown Eyes | 4          | 16        |

13. A thousand individuals are classified according to sex and according to whether they are color-blind:

|                 | Male | Female |
|-----------------|------|--------|
| Not Color-blind | 442  | 514    |
| Color-blind     | 38   | 6      |

What conclusion regarding color-blindness can we draw from these data?

14. To determine whether an engine oil additive decreases the chances of needing an engine overhaul within two years, a truck company with 25 new trucks selects 10 of these at random to be given the additive. The results are shown below.

|             | No Overhaul | Overhaul |
|-------------|-------------|----------|
| Additive    | 5           | 5        |
| No Additive | 3           | 12       |

Do these data confirm that the additive decreases the chances of needing an overhaul within two years?

15. A group of 100 men and 100 women is interviewed regarding interest in a certain radio program. Sixty-five of the men do not listen to the program, and 35 do listen. Eighty of the women are nonlisteners, and 20 are listeners. Is there a significant difference in the listening habits of this group of men and women?

16. The following data show the effect of a certain type of fumigation on fruit spoilage.

|             | Spoiled | Unspoiled |
|-------------|---------|-----------|
| Unfumigated | 8       | 16        |
| Fumigated   | 2       | 14        |

Does the amount of fruit spoiled depend upon whether it has been fumigated (2% level of significance)?

17. A group of 30 men and 80 women is asked to express a preference for the aromas of two pipe tobaccos. The results are shown below.

|       | Brand A | Brand B |
|-------|---------|---------|
| Men   | 9       | 21      |
| Women | 8       | 72      |

(a) Do these data indicate that preference for a particular brand is related to sex?

(b) What is the probability that in part (a) a type 1 error has been committed?

18. Twenty-two animals are suffering from a disease, the severity of which is about the same in each case. In order to test the therapeutic value of a serum, it is administered to 10 of the animals; 12 remain uninoculated as a control. The result is:

|  | Recovered | Died |
|---|---|---|
| Inoculated | 7 | 3 |
| Not Inoculated | 3 | 9 |

Determine the probability of obtaining this result or one more favorable to the treatment.

19. Prove that for a $2 \times 2$ contingency table all values of $|o - e|$ are the same.

20. Show that for a $2 \times 2$ contingency table with observed frequencies $a$, $b$, $c$, $d$ the value of $\chi^2$ used to test for independence can be written as

$$\chi^2 = \frac{n(ad - bc)^2}{(a + b)(c + d)(b + d)(a + c)},$$

where $n = a + b + c + d$.

21. Show that for a $2 \times 2$ contingency table with observed frequencies $a$, $b$, $c$, $d$ the value of adjusted $\chi^2$ can be written as

$$\text{adj. } \chi^2 = \frac{n\left(|ad - bc| - \dfrac{n}{2}\right)^2}{(a + b)(c + d)(b + d)(a + c)},$$

where $n = a + b + c + d$.

22. In three groups of people, chosen from different geographical regions, the distribution of hair color is as follows.

|  | Red Hair | Light Hair | Dark Hair |
|---|---|---|---|
| Group $A$ | 2 | 9 | 9 |
| Group $B$ | 3 | 6 | 21 |
| Group $C$ | 15 | 15 | 20 |

Do these data indicate that hair color is dependent on geographical region? (Use the 2% level of significance.)

23. A gray female zebra finch mated to a gray-cinnamon male produced 3 gray, 2 cinnamon, and 1 gray-cinnamon progeny. A gray-cinnamon female mated to a gray male produced 4 gray, 3 cinnamon, and 3 gray-

cinnamon progeny. On the basis of these results, is there a relation between color distribution of progeny and sex placement (color of the parents) in a cross of gray-cinnamon and gray parents?

24. Questionnaires were mailed to the graduates of a certain university with the following results:

|            | B.S. | M.S. | Ph.D. |
|------------|------|------|-------|
| Returned   | 78   | 44   | 18    |
| Did Not Return | 22 | 6   | 7     |

Do these data indicate that the rate of return of these questionnaires is independent of the degree earned?

25. A company carries two lines of products and has three salesmen. A three-month record shows the following number of units of the two lines sold by each salesman.

|        | Salesman | | |
|--------|----|----|----|
|        | 1  | 2  | 3  |
| Line 1 | 20 | 8  | 15 |
| Line 2 | 17 | 16 | 5  |

Does the record support the claim that each salesman's ability to sell depends on the line he is selling?

26. The following are tabulated data on 82 strains of oats divided into 2 groups according to the presence or absence of awns, and into 3 groups according to yield. Do these data permit the conclusion that more of the awned strains occur in the highest yielding classes than do the awnless strains?

|         | Yield Class (weight in grams) | | |
|---------|---------|---------|---------|
|         | 151–200 | 201–250 | 251–325 |
| Awned   | 6       | 7       | 21      |
| Awnless | 18      | 21      | 9       |

27. The data of exercise 5 of Chapter 2 giving the total seasonal rainfall at Davis, California, for the 70-year period 1871–1940 are represented in the following frequency table.

| Class Boundaries | Frequency | Class Boundaries | Frequency |
|------------------|-----------|------------------|-----------|
| 5– 8             | 2         | 23–26            | 6         |
| 8–11             | 10        | 26–29            | 1         |
| 11–14            | 13        | 29–32            | 1         |
| 14–17            | 8         | 32–35            | 0         |
| 17–20            | 18        | 35–38            | 1         |
| 20–23            | 10        |                  |           |

Can these data be considered as satisfying a normal distribution? Note that for the above frequency table $m = 16.91$, $\sigma = 5.75$.

28. Eighty sets of 10 seeds each are placed on damp filter paper. The frequencies of sets having various numbers of seeds germinating are recorded below. Can these data be assumed to follow a normal distribution?

| Number Germinating | 0 | 1 | 2 | 3 | 4 | 5 | 6 | 7 | 8 | 9 | 10 |
|---|---|---|---|---|---|---|---|---|---|---|---|
| Frequency | 6 | 20 | 28 | 12 | 8 | 6 | 0 | 0 | 0 | 0 | 0 |

# 14   Index Numbers

## 14.1.   Introduction

In many business and economics problems we are interested in reducing data to purely relative numbers which are amenable to comparison. Such numbers which are all relative to the same quantity (or base) are called *index numbers*. Index numbers are used in comparing price, production, employment, or population changes over a certain period of time. They may also be used in studying differences between places or differences between comparable categories such as animals or persons or commodities. Index numbers play an important role today: The wages of many workers in the United States are tied by union contract to the consumer price index, which is an index number compiled by the Bureau of Labor Statistics. This type of agreement between a labor union and management became widespread after General Motors Corporation signed such a contract in May 1948 with the United Automobile Workers (at that time CIO) and in 1950 entered into a five-year pact on this basis.

## 14.2.   Selection of the Base Period

Although many types of index numbers are in use, all of them initially require selection of a base period as a point of reference. For the base period, the index number is set at 100.

The choice of a particular base period is guided by the intended use of the index numbers. Often it is desirable that the base represent as closely as possible a "normal" or "typical" situation. However, because the base period represents the time from which changes are measured, selection of a period not too distant from the present is usually advisable.

Until recently, many of the price indices in use in the United States had as their base the average of prices during the five-year period 1935–1939, a period which can be considered rather normal inasmuch as it was sufficiently far removed from the depression years and was not as yet affected by the economic changes that occurred with the beginning of World War II. Indeed, the Central Statistical Board of the United States Government suggested the selection of indices on this basis. At the present time, the most common base for indices in the United States is the average of the three-year period 1947–1949.

The base need not refer to a single year, month, day, or hour. Frequently it is the average of several consecutive periods. If data have been collected for relatively few years, and no knowledge of what represents a normal or typical result is available, the first year is usually selected as the base period.

## 14.3. Simple Index Numbers

DEFINITION 14-1. *Simple index numbers* are the per cents of each of a set of variates relative to some quantity which is selected as a base.

Consequently, if the variate in the $i$th period is denoted by $p_i$ and the quantity for the base period by $p_o$, the $i$th simple index number is given by

(14-1) $$S_i = \frac{p_i}{p_o} 100.$$

*Example 14-1.* In Table 14-1 are listed the net earnings of General Foods Corporation for each of the fiscal years from 1951 to 1959. Using the year 1951 as the base year, express these earnings as index numbers.

TABLE 14-1. Net Earnings (in thousands of dollars) of General Foods Corporation

| Fiscal Year | Net Earnings | Index Number |
|---|---|---|
| 1951 | 26,407 | 100.0 |
| 1952 | 20,436 | 77.4 |
| 1953 | 24,808 | 93.9 |
| 1954 | 27,913 | 105.7 |
| 1955 | 31,737 | 120.2 |
| 1956 | 39,001 | 147.7 |
| 1957 | 43,866 | 166.1 |
| 1958 | 48,397 | 183.3 |
| 1959 | 54,145 | 205.0 |

*Solution.* Since 26,407 is the variate for the base period, we find for 1952

$$S_1 = \frac{20,436}{26,407} 100 = 77.4.$$

The index numbers for the earnings of the other years are found similarly and are listed in the last column of Table 14-1. Note that these index numbers facilitate comparisons with the base year. For example, we see that from 1951 to 1952 the net earnings of General Foods Corporation declined by 22.6%, whereas from 1951 to 1959 the earnings more than doubled, i.e., increased by 105.0%.

In Example 14-1 our interest was restricted to the study of a single quantity for each year. Most investigations involve a number of quantities corresponding to each period.

> **DEFINITION 14-2.** If the price per unit of a number of items is given for a series of time intervals, the *simple aggregate price index* for a given time interval is the sum of the prices per one unit of each of these items at that time interval expressed as a per cent relative to the corresponding price for the period selected as the base period.

Consequently, if the prices per unit of $k$ items in the base period are denoted by $p_{o,1}, p_{o,2}, p_{o,3}, \cdots, p_{o,k}$, those in the first period by $p_{1,1}, p_{1,2}, \cdots, p_{1,k}$, and in general those in the $i$th period by $p_{i,1}, p_{i,2}, p_{i,3}, \cdots, p_{i,k}$, then the simple aggregate price index for the $i$th period is given by

$$(14\text{-}2) \qquad S_i = \frac{p_{i,1} + p_{i,2} + \cdots + p_{i,k}}{p_{o,1} + p_{o,2} + \cdots + p_{o,k}} \, 100 = \frac{\Sigma p_i}{\Sigma p_o} \, 100.$$

*Example 14-2.* In the third, fourth, and fifth columns of Table 14-2 are listed the prices per pound of three metals used by a certain factory in the years 1950, 1951, 1952 (the other columns of this table are not used in this example). Calculate the simple aggregate price index for these metals for the years 1951 and 1952, using 1950 as the base year.

TABLE 14-2. Prices and Typical Quantities of Three Metals Used by a Certain Factory

| (1) | (2) | (3) | (4) | (5) | (6) | (7) | (8) |
|---|---|---|---|---|---|---|---|
| | Typical Quantities Used | Price per Pound | | | Price of Quantities Used | | |
| | | 1950 | 1951 | 1952 | 1950 | 1951 | 1952 |
| Metal | (w) | $p_o$ | $p_1$ | $p_2$ | $p_o w$ | $p_1 w$ | $p_2 w$ |
| Copper | 20,000 lbs | $0.242 | $0.242 | $0.242 | $4840 | $4840 | $4840 |
| Lead | 12,000 lbs | 0.170 | 0.190 | 0.148 | 2040 | 2280 | 1776 |
| Zinc | 14,000 lbs | 0.175 | 0.195 | 0.125 | 2450 | 2730 | 1750 |
| | | 0.587 | 0.627 | 0.515 | 9330 | 9850 | 8366 |

*Solution.* For the base year 1950, the total price of 1 pound each of copper, lead, and zinc is \$0.587. In 1951 the price of these metals is \$0.627; thus, the simple aggregate price index for 1951 is

$$S_1 = \frac{0.627}{0.587} \, 100 = 107.2.$$

Similarly, the corresponding simple aggregate price index for 1952 is found to be 87.7.

## 14.4. Weighted Index Numbers

As is clear from Example 14-2, simple index numbers do not take into account the relative importance (called the *weight*) of the various items involved. Therefore, simple index numbers are also referred to as *unweighted index numbers*.

Frequently, unweighted index numbers are rather meaningless. For example, if the consumer price index were based upon the unit price of each of the consumer items used by a typical family, and if no consideration were given the relative importance of these items, the price index would not give a true picture of the amount spent for such items by the typical family.

DEFINITION 14-3. An index number which takes into account the weight (used here in the sense of importance) of each of the items involved is called a *weighted index number*.

Since the weights of items may fluctuate during the period under consideration, it is important that the weighted index number be a measure of the change in the item and not a measure of the change in the weight of the item. One method of constructing a weighted index number is to use the same weights for all periods, determining these weights not for any one period but rather as averages of several periods.

Let $w_1, w_2, \cdots, w_k$ be the typical (or average) weights of $k$ items applicable to the period under study, and let $p_{o,1}, p_{o,2}, \cdots, p_{o,k}, p_{1,1}, p_{1,2}, \cdots, p_{1,k}, p_{i,1}, p_{i,2}, \cdots, p_{i,k}$ be defined as before. Then the cost of the $k$ items with weights $w_1, w_2, \cdots, w_k$ in the base period is

$$p_{o,1}w_1 + p_{o,2}w_2 + \cdots + p_{o,k}w_k = \Sigma p_o w,$$

and in the $i$th period is

$$p_{i,1}w_1 + p_{i,2}w_2 + \cdots + p_{i,k}w_k = \Sigma p_i w,$$

and the weighted aggregate price index in the $i$th period is given by

(14-3)
$$W_i = \frac{\Sigma p_i w}{\Sigma p_o w} \, 100.$$

*Example 14-3.* The second column of Table 14-2 lists the average quantities of three metals used by a certain factory in the period 1950–1952. Calculate the weighted aggregate price index for these metals for 1951 and 1952, using 1950 as the base year.

*Solution.* As shown in the sixth column of Table 14-2, the 1950 prices of the average quantities of the three metals are $4840, $2040, and $2450. Therefore, the total cost of these metals for the base period is

$$\Sigma p_o w = 9330.$$

For 1951 the total cost for the same quantities is

$$\Sigma p_1 w = 9850.$$

Thus, the weighted aggregate price index for 1951 is

$$W_1 = \frac{9850}{9330} \, 100 = 105.6.$$

And the weighted aggregate price index for 1952 is **89.7.**

It is rarely possible to use the same weights over long periods of time. Because the relative importance of the items under study changes from day to day or from year to year, and because new items often must be added, weights should be periodically revised. There have been several changes in the United States system of weights used in constructing the consumer price index, the last one having been made in early 1950 in accordance with new conditions following World War II when certain items, such as frozen foods, assumed a major role in the budget of the typical family unit. This change was made at the same time that the base period was changed to the years 1947–1949.

Although defining a weighted index number by formula (14-3) is only one of many ways of constructing weighted index numbers, this method is the one most generally used. Irving Fisher, in his treatise, "The Making of Index Numbers" (1922), listed 134 different formulae which have been suggested for use in constructing weighted index numbers.

## Exercises

1. The following figures show the gross production of crude oil and natural gas liquids in the United States by Standard Oil Company of New Jersey (thousands of barrels per **day).**

| 1950 | 1951 | 1952 | 1953 | 1954 | 1955 | 1956 | 1957 | 1958 |
|------|------|------|------|------|------|------|------|------|
| 423  | 502  | 504  | 516  | 484  | 520  | 546  | 538  | 472  |

Express these production figures as index numbers,
(a) using the year 1950 as the base year;
(b) using the year 1951 as the base year.

2. The sales of gasoline of Standard Oil Company of New Jersey is given by the following figures (thousands of barrels per day).

| 1950 | 1951 | 1952 | 1953 | 1954 | 1955 | 1956 | 1957 | 1958 |
|------|------|------|------|------|------|------|------|------|
| 597  | 664  | 726  | 764  | 798  | 856  | 894  | 897  | 964  |

Express these sales figures as index numbers,
(a) using the year 1950 as the base year;
(b) using the year 1951 as the base year.

3. Residential building cost indices (base period 1947–1949) are shown by the following figures.

| 1915 | 1920 | 1925 | 1930 | 1935 | 1940 | 1945 | 1950 | 1955 |
|------|------|------|------|------|------|------|------|------|
| 26.7 | 59.3 | 47.9 | 48.7 | 40.3 | 50.5 | 70.1 | 107.7 | 123.9 |

If building a house in 1945 cost $7,500, what would it have cost to build the same house in 1955?

4. A company buys three commodities in the typical quantities and at the prices shown in the following table.

| | | | | Price per Unit | |
|-----------|--------|---------|--------|--------|--------|
| Commodity | Units  | Weights | 1957   | 1958   | 1959   |
| A         | pounds | 20,000  | $0.62  | $0.58  | $0.71  |
| B         | dozen  | 50,000  | 2.05   | 2.05   | 2.09   |
| C         | pounds | 60,000  | 0.83   | 0.75   | 0.85   |

Using 1957 as the base year, find for 1958 and 1959
(a) the simple aggregate price index;
(b) the weighted aggregate price index.

5. Every year a farmer purchases four items in the typical quantities and at the prices shown in the following table.

| | | | | Price per Unit | |
|-----------|--------|---------|--------|--------|--------|
| Commodity | Units  | Weights | 1957   | 1958   | 1959   |
| A         | pounds | 120     | $0.45  | $0.46  | $0.48  |
| B         | pounds | 50      | 0.60   | 0.61   | 0.62   |
| C         | pounds | 60      | 0.80   | 0.70   | 0.66   |
| D         | dozen  | 100     | 1.20   | 1.30   | 1.40   |

Using 1957 as the base year, find for 1958 and 1959

(a) the simple aggregate price index;

(b) the weighted aggregate price index.

(c) If from 1959 to 1960 the prices of commodities $A$ and $B$ are expected to increase by 1 cent per pound, and the price of commodity $D$ is expected to increase by 10 cents per dozen, how much must the cost per pound of commodity $C$ decrease during that period in order that the weighted aggregate price index for 1960 remain the same as for 1959?

# 15   Time Series

## 15.1.   Introduction

In this chapter, attention is given to data that show variations with time.

**DEFINITION 15-1.** Series of successive observations of the same phenomenon over a period of time are called *time series*.

Time series are of particular importance in economic and business studies, but their use is not restricted to such data. The data of Tables 14-1 and 15-1 are examples of time series. Ordinarily, the observed values of the variable studied, such as the price of a commodity, are the results of various influences. Discovering and measuring the effects of these influences are the primary purposes of a time series analysis. Although the effects cannot always be determined exactly, they can often be approximated if observations have been made over a sufficiently long period. Time series analyses are basic to understanding past behavior, evaluating current accomplishments, planning future operations, and comparing different time series.

It is customary to consider time series variations as being the result of four well-defined influences: the secular trend, the seasonal variation, the cyclical fluctuation, and the random or erratic variation.

**DEFINITION 15-2.** The *secular trend* is that characteristic of a time series which extends consistently throughout the entire period of time under consideration.

The secular trend is the basic long-term tendency of a particular activity to grow or to decline. It indicates the presence of factors that persist for a considerable duration—factors such as population changes, technological improvements, price level fluctuations, or various conditions that are peculiar to individual industries or establishments.

Frequent and sudden changes in a secular trend are inconsistent with the notion that it represent the regular, steady, long-run movement of a time series. Occasionally an important new element is introduced into the complex of forces affecting the time series, or an old factor is eliminated. Then an abrupt change in the trend is real and should be recognized.

**DEFINITION 15-3.** *Seasonal variations* are variations that occur in regular sequence at specific intervals of time.

Although the word "seasonal" might seem to imply a connection with the seasons of the year, the term is meant to include any kind of variation which is of a periodic nature, and whose repeating cycles are of relatively short duration. Seasonal variations are the result of such seasonal factors as climatic conditions, holidays, business operations, or human habits. Prices of perishable agricultural commodities show pronounced seasonal variation, being high early in the season, then declining sharply as supply is increased at the peak of the season, and finally rising again as supply is diminished. A time series giving the number of visitors per hour at a bank would show a seasonal variation since noon hours and pay days are always busy periods. The borrowing of books at college libraries shows seasonal variation; there is a surprising increase before each examination period and a sharp decline thereafter.

**DEFINITION 15-4.** *Cyclical fluctuations* are long-term movements that represent consistently recurring rises and declines in activity.

Cyclical fluctuations in time series of business activities are usually called business cycles. Although markedly less periodic than seasonal variations, cyclical fluctuations are characterized by considerable regularity. Most business establishments reflect the alternating periods of depression and prosperity experienced by the general economy. An example of this type of fluctuation would be the time series showing building activity in the United States between 1830 and 1940. A graph of this series would reveal more or less regular cycles, with an approximate interval of 18 years between successive tops and bottoms of the curve. In addition to business cycles there are certain other cyclical movements. For example, hog prices move in characteristic cycles averaging about four years in length; the cycles in hog prices are caused by, or at least lag behind, opposite cycles in hog production. Beef cattle prices move in cycles of about 15 years.

**DEFINITION 15-5.** *Random or erratic variations* are variations which occur in a completely unpredictable fashion.

Random variations are due to unforeseeable causes and may be the result of wars, strikes, floods, fires, earthquakes, unusual weather, or some political events. More simply, random or erratic variations in a time series are variations which cannot be accounted for by the secular trend, seasonal variations, or cyclical fluctuations.

Most time series show a definite secular trend, upon which are superimposed seasonal variations, cyclical fluctuations, and random variations. Each observation of a time series can therefore be thought of as being the sum of these four (positive or negative) components. If we denote the secular trend component by $T$, the seasonal component by $S$, the cyclical component by $C$, and the random or erratic component by $E$, we can express each observation $Y$ of a time series as

$$(15\text{-}1) \qquad\qquad Y = T + S + C + E.$$

Isolating those parts of the over-all variation of a time series which are traceable to each of these four components and measuring each part independently are major aims of a time series analysis. In this chapter we shall discuss the various methods employed in isolating and measuring these four components.

## 15.2.   The Secular Trend

### 15.2.1.   The Method of Least Squares

Since the secular trend is the long-term tendency of a time series (disregarding the usually minor seasonal variations and the major cyclical and random variations), we may think of the secular trend as being the main tendency of a time series. It is natural, therefore, to represent a time series graphically by a scatter diagram and to find the curve, preferably a line, which best fits the points of the scatter diagram. If a straight-line trend is indicated, the most widely used procedure of fitting the data is by the method of least squares (see Chapter 12). Inasmuch as the observations $Y$ of a time series are usually measured at uniformly spaced intervals, such as successive hours, days, months, or years, the formulae given by (12-5) are applicable.

Since the secular trend disregards seasonal influences, the calculation can be further simplified by condensing the data in such a way that short-term variations are eliminated. For example, a monthly time series extending over several years is best expressed first as a yearly time series.

*Example 15-1.*   Express the data of Table 15-1 as a yearly time series, and find the corresponding equation of the trend line.

*Solution.*   Determining the average number of hired workers for the twelve months of each year, we obtain the values of $Y'$ listed in the second column

TABLE 15-1.   Number of Hired Farm Workers on Pacific Coast (in thousands)

| Year | Jan. | Feb. | Mar. | Apr. | May | June | July | Aug. | Sept. | Oct. | Nov. | Dec. |
|------|------|------|------|------|-----|------|------|------|-------|------|------|------|
| 1939 | 156 | 156 | 158 | 198 | 205 | 237 | 260 | 317 | 380 | 255 | 210 | 165 |
| 1940 | 146 | 157 | 159 | 202 | 227 | 232 | 283 | 260 | 345 | 340 | 195 | 151 |
| 1941 | 134 | 143 | 154 | 170 | 203 | 275 | 368 | 413 | 430 | 361 | 294 | 231 |
| 1942 | 160 | 162 | 172 | 171 | 210 | 244 | 374 | 394 | 476 | 339 | 332 | 236 |
| 1943 | 153 | 161 | 167 | 185 | 209 | 269 | 356 | 404 | 474 | 350 | 309 | 243 |
| 1944 | 165 | 178 | 184 | 185 | 207 | 285 | 359 | 385 | 460 | 349 | 315 | 236 |
| 1945 | 174 | 179 | 179 | 188 | 211 | 263 | 364 | 417 | 501 | 336 | 341 | 224 |
| 1946 | 176 | 174 | 172 | 188 | 240 | 290 | 388 | 422 | 468 | 357 | 343 | 248 |
| 1947 | 188 | 190 | 201 | 200 | 236 | 313 | 418 | 432 | 453 | 387 | 339 | 249 |
| 1948 | 196 | 187 | 183 | 205 | 239 | 306 | 388 | 436 | 484 | 436 | 373 | 250 |

of Table 15-2. (We use $Y'$ to distinguish the calculated values from the observed values of $Y$ given in Table 15-1.)

Since the values of $Y'$ are averages of twelve observed values for the months January 1 to December 1, they should refer to the midpoint of the twelve-month period, i.e., they should be centered at July 1. The mean of the ten years occurs halfway between July 1, 1943 and July 1, 1944, at January 1, 1944, which therefore corresponds to time $x = 0$. July 1, 1944, half a year later, is represented by $x = 0.5$, July 1, 1945, by $x = 1.5$, and so on, as shown in the third column of Table 15-2. The values of $\Sigma x^2$, $\Sigma x Y'$, required in the calculation of the values for $b$ and $a$, are listed in the fourth and fifth columns of Table 15-2. Thus,

$$b = \frac{706.5}{82.50} = 8.56, \quad a = \frac{2713}{10} = 271.$$

TABLE 15-2.   Calculation of Trend Line for the Data of Table 15-1 by Method of Least Squares

| Year | $Y'$ | $x$ | $x^2$ | $xY'$ |
|------|------|-----|-------|-------|
| 1939 | 225 | −4.5 | 20.25 | −1012.5 |
| 1940 | 225 | −3.5 | 12.25 | −787.5 |
| 1941 | 265 | −2.5 | 6.25 | −662.5 |
| 1942 | 272 | −1.5 | 2.25 | −408.0 |
| 1943 | 273 | −0.5 | 0.25 | −136.5 |
| 1944 | 276 | 0.5 | 0.25 | 138.0 |
| 1945 | 281 | 1.5 | 2.25 | 421.5 |
| 1946 | 289 | 2.5 | 6.25 | 722.5 |
| 1947 | 300 | 3.5 | 12.25 | 1050.0 |
| 1948 | 307 | 4.5 | 20.25 | 1381.5 |
|      | 2713 | 0 | 82.50 | 706.5 |

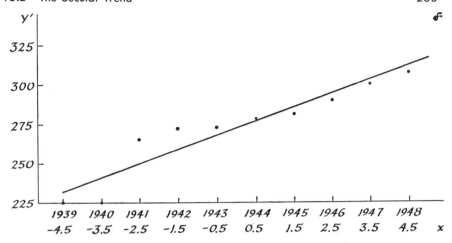

**Fig. 15-1.** Trend line for data of Table 15-2 obtained by method of least squares.

The trend line is given by

$$Y'_e = 271 + 8.56\,x.$$

This line, together with the values of $Y'$, is shown in Figure 15-1.

### 15.2.2.   The Method of Semiaverages

Another method of determining the linear trend is the method of semi-averages. Its chief advantage lies in the simplicity of calculation, its disadvantage in a somewhat greater inaccuracy than the method of least squares.

First, the time series is divided into two equal-length parts. Thus the time series in Table 15-2, covering the years from 1939 to 1948, would be divided into a period 1939–1943 and a period 1944–1948. If a time series consists of an odd number of periods, the middle period is omitted in order to obtain an even number of periods. The means of these two halves are then calculated and graphed as points referring to the midpoints of the two respective time intervals. The line joining these two points is the trend line, as obtained by the method of semiaverages.

*Example 15-2.*   Using the data of Table 15-2, graph the trend line by the method of semiaverages.

*Solution.*   The mean value of $Y'$ for the five-year period 1939–1943 is 252, and the mean value for the five-year period 1944–1948 is 291. Since each half of the time series covers an odd number of years, the two means are centered at July 1, 1941, and July 1, 1946. These two means are plotted and connected

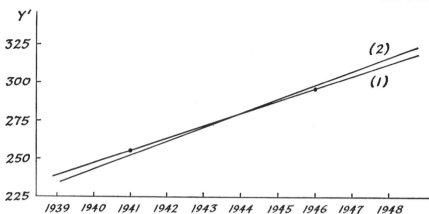

Fig. 15-2. Trend lines for data of Table 15-2 obtained by method of semi-averages (1) and method of least squares (2).

by a straight line, denoted by (1), in Figure 15-2. For comparison, the line obtained by the method of least squares, line (2), is also included in this graph. There is very good agreement between the two lines in this case.

### 15.2.3.   Isolation of the Trend from a Time Series

After the trend line has been determined it is possible to determine the so-called trend value—the values of $Y_e$ obtained from the trend line. From the equation of a straight line, $Y_e = a + bx$, it is evident that the amount of increase (or decrease) in $Y_e$ between two consecutive values of $x$ (i.e., between two consecutive periods) is equal to $b$, the slope of the line of regression. If the trend value for a particular period has been determined, the trend values for the succeeding periods can be obtained by the repeated addition of $b$.

*Example 15-3.*   Determine the trend values for the data of Table 15-2.
*Solution.*   Using the equation of the line obtained in Example 15-1, we find for $x = -4.5$ the trend value for 1939:

$$Y'_e = 271 + 8.56(-4.5) = 232.$$

The trend value for 1940 is $271 + 8.56(-3.5) = 241$. These and the other trend values are listed in the third column of Table 15-3.

Trend values are the values which would be observed if the secular trend is the only factor influencing a time series; i.e., if there is no effect whatsoever due to a seasonal variation, a cyclical fluctuation, or a random disturbance.

In Example 15-3 we confined our attention to the annual trend increment, which was 8.56. In many cases, such as that represented by the data of Table 15-1, it is also of interest to consider the monthly trend increment, which is found by dividing the annual trend increment by 12. Monthly trend increments are of particular importance if it is desired to eliminate the trend for

TABLE 15-3.   Trend Values for the Data of Table 15-2

| Year | Y' | Trend Values | Year | Y' | Trend Values |
|------|-----|-------------|------|-----|-------------|
| 1939 | 225 | 232 | 1944 | 276 | 275 |
| 1940 | 225 | 241 | 1945 | 281 | 284 |
| 1941 | 265 | 250 | 1946 | 289 | 292 |
| 1942 | 272 | 258 | 1947 | 300 | 301 |
| 1943 | 273 | 267 | 1948 | 307 | 310 |

the given data—that is, if it is desired to study the time series which would be obtained in the absence of any trend.

*Example 15-4.*   Eliminate the trend from the data of Table 15-1, considering the number of hired farm workers in January 1939 as being fixed (considering 156 as the base figure).

*Solution.*   From Example 15-1 we find the monthly trend increment to be

$$\frac{8.56}{12} = 0.71.$$

Eliminating the trend from the observed value for February 1939 we obtain

$$156 - 0.71 = 155,$$

rounded off to the nearest integer, and for March 1939 we obtain

$$158 - 2(0.71) = 157.$$

These values, and those for the rest of 1939, are given in Table 15-4.

Clearly, not all trends can be represented by straight lines. The general question of what curves should be fitted to various types of nonlinear trends will not be discussed here. Instead, we shall mention briefly an example that is of particular importance in the study of various types of growth, such as those of bacteria, insects, and animals. Analysis of such growth has revealed that initially the rate of growth is proportional to the size of the population. Later, however, some factor—usually, though not always, attributable to the limitations of space and food—begins to decelerate growth.

TABLE 15-4.   Elimination of the Trend for the Data of Table 15-1 (year 1939)

| Month | Y (observed values) | Values after Elimination of the Trend | Month | Y (observed values) | Values after Elimination of the Trend |
|-------|--------------------|--------------------------------------|-------|--------------------|--------------------------------------|
| Jan. | 156 | 156 | July | 260 | 256 |
| Feb. | 156 | 155 | Aug. | 317 | 312 |
| Mar. | 158 | 157 | Sept. | 380 | 374 |
| Apr. | 198 | 196 | Oct. | 255 | 249 |
| May | 205 | 202 | Nov. | 210 | 203 |
| June | 237 | 233 | Dec. | 165 | 157 |

Fig. 15-3. Growth of wild-type fruit flies in half-pint bottles.

Sometimes this decelerating factor appears long before limitations of land, food, or other resources could conceivably influence the growth of the population. The point at which acceleration of growth has changed to deceleration is called the critical point of the growth curve, and plays an important role in the study of population trends. After the critical point has been determined, the saturation level can be estimated.

The curve that represents the growth pattern just described is called the *logistic curve*. Its equation is

$$(15\text{-}2) \qquad\qquad Y_e = \frac{k}{1 + be^{-aX}},$$

where $a$, $b$, and $k$ are constants determined from the data of the time series and $e$ is approximately $2.71828 \cdots$ , the same number referred to in Chapter 7 in connection with equation (7-1).

The study of the logistic curve originated with work by Raymond Pearl and Lowell J. Reed in 1920. Pearl, a zoologist, found the equation of the curve from an analysis of the growth of fruit flies enclosed in bottles with fixed amounts of food. Figure 15-3 shows the average number of fruit flies in two half-pint bottles, each started on the same day with two adult wild-type flies (one male and one female).

The observations (averages of bottles 1 and 2), indicated by dots in Figure 15-3, were fitted with a logistic curve, as given by equation (15-2), for which it was found that $k = 212$, $a = -0.27$, and $b = 108.85$. It is clear that the observed growth of this fly population is, in general, accurately described by equation (15-2) with the values of $k$, $a$, and $b$ given above. The only serious discrepancies (April 21 and 23) are due to starting both bottles with only one pair of adult flies; we are thus dealing only with the children of the two original parents, not yet with any grandchildren—we are considering only a family, not population growth. Not until April 26 did overlapping of generations begin, and only from then on are we dealing with population growth.

Since for large values of $X$ the denominator of the fraction in (15-2) approaches 1, the constant $k$ is seen to equal the estimated size of the population when it has reached the saturation level. It can also be shown from (15-2) that the critical point of the curve occurs at

$$(15\text{-}3) \qquad\qquad X = \frac{1}{a} \log_e b$$

and that the estimated size of the population at that time is $Y_e = \frac{1}{2} k$.

Thus, for the data in Figure 15-3, the saturation level is 212 flies, and the critical point was reached on April 26, when there were an estimated 106 flies.

Their success in using the logistic curve to estimate population growth in fruit flies led Pearl and Reed to apply the same curve to estimating human population growth in various countries, including the United States. A forecast made by them in 1920 on the basis of the logistic curve predicted the 1950 population of the United States with an error of only about 1%. Use of the same logistic curve, however, resulted in an error of more than 11% in the prediction of the 1960 population of the United States, and thus this logistic curve (which, incidentally, was shown in earlier editions of this text) can no longer be used to predict the growth of the United States population.

Attempts by Pearl and Reed to predict population growth of other countries, e.g., Germany and Algeria, resulted in similar experiences: very good estimates for earlier years, but disappointingly large errors for later years.

It has, therefore, become evident that the early successes of the use of the logistic curve to predict population growth were coincidental. The failure of the logistic curve to describe accurately growth of human populations is not surprising when it is recalled that Pearl and Reed obtained this curve from an experiment with fruit flies in which there was a fixed amount of space, food, and other resources. Their hypothesis is generally not applicable to human populations—except, possibly, in the very long run. Control of the environment has made it increasingly possible to overcome limitations of resources which otherwise might cause a deceleration of population growth. Attempts to determine maximum populations by extrapolation from present technology to future expected improvement appear to be just as hazardous as projecting the number of people directly. It must be concluded that the influences on human population growth are too varied and dependent on too many unpredictable factors to allow accurate description by any particular curve or curves.

## 15.3. The Seasonal Variation

To study the seasonal variation in a time series we first consider a purely hypothetical time series in which all variations are entirely due to seasonal influences. Of course, a time series such as this is hardly ever actually encountered. In such a time series, as shown in the first four columns of Table 15-5, the yearly totals are identical; if they were not, some influence other than seasonal would be present.

TABLE 15-5.  Sales (in thousands of dollars) of a Corporation in the Period
1957–1959

| Quarter | Sales | | | Specific Seasonals | | | Typical Seasonals |
|---|---|---|---|---|---|---|---|
|  | 1957 | 1958 | 1959 | 1957 | 1958 | 1959 |  |
| 1st | 112 | 104 | 115 | 72 | 67 | 74 | 71 |
| 2nd | 172 | 162 | 179 | 110 | 104 | 115 | 110 |
| 3rd | 212 | 221 | 211 | 136 | 142 | 135 | 138 |
| 4th | 128 | 137 | 119 | 82 | 88 | 76 | 82 |
|  | 624 | 624 | 624 | 400 | 401 | 400 | 401 |

**DEFINITION 15-6.** If the variations in a time series are entirely due
to seasonal influences, the *specific seasonal* for a given period of the time
series is an index number whose base is the mean quarterly or monthly
variate (depending on whether the time series is a quarterly or monthly
one).

*Example 15-5.* Calculate the specific seasonals for each quarter of the time
series of Table 15-5.

*Solution.* The mean quarterly sale, in thousands of dollars, for each year
of the time series is 156. The specific seasonal for the first quarter of 1957 is

$$\frac{112}{156}\,100 = 72.$$

The specific seasonals for the other quarters are listed in the fifth, sixth, and
seventh columns of Table 15-5.

To study the typical effect of any particular season in the time series, we
introduce the following definition:

**DEFINITION 15-7.** For a quarterly time series, the *typical seasonal*
for the first quarter is the mean of all specific seasonals for all the first
quarters of the time series. Typical seasonals for the other three quarters
are defined analogously.

For a monthly time series, the typical seasonal for January is the mean of
all specific seasonals for January, and so on.

For a time series showing only seasonal variation, the mean of all typical
seasonals is always 100. The proof of this fact is left as an exercise.

*Example 15-6.* Calculate the typical seasonals for the four quarters of the
time series of Table 15-5.

*Solution.* For the first quarter, the typical seasonal is

$$\frac{72 + 67 + 74}{3} = 71.$$

The typical seasonals for the other three quarters are calculated in like manner; their values are listed in the last column of Table 15-5.

If a time series is influenced by variations other than seasonal ones, the mean quarterly or monthly values are no longer constant. This might suggest that, in the calculation of specific seasonals, a different base be used for each year of the time series. But such a procedure might still give a distorted picture, especially if a seasonal low coincides with the bottom of a business cycle, in which case too much weight might be ascribed to the seasonal influence. In order to avoid this possibility, three methods are commonly used to calculate the seasonal variation in a time series: *the ratio-to-moving-average method, the ratio-to-trend method,* and *the method of link-relatives.* These methods differ only in the way in which they define the specific seasonals. The typical seasonals are defined in terms of the specific seasonals in the same way in all three methods. The first of these methods is used much more frequently than are the other two.

### 15.3.1.   The Ratio-to-moving-average Method

As the name implies, this method makes use of a moving average.

DEFINITION 15-8.   If the observations in a time series are denoted by $Y_1, Y_2, \cdots, Y_n$, then a *moving average* of length $k$ is the series of successive means of $k$ consecutive observations. That is, the series of moving averages is

$$\overline{Y}_1 = \frac{Y_1 + Y_2 + \cdots + Y_k}{k}, \quad \overline{Y}_2 = \frac{Y_2 + Y_3 + \cdots + Y_{k+1}}{k},$$

$$\overline{Y}_3 = \frac{Y_3 + Y_4 + \cdots + Y_{k+2}}{k}, \cdots.$$

Since the values of these means, $\overline{Y}_1, \overline{Y}_2, \cdots$, are based upon $k$ observations, they are centered in a graph at the midpoint of the set of observations for which the mean has been calculated. Thus, if $k = 7$, then $\overline{Y}_1$ is centered at $Y_4$; similarly, $\overline{Y}_2$ is centered at $Y_5$, and so on. If $k = 8$, then $\overline{Y}_1$ is centered at the midpoint between $Y_4$ and $Y_5$; similarly, $\overline{Y}_2$ is centered at the midpoint between $Y_5$ and $Y_6$, and so on.

The ratio-to-moving-average method makes use of the fact that if a monthly time series is affected by the seasonal fluctuations due to the twelve months of the year, then a moving average of length 12 will remove these fluctuations.

DEFINITION 15-9. For a general time series, the *specific seasonal* for a given observation is an index number whose base is the moving average which is centered at that observation.

*Example 15-7.* Calculate the specific seasonals for the data of Table 15-1.
*Solution.* The first twelve-month moving average,

$$\overline{Y}_1 = \frac{156 + 156 + 158 + \cdots + 165}{12} = \frac{2697}{12} = 225,$$

is centered between June 1 and July 1, 1939; the second twelve-month moving average,

$$\overline{Y}_2 = \frac{156 + 158 + 198 + \cdots + 146}{12} = \frac{2687}{12} = 224,$$

is centered between July 1 and August 1, 1939. In order to obtain an average centered at July 1, 1939, we use the mean of $\overline{Y}_1$ and $\overline{Y}_2$:

$$\frac{225 + 224}{2} = 224.5.$$

These centered twelve-month moving averages are listed in the fifth column of Table 15-6. They are used as the bases in the calculation of the specific seasonals. Thus, the specific seasonal for July 1939 is

$$\frac{260}{224.5} 100 = 116.$$

In a similar manner, specific seasonals for all months from July 1939 to June 1940 are calculated; they are listed in the last column of Table 15-6.

Note that each twelve-month moving total (except the first) can be calculated from the preceding one by adding the next following observation and subtracting the first one used to calculate the preceding total. Thus, the second moving total in Table 15-6 is obtained from the first as

$$2697 + 146 - 156 = 2687.$$

In a quarterly time series, centered four-quarter moving averages are used in determining the specific seasonals for each quarter.

The ratio-to-moving-average method does not allow the calculation of moving averages for the first and last six months of the time series under study. Similarly, for quarterly time series, calculation of the moving averages for the first two and last two quarters is impossible. This disadvantage of the ratio-to-moving-average method is not serious when we are dealing with a time series covering an extended period of time, since the omission of a few

TABLE 15-6.   Calculation of Specific Seasonals for 1939 and 1940 for the Data of Table 15-1 by the Ratio-to-moving-average Method

| Year and Month | Y | 12-Month Moving Total | 12-Month Moving Average | Centered 12-Month Moving Average | Specific Seasonal |
|---|---|---|---|---|---|
| 1939 | | | | | |
| Jan. | 156 | | | | |
| Feb. | 156 | | | | |
| Mar. | 158 | | | | |
| Apr. | 198 | | | | |
| May | 205 | | | | |
| June | 237 | | | | |
| | | 2697 | 225 | | |
| July | 260 | | | 224.5 | 116 |
| | | 2687 | 224 | | |
| Aug. | 317 | | | 224 | 142 |
| | | 2688 | 224 | | |
| Sept. | 380 | | | 224 | 170 |
| | | 2689 | 224 | | |
| Oct. | 255 | | | 224 | 114 |
| | | 2693 | 224 | | |
| Nov. | 210 | | | 225 | 93 |
| | | 2715 | 226 | | |
| Dec. | 165 | | | 226 | 73 |
| | | | | | |
| 1940 | | 2710 | 226 | | |
| Jan. | 146 | | | 227 | 64 |
| | | 2733 | 228 | | |
| Feb. | 157 | | | 225.5 | 70 |
| | | 2676 | 223 | | |
| Mar. | 159 | | | 221.5 | 72 |
| | | 2641 | 220 | | |
| Apr. | 202 | | | 223.5 | 90 |
| | | 2726 | 227 | | |
| May | 227 | | | 226.5 | 100 |
| | | 2711 | 226 | | |
| June | 232 | | | 225.5 | 103 |
| | | 2697 | 225 | | |
| July | 283 | | | | |
| Aug. | 260 | | | | |
| Sept. | 345 | | | | |
| Oct. | 340 | | | | |
| Nov. | 195 | | | | |
| Dec. | 151 | | | | |

specific seasonals at the beginning and end of the series hardly affects the calculation of the typical seasonals.

We can now calculate typical seasonals from the specific seasonals. Recalling Definition 15-7, it would seem natural to obtain again the typical seasonal for January as the mean of all available specific seasonals for January. However, this might give undue weight to a few specific seasonals which might be excessively low or high, as compared to the rest. In order to avoid this, one of two procedures is used. Either the median of all specific seasonals is employed, or a certain fixed number of the exceptionally high and low specific seasonals is disregarded and the mean of the remaining specific seasonals is calculated. For simplicity, we shall adopt the first procedure. Usually the results of the two methods will differ little. However, the medians (or means) thus obtained for each season will not in general have a mean of 100. But since typical seasonals were previously defined in such a way that their mean is 100, the set of medians (or means) obtained must be expressed as index numbers whose base is the average of these medians (or means). Thus the index numbers will have a mean of 100 and will therefore represent the typical seasonals.

*Example 15-8.* Calculate the typical seasonals for the data of Table 15-1.
*Solution.* Using the results of Table 15-6 and extending the calculations to include all the data of Table 15-1, we obtain the specific seasonals listed in Table 15-7 (1939 and 1948 are omitted, since for the first and last six months of a monthly time series no specific seasonals can be calculated by the ratio-to-moving-average method).

**TABLE 15-7. Specific Seasonals for 1940–1947 for the Data of Table 15-1**

| Year | Jan. | Feb. | Mar. | Apr. | May | June | July | Aug. | Sept. | Oct. | Nov. | Dec. |
|---|---|---|---|---|---|---|---|---|---|---|---|---|
| 1940 | 64 | 70 | 72 | 90 | 100 | 103 | 126 | 116 | 155 | 154 | 89 | 69 |
| 1941 | 60 | 61 | 63 | 68 | 80 | 105 | 138 | 154 | 160 | 135 | 109 | 86 |
| 1942 | 60 | 61 | 64 | 63 | 78 | 90 | 138 | 145 | 175 | 125 | 122 | 86 |
| 1943 | 56 | 59 | 61 | 67 | 76 | 99 | 130 | 147 | 171 | 126 | 112 | 88 |
| 1944 | 59 | 64 | 67 | 67 | 75 | 103 | 130 | 139 | 167 | 126 | 114 | 86 |
| 1945 | 63 | 65 | 64 | 67 | 75 | 93 | 129 | 148 | 178 | 120 | 121 | 79 |
| 1946 | 62 | 61 | 60 | 66 | 84 | 101 | 134 | 145 | 160 | 121 | 116 | 84 |
| 1947 | 63 | 63 | 67 | 67 | 79 | 104 | 139 | 144 | 151 | 129 | 113 | 83 |
| Median | 61 | 62 | 64 | 67 | 78.5 | 102 | 132 | 145 | 163.5 | 126 | 113.5 | 85 |
| Typical Seasonal | 61 | 62 | 64 | 67 | 78.5 | 102 | 132 | 145 | 163.5 | 126 | 113.5 | 85 |

The median of the eight specific seasonals for January is found to be 61, that for February is 62, and so on, as listed in the next-to-last row of Table 15-7. Since the mean of the twelve medians is 100, i.e.,

$$\frac{61 + 62 + 64 + \cdots + 85}{12} = \frac{1199.5}{12} = 100,$$

we find the typical seasonal for January to be

$$\frac{61}{100} \, 100 = 61.$$

In this special case the typical seasonals are identical to the corresponding medians.

### 15.3.2.   The Ratio-to-trend Method

This method differs from the ratio-to-moving-average method in that the specific seasonals are not calculated by use of moving averages but are based upon the trend values. Thus, each observation is expressed as a percentage of the trend value corresponding to that particular observation. This method is particularly suitable where an abrupt change occurs in the trend: In 1941 fresh citrus shipments showed a sudden change in trend when there was a material decrease due to the introduction of and subsequent increase in processing, initially by canning, then by concentration of juice, and later by freezing (see exercise 5). The ratio-to-trend method has the disadvantage that it does not differentiate between seasonal influences and cyclical and random influences.

### 15.3.3.   The Method of Link-relatives

In the method of link-relatives, each successive variate is expressed as a per cent of the preceding variate. The "typical link-relatives," representing the medians of the respective specific link-relatives, can be expressed as a chain, the first entry (for January) being set equal to 100. Thus, if the medians for January, February, March are 98.2, 99.0, 100.7, respectively, the corresponding numbers in the chain are 100 for January, 99.0% of 100 = 99.0 for February, and 100.7% of 99.0 = 99.7 for March. From the entry in the chain for December (say, 97.5), a number for January can be obtained: 98.2% of 97.5 = 95.7. But the entry for January was initially set equal to 100. Any difference between the two figures for January represents the presence within the time series of the effects of factors other than seasonal. In order to eliminate these influences we shall assume that variations other than seasonal have taken place uniformly over the whole period, i.e., that they can be approximated by a straight line, which implies that the change in any two consecutive months has been constant. For the above example, this constant change is

$$\frac{95.7 - 100}{12} = -0.36,$$

which should be applied to each of the entries of the chain in order to eliminate the other-than-seasonal influences. Thus we obtain the following adjusted chain: 100 for January, $99.0 - (-0.36) = 99.4$ for February, $99.7 - 2(-0.36) = 100.4$ for March. From this adjusted chain, the typical seasonals are obtained as index numbers having as a base the mean of the twelve entries of the adjusted chain.

Frequently, the typical seasonals obtained by the method of link-relatives are in fairly good agreement with those obtained by the ratio-to-moving-average method. Obviously, the latter method gives more accurate results, since it employs a more representative base for calculating the typical seasonals; on the other hand, the method of link-relatives requires considerably less computation, since the base for each link-relative is simply the previous observation.

### 15.3.4. Adjustment of a Time Series for Seasonal Variation

Typical seasonals give information about the usual effect of a season on a particular observation in that season. For the data of Table 15-1, the typical seasonal of 61 found for January in Example 15-8 tells us that in January the number of farm workers hired is 61% of that of the average month. In many situations, it is important to determine what the time series would have been if there had been no seasonal variation—we desire to eliminate the seasonal variation from the series. Knowing the typical seasonals, we can do this easily. If we denote the typical seasonal, also called seasonal index, corresponding to a given time by $s$ and the corresponding observation by $Y$, we have

$$(15\text{-}4) \qquad\qquad Y = \frac{s}{100}(T + C + E),$$

since the typical seasonal is the per cent of the result in the average month (when only components other than seasonal are present). To find the theoretical value which would have occurred in the absence of any seasonal variation, we solve equation (15-4) for $(T + C + E)$. This value of $(T + C + E)$ represents the sum of all non-seasonal influences.

*Example 15-9.* Using the typical seasonals obtained by the ratio-to-moving-average method in Table 15-7, adjust for seasonal variation the data for 1940 of the time series of Table 15-1.

*Solution.* To calculate the adjusted value for January 1940 we find, since $Y = 146$ and $s = 61$,

$$T + C + E = \frac{146}{0.61} = 239.$$

TABLE 15-8.   Number of Hired Farm Workers on Pacific Coast in 1940 Adjusted
              for Seasonal Variation and Trend

| Month | Y | Adjusted for Seasonal Variation $(T + C + E)$ | Trend Value $(T)$ | Sum of Cyclical and Random Influences $(C + E)$ | Seasonally Adjusted Number as a Per Cent of the Trend |
|---|---|---|---|---|---|
| Jan. | 146 | 239 | 237 | 2 | 101 |
| Feb. | 157 | 256 | 238 | 18 | 108 |
| Mar. | 159 | 249 | 238 | 11 | 105 |
| Apr. | 202 | 301 | 239 | 62 | 126 |
| May | 227 | 289 | 239 | 50 | 121 |
| June | 232 | 227 | 240 | −13 | 95 |
| July | 283 | 214 | 241 | −27 | 89 |
| Aug. | 260 | 179 | 242 | −63 | 74 |
| Sept. | 345 | 211 | 243 | −32 | 87 |
| Oct. | 340 | 270 | 243 | 27 | 111 |
| Nov. | 195 | 172 | 244 | −72 | 70 |
| Dec. | 151 | 178 | 245 | −67 | 73 |

This and the adjusted values for all months of 1940 are listed in the third
column of Table 15-8.

Many time series issued monthly by the United States Government are
published on a seasonally adjusted basis in order that any changes which
might occur between consecutive months can be ascribed to other-than-
seasonal factors.

Typical seasonals are rarely constant over long periods of time, though in
a short period their variation is ordinarily so small that they can be assumed
to be constant. However, a particular event may have sufficient impact to
alter materially the typical seasonals. For example, in a time series giving
the quantity of oranges produced each month in recent years in the United
States, the Texas freeze of 1949 changes the typical seasonals considerably.
Therefore a new set of typical seasonals should be calculated for the period
following the freeze.

Now that we can eliminate both the trend and the seasonal variation from
a time series, we can calculate for each observation the sum of the cyclical
and random components.

*Example 15-10.* Calculate the sum of the cyclical and random components
for the data of the times series of Table 15-1 for 1940.

*Solution.* The values of $(T + C + E)$ and the trend values obtained
from the regression equation found in Example 15-1 are listed in the third
and fourth columns of Table 15-8. Subtracting the $T$-values from the

$(T + C + E)$-values gives the $(C + E)$-values, which are listed in the fifth column of Table 15-8.

Frequently, in order to indicate the relative importance of the cyclical and random influences, the $(T + C + E)$-values are expressed as a per cent of the trend. These per cents for the data of Example 15-10 are listed in the last column of Table 15-8.

## 15.4. The Cyclical Fluctuation

The study of cyclical fluctuations is quite similar to the study of seasonal variations except that the latter refers to long cycles whereas the former refers to short cycles. In order to determine the length of the cycles, it is advisable to study the scatter diagram carefully and to try to find from it the period between successive tops or bottoms. Frequently, the study of cyclical fluctuations is complicated by the fact that cycles of different lengths may be superimposed upon one another, making the isolation of the individual cycles difficult. We shall consider only a single, discernible, long-term cycle in a time series. The procedures used in its isolation from the time series are analogous to the method of moving averages used in the study of the seasonal variation. The moving averages therefore represent the hypothetical values which would be observed in the absence of any cyclical fluctuation. Consequently, in a yearly time series (in which there is no seasonal variation), the random or irregular variation can be obtained by subtracting the trend values from the corresponding moving averages. Sometimes, particularly when the random variation is very small, the moving averages themselves can be employed as representing the trend of the original time series. These principles are illustrated with fictitious data in Example 15-11.

*Example 15-11.* The number of items of a certain product sold within a country is given in Table 15-9. Find the length of the cyclical fluctuation, and graph the moving averages.

TABLE 15-9. Number of Items Sold (in thousands)

| Year | Sales | Year | Sales | Year | Sales |
|------|-------|------|-------|------|-------|
| 1930 | 458 | 1937 | 650 | 1944 | 308 |
| 1931 | 672 | 1938 | 329 | 1945 | 507 |
| 1932 | 611 | 1939 | 365 | 1946 | 693 |
| 1933 | 266 | 1940 | 574 | 1947 | 762 |
| 1934 | 207 | 1941 | 754 | 1948 | 415 |
| 1935 | 410 | 1942 | 601 | 1949 | 368 |
| 1936 | 720 | 1943 | 365 | 1950 | 575 |

*Solution.*   First we construct the scatter diagram for the data of Table 15-9. A curve drawn through the scatter diagram (Figure 15-4) reveals that the time between successive tops or bottoms of the graph is about 5 years.

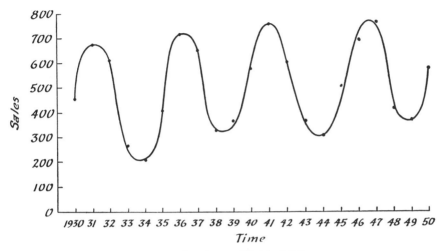

**Fig. 15-4.   Scatter diagram for data of Table 15-9.**

Applying a moving average of 5 years to the observations of the time series of Table 15-9, and centering each average at the middle observation of the five used in the average, we obtain the moving averages listed in Table 15-10. These represent the $(T + E)$-values for the time series. Calculating the trend line by use of equation (12-5), we find

$$Y_e = 503 + 7.01\ x,$$

from which we obtain the trend values given in Table 15-10. Finally, we calculate the values of the random variations by subtracting the trend values, $T$, from the corresponding moving averages, $T + E$. These are also listed in Table 15-10. Graphing both the trend line and the moving averages, we see from Figure 15-5 that, owing to the small values of random variation, there is close agreement between the curve of moving averages and the trend line.

Considerable attention has been devoted to business cycles which may exist in the over-all economy of a country. Various claims concerning the existence of such cycles have been made. Although some of these claims might have been valid for periods up to World War II, they have not proved valid for the period thereafter. The existence of such cycles in an entire economy is being regarded, therefore, with increasing skepticism. Some modern economists have completely abandoned the idea of business cycles in the economy of the United States.

**TABLE 15-10.** Number of Items Sold (in thousands) Adjusted for Cyclical Fluctuation and Trend

| Year | Y | Moving Average (T + E) | Trend Value (T) | Random Variation (E) | Year | Y | Moving Average (T + E) | Trend Value (T) | Random Variation (E) |
|------|-----|------|-----|-----|------|-----|------|-----|-----|
| 1930 | 458 |      |     |     | 1941 | 754 | 532 | 510 | 22 |
| 1931 | 672 |      |     |     | 1942 | 601 | 520 | 517 | 3 |
| 1932 | 611 | 443 | 447 | −4  | 1943 | 365 | 507 | 524 | −17 |
| 1933 | 266 | 433 | 454 | −21 | 1944 | 308 | 495 | 531 | −36 |
| 1934 | 207 | 443 | 461 | −18 | 1945 | 507 | 527 | 538 | −11 |
| 1935 | 410 | 451 | 468 | −17 | 1946 | 693 | 537 | 545 | −8 |
| 1936 | 720 | 463 | 475 | −12 | 1947 | 762 | 549 | 552 | −3 |
| 1937 | 650 | 495 | 482 | 13  | 1948 | 415 | 563 | 559 | 4 |
| 1938 | 329 | 528 | 489 | 39  | 1949 | 368 |     |     |   |
| 1939 | 365 | 534 | 496 | 38  | 1950 | 575 |     |     |   |
| 1940 | 574 | 525 | 503 | 22  |      |     |     |     |   |

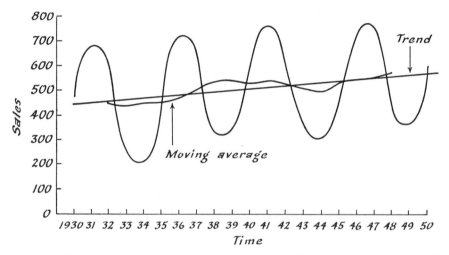

Fig. 15-5. Graph of moving averages and trend line for data of Table 15-9.

## Exercises

1. The following data give the net income per share of the Standard Oil Company of California for the years 1949–1958.

|              | 1949 | 1950 | 1951 | 1952 | 1953 | 1954 | 1955 | 1956 | 1957 | 1958 |
|--------------|------|------|------|------|------|------|------|------|------|------|
| Income per Share ($) | 2.15 | 2.39 | 2.74 | 2.75 | 3.00 | 3.35 | 3.66 | 4.24 | 4.56 | 4.08 |

    (a) Find the equation of the trend line by the method of least squares, and graph that line.

    (b) Graph the trend line by the method of semiaverages.

    (c) Find the trend value for each of the years listed.

2. The following data show average hourly earnings of workers employed by United States Steel Corporation for the period 1950–1958.

| | 1950 | 1951 | 1952 | 1953 | 1954 | 1955 | 1956 | 1957 | 1958 |
|---|---|---|---|---|---|---|---|---|---|
| Earnings ($) | 1.83 | 2.05 | 2.26 | 2.39 | 2.49 | 2.70 | 2.93 | 3.19 | 3.50 |

    (a) Find the equation of the trend line by the method of least squares, and graph that line.

    (b) Graph the trend line by the method of semiaverages.

    (c) Find the trend value for each of the years listed.

3. Calculate the specific seasonals and typical seasonals for the following time series (showing the number of absences in a factory) whose variations are due entirely to seasonal influences.

| Month | 1948 | 1949 | 1950 | 1951 |
|---|---|---|---|---|
| Jan. | 337 | 321 | 339 | 319 |
| Feb. | 312 | 320 | 321 | 305 |
| Mar. | 309 | 301 | 315 | 305 |
| Apr. | 308 | 309 | 299 | 305 |
| May | 312 | 301 | 296 | 300 |
| June | 298 | 279 | 297 | 300 |
| July | 275 | 281 | 281 | 290 |
| Aug. | 278 | 299 | 275 | 279 |
| Sept. | 262 | 260 | 265 | 269 |
| Oct. | 295 | 301 | 292 | 299 |
| Nov. | 299 | 303 | 309 | 300 |
| Dec. | 321 | 331 | 317 | 335 |

4. The following data give the cold storage holdings of frozen eggs in millions of pounds.

| Month | 1941 | 1942 | 1943 | 1944 |
|---|---|---|---|---|
| Jan. | 73.3 | 95.5 | 82.9 | 102.3 |
| Feb. | 53.8 | 76.3 | 59.8 | 81.7 |
| Mar. | 45.2 | 73.8 | 56.5 | 98.6 |
| Apr. | 63.4 | 107.4 | 99.2 | 148.6 |
| May | 99.5 | 159.6 | 172.3 | 218.0 |
| June | 142.0 | 223.8 | 251.5 | 292.4 |

| Month | 1941 | 1942 | 1943 | 1944 |
|-------|------|------|------|------|
| July  | 178.6 | 278.5 | 323.2 | 354.2 |
| Aug.  | 195.2 | 290.5 | 351.2 | 388.5 |
| Sept. | 194.0 | 272.0 | 343.6 | 371.6 |
| Oct.  | 178.4 | 234.9 | 306.2 | 332.6 |
| Nov.  | 153.8 | 180.3 | 242.3 | 279.2 |
| Dec.  | 129.5 | 126.3 | 172.4 | 219.8 |

(a) Calculate the specific seasonals by the ratio-to-moving-average method for all months of the table, where such calculation is possible.

(b) Use the specific seasonals obtained in part (a) to calculate the typical seasonal for each month.

(c) Adjust the time series for the year 1942 for seasonal variation.

(d) Find the trend line by the method of least squares.

(e) Determine the trend value for each month of 1942.

(f) Find the sum of the cyclical and random components for each month of 1942.

5. The following data give the fresh lemon shipments from California and Arizona in thousands of boxes.

| Year | Nov.–Jan. | Feb.–Apr. | May–July | Aug.–Oct. |
|------|-----------|-----------|----------|-----------|
| 1930–31 | 906 | 1,249 | 2,816 | 1,133 |
| 31–32 | 869 | 1,293 | 2,336 | 869 |
| 32–33 | 892 | 941 | 2,448 | 1,125 |
| 33–34 | 952 | 1,233 | 2,957 | 1,219 |
| 34–35 | 1,139 | 1,614 | 3,036 | 1,515 |
| 1935–36 | 1,124 | 1,628 | 3,116 | 1,508 |
| 36–37 | 1,203 | 1,467 | 2,784 | 1,188 |
| 37–38 | 988 | 1,437 | 3,152 | 1,767 |
| 38–39 | 1,155 | 1,595 | 3,451 | 1,798 |
| 39–40 | 1,242 | 1,705 | 3,113 | 1,739 |
| 1940–41 | 1,549 | 1,789 | 3,801 | 2,081 |
| 41–42 | 1,361 | 1,684 | 3,106 | 1,836 |
| 42–43 | 1,415 | 1,945 | 3,961 | 2,293 |
| 43–44 | 1,783 | 1,928 | 4,007 | 1,767 |
| 44–45 | 1,850 | 2,173 | 3,616 | 1,955 |
| 1945–46 | 1,837 | 2,029 | 3,534 | 1,755 |
| 46–47 | 1,480 | 1,818 | 3,546 | 2,330 |
| 47–48 | 1,413 | 1,702 | 3,612 | 1,763 |
| 48–49 | 1,287 | 1,619 | 3,473 | 1,572 |
| 49–50 | 1,049 | 1,563 | 3,313 | 1,459 |

(a) Calculate the specific seasonals by the ratio-to-moving-average method for the period 1931–1932 to 1948–1949.

(b) Use the specific seasonals obtained in part (a) to calculate the typical seasonals for the four quarters Nov.–Jan., Feb.–Apr., May–July, Aug.–Oct.

(c) Adjust the time series for the period 1931–1932 and 1932–1933 for seasonal variation.

(d) Make up a yearly time series from the given data; graph these data; and observe a change in trend in 1939–1940. (Therefore, two different trend lines should be used—one for the period 1931–1932 to 1939–1940, and another for the period 1940–1941 to 1948–1949.) Find the equations of these two trend lines by the method of least squares, and graph them.

(e) Determine the trend value for each period of 1931–1932 and 1932–1933.

(f) Find the sum of the cyclical and random components for each period of 1931–1932 and 1932–1933.

6. The number of items of a certain product imported into the United States is given below in thousands of units.

| Year | Number | Year | Number | Year | Number |
|------|--------|------|--------|------|--------|
| 1910 | 170 | 1917 | 182 | 1924 | 60 |
| 1911 | 210 | 1918 | 90 | 1925 | 107 |
| 1912 | 188 | 1919 | 92 | 1926 | 140 |
| 1913 | 98 | 1920 | 141 | 1927 | 154 |
| 1914 | 83 | 1921 | 183 | 1928 | 61 |
| 1915 | 131 | 1922 | 141 | 1929 | 44 |
| 1916 | 205 | 1923 | 80 | 1930 | 92 |

(a) Find the length of the cyclical fluctuation, and apply a moving average of that length to these data.

(b) Find the trend line by use of these moving averages.

(c) Calculate the trend values from the equation obtained in part (b), and find for each of the years of the table the random component.

# 16    The F-Distribution

## 16.1.    Definition

Another very important distribution frequently used in making tests of hypotheses is the $F$-distribution. In Section 10.4 it was pointed out in studying the distribution of the difference between means that the $F$-distribution is used to determine the validity of the assumption of identical standard deviations of two populations. It is also the distribution on which the whole analysis of variance procedure, discussed briefly in Chapter 17, is based.

> **DEFINITION 16-1.**    If the probability of occurrence of a quantity $F$ is given by
>
> (16-1)
> $$y = \frac{cF^{(\nu_1 - 2)/2}}{(\nu_2 + \nu_1 F)^{(\nu_1 + \nu_2)/2}},$$
>
> the distribution is called an *F-distribution*, where both $\nu_1$ and $\nu_2$ are numbers of degrees of freedom, and $c$ is a constant dependent on $\nu_1$ and $\nu_2$ and is chosen in such a way that the total area under the probability curve (16-1) is equal to 1.

This distribution primarily distinguishes itself from distributions studied in previous chapters in that it involves two numbers of degrees of freedom, $\nu_1$ and $\nu_2$. Since $\nu_2$ appears only in the denominator of the fraction given above, it is frequently referred to as the denominator degrees of freedom, and $\nu_1$ is referred to as the numerator degrees of freedom.

The graphs of (16-1) vary considerably as $\nu_1$ and $\nu_2$ change. Figure 16-1 shows the graph of equation (16-1) for a typical case. If $\nu_1$ is greater than 2, the curve reaches its highest point at

(16-2)
$$F = \frac{\nu_1 - 2}{\nu_1} \cdot \frac{\nu_2}{\nu_2 + 2},$$

which is always less than 1, since each of the two fractions in (16-2) is smaller than 1. But as both $\nu_1$ and $\nu_2$ become larger and larger both fractions approach 1, so that for large $\nu_1$ and $\nu_2$ the highest point of (16-1) occurs very nearly at $F = 1$.

The $F$-distribution has the following important property: If a quantity $F$ satisfies an $F$-distribution with $\nu_1$ and $\nu_2$ degrees of freedom for numerator and denominator, respectively, then the reciprocal of that quantity, $1/F$, also satisfies an $F$-distribution, but with the numerator degrees of freedom now being $\nu_2$ and the denominator degrees of freedom being $\nu_1$.

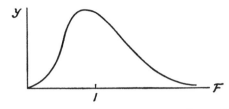

Fig. 16-1. A typical F-distribution $(\nu_1 > 2)$.

By introducing the notation $F(\nu_1, \nu_2)$ for a quantity which satisfies the $F$-distribution with $\nu_1$ and $\nu_2$ degrees of freedom, respectively, we have the following theorem.

**THEOREM 16-1.** If $F(\nu_1, \nu_2)$ satisfies the $F$-distribution, then

$$F'(\nu_2, \nu_1) = \frac{1}{F(\nu_1, \nu_2)}$$

satisfies the $F$-distribution also.

The proof of this theorem requires calculus and therefore will not be given here.

Construction of tables for the $F$-distribution is complicated by the fact that two degrees of freedom, $\nu_1$ and $\nu_2$, are involved. Table Va in the Appendix gives for various values of $\nu_1$ and $\nu_2$ ($\nu_1$ being listed in the first row and $\nu_2$ in the first column) the value of $F$ required such that the total area under the curve to the left of that $F$-value is 0.95. This $F$-value will from now on be denoted by $F_{.95}$. Thus, from Table Va, for $\nu_1 = 7$, $\nu_2 = 10 : F_{.95} = 3.14$, which means that in this case the total area under the curve from $F = 0$ to $F = 3.14$ equals 0.95. Table Vb gives values of $F_{.975}$ and Table Vc values of $F_{.99}$.

Although Table V does not give values of $F_{.05}$, $F_{.025}$, and $F_{.01}$, these values of $F$ can easily be obtained by means of the formula

$$(16\text{-}3) \qquad F_\alpha(\nu_1, \nu_2) = \frac{1}{F_{1-\alpha}(\nu_2, \nu_1)}.$$

*Proof of Formula (16-3).* To fix our ideas let $\alpha = 0.025$, and let $P[F < F_{.025}]$ denote the probability that $F(\nu_1, \nu_2)$ is less than $F_{.025}$. Then, since this probability equals the area under the curve to the left of $F_{.025}$, we have

$$(16\text{-}4) \qquad 0.025 = P[F < F_{.025}] = P\left[\frac{1}{F} > \frac{1}{F_{.025}}\right] = P\left[F' > \frac{1}{F_{.025}}\right].$$

But, since we know from Theorem 16-1 that $F'$ satisfies the $F$-distribution with the number of degrees of freedom reversed and since from (16-4)

$$P\left[F' > \frac{1}{F_{.025}}\right] = 0.025,$$

$1/F_{.025}$ is the point in the distribution of $F(\nu_2, \nu_1)$ for which the total area to the right is 0.025, or the total area to the left is 0.975. Thus,

$$F_{.025}(\nu_1, \nu_2) = \frac{1}{F_{.975}(\nu_2, \nu_1)}.$$

Formula (16-3) can be proved in general by replacing in the statements above 0.025 by $\alpha$, and 0.975 by $1 - \alpha$.

*Example 16-1.*   Find $F_{.025}(3, 5)$.
*Solution.*   From (16-3) we find

$$F_{.025}(3, 5) = \frac{1}{F_{.975}(5, 3)} = \frac{1}{14.9} = 0.067.$$

An important relationship exists between Student's $t$-distribution and the $F$-distribution for the special case where $\nu_1 = 1$. It is expressed in Theorem 16-2.

**THEOREM 16-2.**   If a quantity $t$ satisfies Student's $t$-distribution with $\nu_2$ degrees of freedom, then its square, $t^2$, satisfies the $F$-distribution with $\nu_1 = 1$ and $\nu_2$ degrees of freedom for the denominator.

From Theorem 16-2, it can be proved that

(16-5)                                $F_{1-\alpha}(1, \nu_2) = t_\alpha^2(\nu_2),$

where $t_\alpha(\nu_2)$ denotes the $t$-value for $\nu_2$ degrees of freedom for which the two tail areas total $\alpha$.

*Proof of Formula (16-5).*   Since $F_{1-\alpha}(1, \nu_2)$ is the point of the $F$-distribution for which the area under the curve to the right equals $\alpha$, we have

(16-6)
$$\alpha = P[F > F_{1-\alpha}(1, \nu_2)] = P[t^2 > F_{1-\alpha}] = P[t > \sqrt{F_{1-\alpha}} \quad \text{or} \quad t < -\sqrt{F_{1-\alpha}}].$$

From (16-6), we see that $\sqrt{F_{1-\alpha}}$ is that point in the $t$-distribution for which the two tail areas (that is, to the right of $\sqrt{F_{1-\alpha}}$ and to the left of $-\sqrt{F_{1-\alpha}}$) total $\alpha$, which means that

$$\sqrt{F_{1-\alpha}(1, \nu_2)} = t_\alpha(\nu_2),$$

and, squaring both sides,

$$F_{1-\alpha}(1, \nu_2) = t_\alpha^2(\nu_2).$$

By means of this formula it is possible to find from Table II all values of $F$ of the columns for $\nu_1 = 1$ in Table V.

*Example 16-2.*   Use the $t$-table (Table II) to find $F_{.95}(1, 10)$.
*Solution.*

$$F_{.95}(1, 10) = t_{.05}^2(10) = (2.228)^2 = 4.964,$$

which agrees with the value of $F_{.95}(1, 10)$ given in Table Va.

## 16.2.   Testing the Homogeneity of Two Variances

DEFINITION 16-2.   The variances of two samples are said to be *homogeneous* if the populations from which the two samples are taken have identical variances (or identical standard deviations).

In many problems, as was already indicated in Chapter 10, it is important to have a test which helps to decide whether two variances are homogeneous. Such a test will now be developed.

Consider two populations with identical standard deviations. Let $N$ denote the number of all possible pairs of samples which can be taken from these populations such that the first of each pair is from the first population and has $n_1$ variates and the other is from the second population and has $n_2$ variates. Let the means of the samples from the first population be denoted by $\overline{X}_1, \overline{X}_2, \cdots, \overline{X}_N$, and those from the second by $\overline{Y}_1, \overline{Y}_2, \cdots, \overline{Y}_N$. By use of formula (10-2), calculate from each of these samples the best estimate of the standard deviation of the population, and denote the best estimates obtained from samples of the first population by $s_{x,1}, s_{x,2}, \cdots, s_{x,N}$ and those obtained from samples of the second population by $s_{y,1}, s_{y,2}, \cdots, s_{y,N}$, that is,

$$s_{x,1} = \sqrt{\frac{\Sigma(X - \overline{X}_1)^2}{n_1 - 1}}, \qquad s_{y,1} = \sqrt{\frac{\Sigma(Y - \overline{Y}_1)^2}{n_2 - 1}}.$$

Calculate for each pair the ratio of the squares of the best estimates of the standard deviations of the two samples; thereby $N$ such ratios are obtained which we shall denote by $F_1, F_2, \cdots, F_N$, as shown in Figure 16-2.

The $F$-values thus obtained satisfy an $F$-distribution with $\nu_1 = n_1 - 1$ and $\nu_2 = n_2 - 1$. This is restated in the following theorem.

THEOREM 16-3.   If $X$ and $Y$ are normally distributed with identical standard deviations, and if all possible pairs of samples are drawn from these populations (as shown in Figure 16-2), then the ratio of the squares of the best estimates of the standard deviations, that is,

(16-7)
$$F = \frac{s_x^2}{s_y^2},$$

where

(16-8)
$$s_x = \sqrt{\frac{\Sigma(X - \bar{X})^2}{n_1 - 1}}, \qquad s_y = \sqrt{\frac{\Sigma(Y - \bar{Y})^2}{n_2 - 1}},$$

satisfies an $F$-distribution with $\nu_1 = n_1 - 1$ and $\nu_2 = n_2 - 1$.

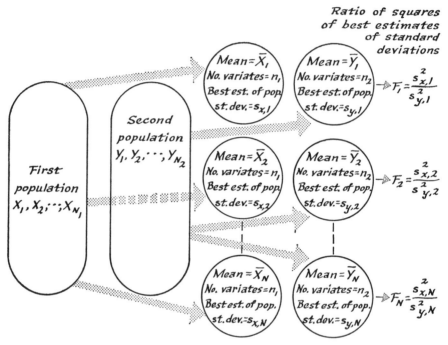

Fig. 16-2.   Distribution of variance ratios for two populations with identical standard deviations.

From Theorem 16-2 it follows immediately that, for the arrangement described in Figure 16-2, also the reciprocal of $F$, that is,

(16-9)
$$F' = \frac{s_y^2}{s_x^2}$$

satisfies the $F$-distribution with $\nu_1 = n_2 - 1$, and $\nu_2 = n_1 - 1$.

To test for the homogeneity of variances, we set up the hypothesis that the standard deviations of the two populations under consideration are identical. Thus the value of $F$ as obtained from (16-7) is expected to be near 1. If a very large or very small value of $F$ is obtained, it would be an indication that the hypothesis of equal standard deviations should be rejected, or, more precisely, we reject the hypothesis if the calculated value of $F$ is such that the two tail areas corresponding to it are less than 0.05 (assuming a 5% level of significance). This means that we reject the hypothesis if the calculated $F$-value is either larger than $F_{.975}$ or less than $F_{.025}$; otherwise we accept it.

A two-tailed test is always applied in this case, since the problem is to find whether $s_x$ and $s_y$ differ significantly. We must be prepared to reject the hypothesis of identical population standard deviations if $F$ is either significantly larger or significantly smaller than 1. Here, the hypothesis $\sigma_x = \sigma_y$ is considered as having the alternative $\sigma_x \neq \sigma_y$. In many other problems, indeed in most problems where the $F$-test is applied, as in the analysis of variance (see Chapter 17), one variance is assumed given, and the question is raised whether another variance exceeds the given one by a significant amount. This situation calls for a one-tailed test, as the alternative to the hypothesis $\sigma_x = \sigma_y$ then is $\sigma_x > \sigma_y$, where $\sigma_y$ is the given or fixed variance.

Since Table V gives only values of $F_{.95}$, $F_{.975}$, $F_{.99}$, which are critical points on the right side of the distributions, it is advisable in calculating $F$ to use (16-7) or (16-9), whichever gives the larger value. Clearly, this occurs when the larger standard deviation is placed in the numerator. The procedure then in testing for the homogeneity of two variances is always to divide the larger variance by the smaller, which results in an $F$-value larger than 1, which can then be compared with the critical $F$-value given in Table V.

*Example 16-3.*   Assuming the data of Example 10-4, determine whether the variances of the two samples can be considered homogeneous on the basis of the 5% level of significance.

*Solution.*   From the solution of Example 10-4 we find

$$s_x^2 = \frac{\Sigma(X - \bar{X})^2}{n_1 - 1} = \frac{110}{3} = 36.67,$$

$$s_y^2 = \frac{\Sigma(Y - \bar{Y})^2}{n_2 - 1} = \frac{56}{5} = 11.20$$

and

$$F = \frac{36.67}{11.20} = 3.27.$$

From Table Vb we find

$$F_{.975}(3, 5) = 7.76.$$

Since the calculated $F$-value does not exceed $F_{.975}(3, 5)$, we conclude that the two variances can be assumed to be homogeneous. These two samples can be considered as coming from two populations with identical standard deviations, and the assumption which we made in Example 10-4 was valid.

It may appear surprising that in Example 16-3 where the variance of one sample is more than three times that of the other, the hypothesis of equal standard deviations of the two populations is still acceptable. Indeed, the value of $F_{.975}(3, 5) = 7.76$ indicates that one sample variance could have been more than seven times that of the other without violating the hypothesis of homogeneous variances. This shows that, for small samples taken from populations with identical standard deviations, the variances can differ very greatly. Consequently, the assumption of homogeneous variances can safely be made in most situations and, in particular, in applying Theorem 10-2. If, however, the $F$-value indicates that the standard deviations of the two populations are different, then Theorem 10-2 should not be used to test for significant differences between means. A special theorem, not discussed here, is applicable in that case.

## Exercises

1. Find the following:
   (a) $F_{.01}(5, 9)$;          (b) $F_{.025}(6, 8)$;          (c) $F_{.05}(20, 15)$.

2. Use the $t$-table to find, accurate to three decimal places:
   (a) $F_{.99}(1, 10)$;          (b) $F_{.95}(1, 15)$;          (c) $F_{.05}(8, 1)$.

3. Can the variances for the data of exercise 11, Chapter 10, be considered as being homogeneous (5% level)?

4. From a sample of 13 variates the best estimate of the standard deviation of the population was calculated as 8.32, and from another sample of 15 variates it was calculated to be 4.47. Can these samples be considered as having homogeneous variances?

5. Cochran presents an example of an experiment with a control and a treatment consisting of a large amount of chalk or lime on the number of marigolds per plot. The results are given below.

   Control: 140, 142, 36, 129, 49, 37, 114, 125
   Treated: 117, 137, 137, 143, 130, 112, 130, 121.
   Test for homogeneity of variances.

6. To test the effect of phosphorus as a fertilizer, 10 plots were treated with phosphorus, and 10 other plots were not treated. The yields in bushels of corn for the treated plots and those used as control are as follows:

   Treated: 6.2, 5.7, 6.5, 6.0, 6.3, 5.8, 5.7, 6.0, 6.0, 5.8
   Control: 5.6, 5.9, 5.6, 5.7, 5.8, 5.7, 6.0, 5.5, 5.7, 5.5

Does this indicate that the fertilizer increased the yield significantly on the basis of the 5% level of significance (test for homogeneity of variances first)?

7. In a sample of 11 variates the best estimate of the standard deviation of the population was calculated to be $s_x = 9.76$. If another sample has 16 variates, find the limits within which $s_y$ must lie in order that the two samples can be considered to have homogeneous variances on the basis of the 5% level of significance.

8. If the variates in a sample are 80, 70, 65, 69, 74, 79, 53 and those in another sample are 60, 45, 49, 70, $X$, find the limits within which $X$ must be in order that the two samples could be considered as having homogeneous variances (5% level).

9. For a sample of 21 variates the sum of the squares of the deviations from the mean was found to be $\Sigma(X - \bar{X})^2 = 483$. From a sample taken from another population the best estimate of the standard deviation of that population was found to be 2.59. Within what range must the size of the second sample be in order that the variances of the two populations can be considered different at the 5% level of significance?

10. Two samples of 7 and 14 variates, respectively, are checked for homogeneity of variances. If the best estimate of the standard deviation of the population as obtained from the sample of 7 variates is exactly 3 units larger than the best estimate of the standard deviation obtained from the other sample, what are the smallest values the best estimates of the two standard deviations can have in order that the variances can be considered homogeneous at the 5% level of significance?

# 17 The Analysis of Variance, One Criterion of Classification

## 17.1. Introduction

In Chapter 10 we saw that by means of Student's $t$-test it is possible to determine whether the means of two given samples differ significantly. In this chapter we shall consider the problem of determining whether among a given set of more than two samples (say $k$ samples) there are means which differ significantly.

At first glance this problem might appear to be easily solved by taking all possible pairs of samples and testing them individually for significant differences by means of Student's $t$-test. Closer inspection, however, will show that such a procedure must be rejected not only on the grounds that it is laborious, but much more importantly on the grounds that it has a good chance of leading to a false conclusion.

Let us consider seven samples taken from populations with identical means. If we were to test all possible pairs of samples for significant differences among their means, we would have to carry out the $t$-test on $C_{7,2} = 21$ pairs, for each of which the probability of arriving at the correct conclusion of no significant difference would be $0.95 = 19/20$ (assuming that we use the 5% level of significance). Consequently, the probability that we would arrive at the correct conclusion for all 21 pairs is $(19/20)^{21}$, which means that the probability of obtaining at least one incorrect conclusion is given by

$$1 - \left(\frac{19}{20}\right)^{21} = 1 - 0.340 = 0.660.$$

Thus, 66% of the time, we would be drawing a wrong conclusion, i.e., committing a type 1 error. Clearly a statistical test in which the probability of obtaining an incorrect conclusion is of such magnitude cannot be considered an acceptable test. For larger numbers of samples this probability would be still higher, and even for smaller numbers of samples it may be quite high. Thus, if only five samples were considered, it can easily be shown that we would be wrong 40.1% of the time by testing pairs of samples individually, assuming that they all came from populations with identical means.

It is therefore necessary to develop a different method, one which takes into consideration all the sample means together. This procedure is called the *analysis of variance* and is based on two principles:

1. The partitioning of the sum of squares.
2. The estimating of the standard deviation of the population by two methods and a comparison of these estimates.

These two principles will now be discussed separately.

## 17.2.   Partitioning of the Sum of Squares, Equal Sample Sizes

Consider $k$ samples, all of which have the same number of variates, say $n$. Denote the total of all variates in the first sample by $T_1$, the total of all variates in the second sample by $T_2$, and so on, and the total of all variates, or *grand total*, by $T$; similarly denote the mean of the first sample by $\overline{X}_1$, that of the second sample by $\overline{X}_2$, and so on, and the mean of all variates, or *grand mean*, by $\overline{X}$. Since in most practical applications with which we shall be concerned the various samples represent the results of different treatments which have been applied, we shall consider hereafter the term treatment as having the same meaning as sample. The notation applicable to this case is summarized in Table 17-1.

**TABLE 17-1.   The Case of $k$ Samples of $n$ Variates Each**

|  | 1st Sample or 1st Treatment | 2nd Sample or 2nd Treatment |  | kth Sample or kth Treatment |  |
|---|---|---|---|---|---|
|  | $X_{11}$ | $X_{12}$ | $\cdots$ | $X_{1k}$ |  |
|  | $X_{21}$ | $X_{22}$ | $\cdots$ | $X_{2k}$ |  |
|  | . | . |  | . |  |
|  | . | . |  | . |  |
|  | . | . |  | . |  |
|  | $X_{n1}$ | $X_{n2}$ | $\cdots$ | $X_{nk}$ |  |
| Total | $T_1$ | $T_2$ | $\cdots$ | $T_k$ | Grand Total $= T$ |
| Mean | $\overline{X}_1$ | $\overline{X}_2$ | $\cdots$ | $\overline{X}_k$ | Grand Mean $= \overline{X}$ |

In Table 17-1 we introduce double subscript notation. The first subscript identifies the particular variate within a sample, the second subscript the sample to which the variate belongs. Thus, $X_{21}$ denotes the second variate in the first sample, in general $X_{ij}$ the $i$th variate in the $j$th sample.

In order to explain the principle of the partitioning of the sum of squares it is necessary first to introduce a set of definitions.

DEFINITION 17-1.  The *total sum of squares* is defined as

(17-1) $$S.S. = \sum_{i=1}^{n} \sum_{j=1}^{k} (X_{ij} - \overline{X})^2.$$

The double sum appearing in (17-1) means that the sum is to be taken for all integral values of the first subscript from 1 to $n$ and all integral values of the second subscript from 1 to $k$. In other words, the total sum of squares is the sum of the squares of the deviations from the grand mean for all the variates; it is therefore a measure of the dispersion of all the variates about the grand mean.

DEFINITION 17-2.  The *between means* (or *among-means*) *sum of squares* (or *sum of squares for treatments*) is defined as

(17-2) $$S.S.T. = n \sum_{j=1}^{k} (\overline{X}_j - \overline{X})^2.$$

Since the sum appearing in (17-2) is the sum of the squares of the deviations of the sample (or treatment) means about the grand mean, $S.S.T.$ is a measure of the dispersion of the sample means about the grand mean. The less the sample means differ from each other, the smaller $S.S.T.$ will be. If, on the other hand, the treatments show widely differing effects, there will be a large difference among the sample means and consequently a large value of $S.S.T.$

DEFINITION 17-3.  The *within-samples sum of squares* (or *sum of squares for error*) is defined as

(17-3) $$S.S.E. = \sum_{i=1}^{n} (X_{i1} - \overline{X}_1)^2 + \sum_{i=1}^{n} (X_{i2} - \overline{X}_2)^2 + \cdots$$
$$+ \sum_{i=1}^{n} (X_{ik} - \overline{X}_k)^2$$
$$= \sum_{i=1}^{n} \sum_{j=1}^{k} (X_{ij} - \overline{X}_j)^2.$$

In the first of the $k$ sums appearing on the right-hand side of (17-3) the deviations are taken about the mean of the first sample; this term therefore represents a measure of the dispersion within the first sample. Similarly, the second term represents a measure of the dispersion within the second sample, and so on. Consequently, $S.S.E.$ is a measure of the dispersion of the variates within the samples about their respective sample means and is independent of any differences between sample means; its value depends only on the random changes occurring in almost any experiment and thus represents the experimental error of the experiment.

*Example 17-1.*   Consider the following five samples of three variates each:

|       | 3 | 5 | 7 | 6 | 4 |            |
|-------|---|---|---|---|---|------------|
|       | 2 | 8 | 8 | 8 | 9 |            |
|       | 4 | 8 | 6 | 7 | 5 |            |
| Total | 9 | 21 | 21 | 21 | 18 | $T = 90$ |
| Mean  | 3 | 7 | 7 | 7 | 6 | $\overline{X} = 6$ |

Calculate for these data the total sum of squares, the between-means sum of squares, and the within-samples sum of squares by use of the definitions of these quantities.

*Solution*

$$
\begin{aligned}
S.S. &= (3 - 6)^2 + (2 - 6)^2 + (4 - 6)^2 + (5 - 6)^2 + (8 - 6)^2 + \cdots \\
&\quad + (5 - 6)^2 = 9 + 16 + 4 + 1 + 4 \cdots + 1 = 62; \\
S.S.T. &= 3[(3 - 6)^2 + (7 - 6)^2 + (7 - 6)^2 + (7 - 6)^2 + (6 - 6)^2] \\
&= 3(9 + 1 + 1 + 1 + 0) = 36; \\
S.S.E. &= (3 - 3)^2 + (2 - 3)^2 + (4 - 3)^2 + (5 - 7)^2 + (8 - 7)^2 + (8 - 7)^2 \\
&\quad + \cdots + (5 - 6)^2 = 26.
\end{aligned}
$$

The procedure used to calculate $S.S.$, $S.S.T.$, and $S.S.E.$ in Example 17-1 is not the one commonly employed in practice since it is much easier to obtain these quantities, especially in machine calculations, by use of the following formulae, sometimes referred to as their computing forms:

$$(17\text{-}4) \qquad S.S. = \sum_{i=1}^{n} \sum_{j=1}^{k} X_{ij}^2 - \frac{T^2}{kn};$$

$$(17\text{-}5) \qquad S.S.T. = \frac{\sum_{j=1}^{k} T_j^2}{n} - \frac{T^2}{kn};$$

$$(17\text{-}6) \qquad S.S.E. = \sum_{i=1}^{n} \sum_{j=1}^{k} X_{ij}^2 - \frac{\sum_{j=1}^{k} T_j^2}{n}.$$

*Example 17-2.*   Calculate $S.S.$, $S.S.T.$, and $S.S.E.$ for the data of Example 17-1 by use of their computing forms.

$$S.S. = 3^2 + 2^2 + 4^2 + 5^2 + 8^2 + \cdots + 5^2 - \frac{8100}{15} = 602 - 540 = 62;$$

$$S.S.T. = \frac{9^2 + 21^2 + 21^2 + 21^2 + 18^2}{3} - \frac{8100}{15} = 576 - 540 = 36;$$

$$S.S.E. = 3^2 + 2^2 + 4^2 + 5^2 + 8^2 + \cdots + 5^2 - \frac{9^2 + 21^2 + 21^2 + 21^2 + 18^2}{3}$$

$$= 602 - 576 = 26.$$

*Proof of Formulae (17-4), (17-5), and (17-6).* All three formulae are consequences of the result of Example 3-4, namely that for a given set of $N$ numbers, whose mean is $m$,

$$(17\text{-}7) \qquad \sum_{i=1}^{N} (X_i - m)^2 = \sum_{i=1}^{N} X_i^2 - \frac{\left(\sum\limits_{i=1}^{N} X_i\right)^2}{N}.$$

For purposes of application, it is more convenient to state (17-7) in words: For a set of $N$ numbers $X_1, X_2, \cdots, X_N$, the sum of squares of the deviations from the mean equals the sum of the squares of these numbers minus $1/N$ times the square of the total of these numbers.

From Definition 17-1 we see that $S.S.$ represents the sum of the squares of the deviations of the $kn$ numbers $X_{11}, X_{21}, \cdots, X_{kn}$ from their mean; in accordance with the above statement this sum can be rewritten as the sum of the squares of these numbers minus $1/kn$ times $T^2$, the square of the total of these numbers. Formula (17-4) therefore follows from (17-1).

To prove (17-5) from (17-2) we apply (17-7) to the $k$ numbers $\overline{X}_1, \overline{X}_2, \cdots, \overline{X}_k$, whose mean is $\overline{X}$; (17-2) can then be written as

$$S.S.T. = n\left[\sum_{j=1}^{k} \overline{X}_j^2 - \frac{\left(\sum\limits_{j=1}^{k} \overline{X}_j\right)^2}{k}\right] = n\left[\sum_{j=1}^{k} \frac{T_j^2}{n^2} - \frac{\left(\sum\limits_{j=1}^{k} T_j\right)^2}{kn^2}\right] = \frac{\sum\limits_{j=1}^{k} T_j^2}{n} - \frac{T^2}{kn},$$

which proves (17-5).

To prove (17-6) we apply (17-7) to each of the $k$ sums appearing in (17-3) and obtain

$$S.S.E. = \sum_{i=1}^{n} X_{i1}^2 - \frac{\left(\sum\limits_{i=1}^{n} X_{i1}\right)^2}{n} + \sum_{i=1}^{n} X_{i2}^2 - \frac{\left(\sum\limits_{i=1}^{n} X_{i2}\right)^2}{n}$$

$$+ \cdots + \sum_{i=1}^{n} X_{ik}^2 - \frac{\left(\sum\limits_{i=1}^{n} X_{ik}\right)^2}{n}$$

$$= \sum_{i=1}^{n} \sum_{j=1}^{k} X_{ij}^2 - \frac{T_1^2}{n} - \frac{T_2^2}{n} - \cdots - \frac{T_k^2}{n} = \sum_{i=1}^{n} \sum_{j=1}^{k} X_{ij}^2 - \frac{\sum\limits_{j=1}^{k} T_j^2}{n}.$$

From the solution of Example 17-1 the reader may have observed that the sum of $S.S.T.$ and $S.S.E.$ equals $S.S.$, i.e., $36 + 26 = 62$, and he may wonder whether this property is true for any set of data. This indeed is the case, and it is the partitioning principle stated in Theorem 17-1.

**THEOREM 17-1.** The total sum of squares for a set of variates as shown in Table 17-1 is equal to the sum of the between-means sum of squares and the within-samples sum of squares, or

$$(17\text{-}8) \qquad\qquad S.S. = S.S.T. + S.S.E.$$

This means that we can always partition the total dispersion in such a set of data into two components, one due to the dispersion existing between the sample means, the other due to the dispersion existing within the samples.

*Proof of Theorem 17-1.* Formula (17-8) is immediately seen to be true if we add the expressions for $S.S.T.$ and $S.S.E.$ as given by (17-5) and (17-6), respectively, and obtain

$$S.S.T. + S.S.E. = \frac{\sum\limits_{j=1}^{k} T_j^2}{n} - \frac{T^2}{kn} + \sum\limits_{i=1}^{n}\sum\limits_{j=1}^{k} X_{ij}^2 - \frac{\sum\limits_{j=1}^{k} T_j^2}{n}$$

$$= \sum\limits_{i=1}^{n}\sum\limits_{j=1}^{k} X_{ij}^2 - \frac{T^2}{kn} = S.S.$$

From (17-1) we see that if $\overline{X} = 0$, then $S.S.$ reduces to $\sum\limits_{i=1}^{n}\sum\limits_{j=1}^{k} X_{ij}^2$, i.e., the first term appearing on the right-hand side of (17-4). Thus, the term $T^2/kn$ corrects for the fact that the sum of squares is required about the grand mean $\overline{X}$ and not about 0. This results in Definition 17-4.

**DEFINITION 17-4.** The *correction term* for a set of variates as shown in Table 17-1 is defined as

$$(17\text{-}9) \qquad\qquad C = \frac{T^2}{kn}.$$

## 17.3.  Partitioning of the Sum of Squares, Unequal Sample Sizes

The case where the various samples do not all have the same number of variates arises less frequently and will therefore be discussed only briefly. Again let us consider $k$ samples, but now with $n_1$ variates in the first sample, $n_2$ variates in the second sample, and so on; the meaning of $T_1, T_2, \cdots, T_k$,

$T, \overline{X}_1, \overline{X}_2, \cdots, \overline{X}_k, \overline{X}$ will be the same as before. The notation for this case is summarized in Table 17-2.

TABLE 17-2. The Case of $k$ Samples with $n_1, n_2, \cdots, n_k$ Variates, Respectively.

|  | 1st Sample or 1st Treatment | 2nd Sample or 2nd Treatment |  | kth Sample or kth Treatment |  |
|---|---|---|---|---|---|
|  | $X_{11}$ | $X_{12}$ | $\cdots$ | $X_{1n}$ |  |
|  | $X_{21}$ | $X_{22}$ | $\cdots$ | $X_{2n}$ |  |
|  | . | . |  | . |  |
|  | . | . |  | . |  |
|  | . | . |  | . |  |
|  | $X_{n_1,1}$ | $X_{n_2,2}$ | $\cdots$ | $X_{n_k,n}$ |  |
| Total | $T_1$ | $T_2$ | $\cdots$ | $T_k$ | Grand Total $= T$ |
| Mean | $\overline{X}_1$ | $\overline{X}_2$ | $\cdots$ | $\overline{X}_k$ | Grand Mean $= \overline{X}$ |

The reader should not be deceived by the appearance of equal length of all columns; this was done for conciseness in presenting the table. In any actual case of unequal number of variates the columns would be of unequal lengths; for a numerical case see Table 17-6, where $n_1 = 6$, $n_2 = 4$, $n_3 = 5$, $n_4 = 4$.

The expressions defined by (17-1), (17-2), and (17-3) need be modified very slightly to apply to an unequal number of variates. Here the definitions take the following forms:

(17-10)    $S.S. = \sum_{i=1}^{n_1} (X_{i1} - \overline{X})^2 + \sum_{i=1}^{n_2} (X_{i2} - \overline{X})^2 + \cdots + \sum_{i=1}^{n_k} (X_{ik} - \overline{X})^2.$

(17-11)   $S.S.T. = n_1(\overline{X}_1 - \overline{X})^2 + n_2(\overline{X}_2 - \overline{X})^2 + \cdots + n_k(\overline{X}_k - \overline{X})^2.$

(17-12)   $S.S.E. = \sum_{i=1}^{n_1} (X_{i1} - \overline{X}_1)^2 + \sum_{i=1}^{n_2} (X_{i2} - \overline{X}_2)^2 + \cdots + \sum_{i=1}^{n_k} (X_{ik} - \overline{X}_k)^2.$

Clearly, the interpretations of (17-10), (17-11), and (17-12) are identical to those for (17-1), (17-2), and (17-3). Also, each of the above expressions again can be written in a form suitable for machine calculation. This results in the following formulae:

(17-13)      $S.S. = \sum_{i=1}^{n_1} X_{i1}^2 + \sum_{i=1}^{n_2} X_{i2}^2 + \cdots + \sum_{i=1}^{n_k} X_{ik}^2 - \dfrac{T^2}{n_1 + n_2 + \cdots + n_k}.$

(17-14)    $S.S.T. = \dfrac{T_1^2}{n_1} + \dfrac{T_2^2}{n_2} + \cdots + \dfrac{T_k^2}{n_k} - \dfrac{T^2}{n_1 + n_2 + \cdots + n_k}.$

(17-15)

$$S.S.E. = \sum_{i=1}^{n_1} X_{i1}^2 + \sum_{i=1}^{n_2} X_{i2}^2 + \cdots + \sum_{i=1}^{n_k} X_{ik}^2 - \left( \dfrac{T_1^2}{n_1} + \dfrac{T_2^2}{n_2} + \cdots + \dfrac{T_k^2}{n_k} \right).$$

The proofs of the above three formulae are so similar to those of formulae (17-4), (17-5), and (17-6) that they will be left as an exercise for the student (see Exercise 6).

Similarly, it is obvious that the principle of the partitioning of the sum of squares holds also here, since the sum of (17-14) and (17-15) equals that of (17-13). We thus have the following theorem, which is completely analogous to Theorem 17-1.

> **THEOREM 17-2.** The total sum of squares for a set of variates as shown in Table 17-2 is equal to the sum of the between-means sum of squares and the within-samples sum of squares.

As before, the second term appearing on the right-hand sides of both (17-13) and (17-14) is referred to as the correction term.

## 17.4.   Comparison of Variances in Analysis of Variance Table, Equal Sample Sizes

Considering again $k$ samples of $n$ variates each, i.e., the situation of Table 17-1, we make the hypothesis that all of the $k$ samples are taken from the same population. We then can estimate the variance of that population, $\sigma^2$, in two ways:

1. We can estimate $\sigma^2$ by pooling the variates of the $k$ samples by a generalization of the procedure used for two samples where we applied formula (10-7). The numerator then becomes the sum of the squares of the deviations of the variates of all $k$ samples from their respective sample means and the denominator $n_1 + n_2 + \cdots + n_k - k$, or, since all samples are assumed to have the same number of variates, $n$, we have for the denominator $kn - k = k(n-1)$, so that we obtain the following best estimate of $\sigma^2$ by pooling the sums of the squares of the deviations:

$$(17\text{-}16) \qquad s_p^2 = \frac{\sum\limits_{i=1}^{n}(X_{i1}-\overline{X}_1)^2 + \sum\limits_{i=1}^{n}(X_{i2}-\overline{X}_2)^2 + \cdots + \sum\limits_{i=1}^{n}(X_{ik}-\overline{X}_k)^2}{k(n-1)}.$$

We use the subscript $p$ in $s_p^2$ to indicate that this estimate was obtained by pooling the sums of the squares of the deviations.

Since the numerator of the fraction appearing in (17-16) equals $S.S.E.$ we can rewrite (17-16) as

$$(17\text{-}17) \qquad\qquad\qquad s_p^2 = \frac{S.S.E.}{k(n-1)}.$$

2. Another estimate of $\sigma^2$ can be obtained by estimating first the variance of the sample means, $\sigma_{\bar{x}}^2$. An estimate of $\sigma_{\bar{x}}^2$ can be obtained by considering $\bar{X}_1, \bar{X}_2, \cdots, \bar{X}_k$ as a sample of all possible treatment means. From formula (10-2) we have

$$(17\text{-}18) \qquad s_{\bar{x}}^2 = \frac{\sum\limits_{j=1}^{k} (\bar{X}_j - \bar{X})^2}{k-1}.$$

But, since $\sigma_{\bar{x}}^2 = \sigma^2/n$, or $\sigma^2 = n\sigma_{\bar{x}}^2$, we have a second estimate of $\sigma^2$ from the sample (or treatment) means, which we shall denote by $s_t^2$ (since it was obtained by use of the treatment means), which is given by

$$(17\text{-}19) \qquad s_t^2 = ns_{\bar{x}}^2 = \frac{n \sum\limits_{j=1}^{k} (\bar{X}_j - \bar{X})^2}{k-1}.$$

Since the numerator of the fraction appearing in (17-19) equals $S.S.T.$, we can rewrite (17-19) as

$$(17\text{-}20) \qquad s_t^2 = \frac{S.S.T.}{k-1}.$$

The analysis of variance procedure consists in comparing these two estimates of $\sigma^2$. Since both quantities represent estimates of the same variance $\sigma^2$, their ratio should not differ significantly from 1. More precisely, the following can be proved: If repeatedly $k$ samples of $n$ variates each are taken from a population and for each of these sets of $k$ samples the ratio $s_t^2/s_p^2$ is calculated, these ratios satisfy the $F$-distribution which results in the following theorem.

**THEOREM 17-3.** If all possible sets of $k$ samples of $n$ variates each are taken from a normally distributed population, then the quantity

$$(17\text{-}21) \qquad F = \frac{s_t^2}{s_p^2},$$

where $s_p^2$ and $s_t^2$ are given by (17-17) and (17-20), respectively, satisfy the $F$-distribution with $\nu_1 = k - 1$ and $\nu_2 = k(n-1)$.

It is important to note that the sum of the numbers of degrees of freedom associated with $s_t^2$, i.e., $k - 1$, and with $s_p^2$, i.e., $k(n-1)$, add up to $k - 1 + k(n-1) = kn - 1$, which is the number of degrees of freedom associated with the total number of variates. Consequently, there is not only a partitioning principle for the sum of squares, but also for the degrees of freedom.

If now our hypothesis fails to be true, i.e., if the $k$ samples are in fact taken from populations with different means, then $s_t^2$ will be considerably greater than $s_p^2$, owing to the wider dispersion of the sample means about the grand mean. If $s_t^2$ is so large that in comparison with $s_p^2$ it yields an $F$-value exceeding $F_{.95}$, we consider the sample means significantly different and conclude that there must be at least one pair of samples whose means differ significantly. It should be carefully observed that a significant result can occur only if $s_t^2$ exceeds $s_p^2$, i.e., if $F$, as defined by (17-21), exceeds 1; thus, a one-tailed test must always be used in the analysis of variance. Whenever $s_t^2$ is less than or equal to $s_p^2$, the result is never considered significant; the dispersion of the sample means about the grand mean would be no more than that expected ordinarily from a set of $k$ samples, all of which were taken from the same population. Thus, whenever $s_t^2 \leq s_p^2$, it is unnecessary to calculate an $F$-value, since it obviously would be insignificant.

The use of the analysis of variance in testing for significant differences between sample means requires, therefore, the calculation of $s_p^2$ and $s_t^2$ and the determination, on the basis of a one-tailed test, whether their ratio is significantly different from 1. This calculation is most conveniently performed in the following sequence of steps.

Step 1.   Find $C = \dfrac{T^2}{kn}$;

Step 2.   Find $S.S. = \sum\limits_{i=1}^{n} \sum\limits_{j=1}^{k} X_{ij}^2 - C$;

Step 3.   Find $S.S.T. = \dfrac{\sum\limits_{j=1}^{k} T_j^2}{n} - C$;

Step 4.   Find $S.S.E. = S.S. - S.S.T.$;

Step 5.   Find $d.f.$ associated with each of the above expressions;

Step 6.   Find $s_t^2 = \dfrac{S.S.T.}{k-1}$;

Step 7.   Find $s_p^2 = \dfrac{S.S.E.}{k(n-1)}$;

Step 8.   Find $F = \dfrac{s_t^2}{s_p^2}$;

Step 9.   Find $F_{.95}$, the tabular $F$-value for $\nu_1 = k-1$ and $\nu_2 = k(n-1)$, and compare with the $F$-value obtained in step 8.

It is customary to summarize these calculations in a so-called analysis of variance table as shown in Table 17-3.

*Example 17-3.*   On the basis of the 5% level of significance, are there significant differences between the means of the five samples given in Table 17-4?

**TABLE 17-3.** Analysis of Variance Table for Equal Sample Sizes

| Source of Variation | Sum of Squares | d.f. | Mean Square | F | $F_{.95}$ |
|---|---|---|---|---|---|
| Total | $S.S. = \sum\limits_{i=1}^{n} \sum\limits_{j=1}^{k} X_{ij}^2 - C$ | $kn - 1$ | | | |
| Between-means (or treatments) | $S.S.T. = \dfrac{\sum\limits_{j=1}^{k} T_j^2}{n} - C$ | $k - 1$ | $s_t^2 = \dfrac{S.S.T.}{k - 1}$ | $\dfrac{s_t^2}{s_p^2}$ | Tabula value |
| Within-samples (or error) | $S.S.E. = S.S. - S.S.T.$ | $k(n - 1)$ | $s_p^2 = \dfrac{S.S.E.}{k(n - 1)}$ | | |

**TABLE 17-4.** An Experiment with Five Samples of Four Variates Each

| | | Sample (or Treatment) | | | | | |
|---|---|---|---|---|---|---|---|
| | | A | B | C | D | E | |
| | | 10 | 12 | 9 | 14 | 10 | |
| | | 4 | 10 | 4 | 9 | 6 | |
| | | 6 | 13 | 4 | 10 | 8 | |
| | | 4 | 7 | 5 | 11 | 4 | |
| Total | | 24 | 42 | 22 | 44 | 28 | Grand Total = 160 |
| Mean | | 6.0 | 10.5 | 5.5 | 11.0 | 7.0 | Grand Mean = 8.0 |

*Solution.* Following the suggested procedure, we find

1. $C = \dfrac{160^2}{20} = 1280;$

2. $S.S. = 10^2 + 4^2 + \cdots + 4^2 - C = 1482 - 1280 = 202;$

3. $S.S.T. = \dfrac{24^2 + 42^2 + \cdots + 28^2}{4} - C = 1386 - 1280 = 106;$

4. $S.S.E. = 202 - 106 = 96.$

The results can now be entered into an analysis of variance table (see Table 17-5) and the remaining calculations completed in the table.

**TABLE 17-5.** Analysis of Variance Table for the Data of Table 17-4

| Source of Variation | Sum of Squares | d.f. | Mean Square | F | $F_{.95}$ |
|---|---|---|---|---|---|
| Total | 202 | 19 | | | |
| Between-means (or treatments) | 106 | 4 | 26.5 | 4.14 | 3.06 |
| Within-samples (or error) | 96 | 15 | 6.4 | | |

Since the calculated $F$-value of 4.14 exceeds the tabular value of $F_{.95}$ for $\nu_1 = 4$, $\nu_2 = 15$, we conclude that the hypothesis that all of the given samples were taken from the same population is not justified at the 5% level of significance; thus, there is at least one pair of samples whose means differ significantly. Since, however, $F_{.99}(4, 15) = 4.89$, the differences in means are not highly significant. A further question which arises is the problem of deciding which pairs of samples of Table 17-4 have significantly different means. This can be answered quite easily by a method to be shown in Section 17-5.

## 17.5.  The Least Significant Difference

If the $F$-ratio indicates significant differences between sample means, it becomes important to determine which means cause the significance. A simple procedure to answer this question is available for the case of equal sample sizes. It is based on the following definition.

DEFINITION 17-5.  For a set of $k$ samples of $n$ variates each, showing significant differences between sample means as indicated by the $F$-value in the analysis of variance, the *least significant difference*, denoted by *L.S.D.*, is defined as the smallest difference which could exist between two significantly different sample means.

A formula for the *L.S.D.* is easily derived. Let $\bar{X}_1$ and $\bar{X}_2$ be any two sample means (not necessarily the first two sample means), then by Chapter 10, $\bar{X}_1$ and $\bar{X}_2$ differ significantly—see formula (10-8)—if

$$t = \frac{\bar{X}_1 - \bar{X}_2}{s_{\bar{x}_1 - \bar{x}_2}}$$

exceeds $t_{.05}$ (assuming the 5% level of significance). Thus, the *L.S.D.* is the difference between two sample means, $\bar{X}_1 - \bar{X}_2$, for which $t = t_{.05}$, i.e.,

$$L.S.D. = t_{.05} s_{\bar{x}_1 - \bar{x}_2}.$$

But, from Chapter 10, for $n_1 = n_2 = n$,

$$s_{\bar{x}_1 - \bar{x}_2} = \sqrt{s_{\bar{x}_1}^2 + s_{\bar{x}_2}^2} = \sqrt{\frac{s^2}{n} + \frac{s^2}{n}} = \sqrt{\frac{2s^2}{n}},$$

where $s$ equals $s_p$ as defined by (17-16). From here on we shall omit the subscript $p$ and understand $s$ to equal $s_p$. The formula for the *L.S.D.*, the least significant difference, then becomes

(17-22)
$$L.S.D. = t_{.05} \sqrt{\frac{2s^2}{n}},$$

where $t_{.05}$ is the tabular value of $t$ at the 5% level for the number of degrees of freedom, on which $s$ is based, which according to (17-16) equals $k(n-1)$.

*Example 17-4.* On the basis of the 5% level of significance, which of the pairs of samples in Example 17-3 differ significantly in their means?

*Solution.* From (17-22) we find the least significant difference to be

$$L.S.D. = 2.131 \sqrt{\frac{2(6.4)}{4}}$$
$$= 3.812,$$

since $s^2 = 6.4$ from Table 17-5 and $t_{.05} = 2.131$ for $\nu = 15$. Thus, a look at Table 17-4 shows that the first two sample means differ significantly, since $\overline{X}_1 - \overline{X}_2 = 4.5$ exceeds 3.812. A complete investigation of all possible pairs reveals that for the following pairs the sample means differ significantly: $AB$, $AD$, $BC$, $CD$, $DE$.

It is important to realize that the formula for the *L.S.D.* should never be used when the $F$-value obtained in the analysis of variance is not significant. It is entirely possible—and even very likely—that if the formula for the *L.S.D.* is mistakenly used in a situation where the $F$-value is insignificant, some differences between sample means will exceed the *L.S.D.* In such situations we could not call these differences significant, but would have to regard them as the kind of large differences expected to occur in samples from populations with identical means.

Use of the *L.S.D.* has the advantage that for the special case of two samples its use will always result in precisely the same conclusion as obtained in a Student $t$-test (see Section 17.7). If, however, the analysis of variance involves more than two samples, it is clear that the two extreme means differ more widely just by chance alone than do other means. Consequently, the value given by the usual formula for an *L.S.D.* is too small to compare such two extreme means.

Two possible solutions suggest themselves to resolve this difficulty:

1. Increase the size of the *L.S.D.* so that all possible pairs of treatment means are compared with a fixed value which exceeds that given by the *L.S.D.*

2. Use different significant values (called *multiple ranges*) depending on the number of means which are compared.

The type of test resulting from the first solution is usually referred to as a *fixed range test* since only one range is used for all possible comparisons. The disadvantage of such a test is evident: Two adjacent means which by the ordinary *L.S.D.* test would be called significantly different might not appear significantly different when compared to a somewhat larger range. Thus, the chance of accepting an incorrect hypothesis, or committing a type 2 error, has been increased for two adjacent means while, on the other hand, the chance of rejecting a correct hypothesis, or committing a type 1 error, has been decreased for nonadjacent means. Tests of this type have been given by Fisher in 1935 and Tukey in 1952.

Tests of the type suggested by the second solution are referred to as *multiple range tests*. The first such test was proposed by Newman in 1939 and was modified slightly by Keuls in 1952. Tukey proposed a test in 1953 which can be considered a compromise between the Newman-Keuls test and the earlier test proposed by Tukey. Finally in 1953 and 1955 Duncan proposed a test making use of so-called special *protection levels* based upon degrees of freedom. Though it might be too early to judge at this time which of these tests will ultimately have the widest appeal, it seems that Duncan's test, as proposed in 1955, appears to have the best chance of becoming generally adopted. Indeed, much evidence is available that this test, referred to as *Duncan's multiple range test*, is used extensively both in this and other countries. For an explanation of this test the reader is referred to Duncan's paper "Multiple range and multiple *F*-tests," *Biometrics*, 11, 1–42, 1955.

## 17.6. Comparison of Variances in Analysis of Variance Table, Unequal Sample Sizes

Modifications necessary in the formulae developed for equal numbers of variates are very minor if unequal numbers of variates are involved. Consider again the case where the first sample has $n_1$ variates, the second $n_2$ variates, and so on, i.e., the situation of Table 17-2. The two estimates of the variance of the population, $\sigma^2$, then take the following forms:

$$(17\text{-}23) \quad s_p^2 = \frac{\sum\limits_{i=1}^{n_1} (X_{i1} - \overline{X}_1)^2 + \sum\limits_{i=1}^{n_2} (X_{i2} - \overline{X}_2)^2 + \cdots + \sum\limits_{i=1}^{n_k} (X_{ik} - \overline{X}_k)^2}{n_1 + n_2 + \cdots + n_k - k}$$

$$= \frac{S.S.E.}{n_1 + n_2 + \cdots + n_k - k},$$

$$(17\text{-}24) \quad s_t^2 = \frac{n_1(\overline{X}_1 - \overline{X})^2 + n_2(\overline{X}_2 - \overline{X})^2 + \cdots + n_k(\overline{X}_k - \overline{X})^2}{k - 1} = \frac{S.S.T.}{k - 1}.$$

Theorem 17-3 can then be restated for the case of unequal numbers of variates.

**THEOREM 17-4.** If all possible sets of $k$ samples of $n_1, n_2, \cdots, n_k$ variates, respectively, are taken from a normally distributed population, then the quantity

$$F = \frac{s_t^2}{s_p^2},$$

where $s_p^2$ and $s_t^2$ are given by (17-23) and (17-24), respectively, satisfies the $F$-distribution with $\nu_1 = k - 1$ and $\nu_2 = n_1 + n_2 + \cdots + n_k - k$.

It should be noted that again there is also a partitioning principle for the numbers of degrees of freedom in that the sum of the numbers of degrees of freedom $k - 1$ and $n_1 + n_2 + \cdots + n_k - k$, associated with $s_t^2$ and $s_p^2$, respectively, add up to $k - 1 + n_1 + n_2 + \cdots + n_k - k = n_1 + n_2 + \cdots + n_k - 1$, the number of degrees of freedom associated with the total number of variates.

The calculations necessary to obtain the $F$-value are again best arranged in a sequence of steps which are analogous to those listed for equal sample sizes and which can be summarized in an analysis of variance table similar to Table 17-3, but modified in accordance with the slightly different formulae for the sums of squares and degrees of freedom.

*Example 17-5.* Are there significant differences between the means of the four samples given in Table 17-6 on the basis of the 5% level of significance?

TABLE 17-6. An Experiment with Four Samples of Unequal Sizes.

| | Sample (or Treatment) | | | | |
|---|---|---|---|---|---|
| | A | B | C | D | |
| | 12 | 12 | 9 | 12 | |
| | 10 | 16 | 7 | 8 | |
| | 7 | 15 | 6 | 8 | |
| | 8 | 9 | 11 | 10 | |
| | 9 | | 7 | | |
| | 14 | | | | |
| Total | 60 | 52 | 40 | 38 | Grand Total = 190 |
| Mean | 10.0 | 13.0 | 8.0 | 9.5 | Grand Mean = 10.0 |

*Solution.* Following the suggested procedure outlined for equal numbers of variates with the necessary modifications, we find

1. $C = \dfrac{190^2}{19} = 1900;$

2. $S.S. = 12^2 + 10^2 + \cdots + 10^2 - C = 2048 - 1900 = 148;$

3. $S.S.T. = \dfrac{60^2}{6} + \dfrac{52^2}{4} + \dfrac{40^2}{5} + \dfrac{38^2}{4} - C = 1957 - 1900 = 57;$

4. $S.S.E. = 148 - 57 = 91.$

These results and the remaining calculations necessary to arrive at the required $F$-value are shown in Table 17-7.

**TABLE 17-7.** Analysis of Variance Table for the Data of Table 17-6

| Source of Variation | Sum of Squares | d.f. | Mean Square | F | F.95 |
|---|---|---|---|---|---|
| Total | 148 | 18 | | | |
| Between-means (or treatments) | 57 | 3 | 19.0 | 3.13 | 3.29 |
| Within-samples (or error) | 91 | 15 | 6.07 | | |

Since the $F$-value of 3.13 is less than the tabular value of $F_{.95}$ for $\nu_1 = 3$, $\nu_2 = 15$, assuming the 5% level of significance, we accept the hypothesis that all of the given samples are taken from the same population.

Whenever unequal numbers of variates occur in the samples and the $F$-value indicates significance, there is no simple way to decide which pairs of sample means differ significantly. We must test all possible pairs individually by means of the $t$-test, as shown in Chapter 10, using each time the appropriate number of variates for the samples being compared.

## 17.7.   The Special Case of Two Samples

Clearly, the analysis of variance for two samples, whose variates are not paired, must lead to conclusions identical with those of the $t$-test of Chapter 10. This will be shown for equal numbers of variates. The case where the two samples have unequal numbers of variates is left as an exercise (see Exercise 12).

For $k = 2$ we must show that the $F$-ratio as given by (17-21) reduces to the square of the $t$-value as given by formula (10-8). This follows from Theorem 16-2, since, if we let $F = t^2$, where $t$ satisfies the $t$-distribution, then $F$ must satisfy the $F$-distribution with $\nu_1 = 1$. Of course, for this case in formula (10-8) $n_1 = n_2 = n$ and $m_{\bar{x}-\bar{y}} = 0$, and we must replace $\bar{X}$ by $\bar{X}_1$ and $\bar{Y}$ by $\bar{X}_2$. Formula (10-8) then takes the form

$$(17\text{-}25) \qquad t = \frac{\bar{X}_1 - \bar{X}_2}{\sqrt{s_{\bar{x}_1}^2 + s_{\bar{x}_2}^2}} = \frac{\bar{X}_1 - \bar{X}_2}{\sqrt{\dfrac{s^2}{n} + \dfrac{s^2}{n}}} = \frac{\bar{X}_1 - \bar{X}_2}{\sqrt{\dfrac{2s^2}{n}}},$$

where

$$(17\text{-}26) \qquad s^2 = \frac{\displaystyle\sum_{i=1}^{n}(X_{i1} - \bar{X}_1)^2 + \sum_{i=1}^{n}(X_{i2} - \bar{X}_2)^2}{2(n-1)}.$$

Now for $k = 2$ formula (17-16) reduces also to (17-26), while (17-19) becomes

$$s_t^2 = n[(\bar{X}_1 - \bar{X})^2 + (\bar{X}_2 - \bar{X})^2]$$
$$= n\left[\left(\bar{X}_1 - \frac{\bar{X}_1 + \bar{X}_2}{2}\right)^2 + \left(\bar{X}_2 - \frac{\bar{X}_1 + \bar{X}_2}{2}\right)^2\right] = \frac{n}{2}(\bar{X}_1 - \bar{X}_2)^2,$$

and the $F$-ratio of (17-21) takes the form

$$(17\text{-}27) \qquad\qquad F = \frac{\frac{n}{2}(\bar{X}_1 - \bar{X}_2)^2}{s^2} = \frac{(\bar{X}_1 - \bar{X}_2)^2}{\frac{2s^2}{n}},$$

which is the square of the $t$-value given by (17-25).

No numerical example of the analysis of variance for the case of two samples need be carried out here since it is just a special case of the procedure already discussed. However, the reader is asked, in exercise 11, to set up an analysis of variance table for Example 10-4.

The analysis of variance as discussed in this chapter can therefore be considered as a generalization of the procedure for testing two samples for significant differences between their means when the variates are not paired. We have consistently assumed here—although we did not say so explicitly each time—that the variates were not paired or that there was no other common criterion of classification between them. We assumed that the variates were classified only according to the samples or treatments to which they belonged or that there was only one criterion of classification, namely the treatments.

DEFINITION 17-6. A design in which there is only one criterion of classification for the variates—namely the treatments—is called a *completely randomized design*.

## 17.8. Assumptions Made in the Analysis of Variance with One Criterion of Classification

In discussing the procedures of this chapter various assumptions were stated which have to be satisfied to allow use of the analysis of variance. It may be well, however, to write these assumptions in a more concise way by means of a so-called *model*, which is a formula expressing the hypotheses in terms of an equation.

For the analysis of variance with one criterion of classification the model can be stated by the formula

(17-28) $$X_{ij} = m + \tau_j + \epsilon_{ij},$$

where

$X_{ij}$ = the $i$th variate in the $j$th sample,
$m$ = the population grand mean,
$\tau_j$ = the differential effect of the $j$th treatment over the mean $m$,
$\epsilon_{ij}$ = the random sampling effect, also called *residual*.

It is further assumed that

(17-29) $$\sum_{j=1}^{n} \tau_j = 0,$$

i.e., that the sum of all treatment effects equals zero, and that the $\epsilon_{ij}$ satisfy a normal distribution with mean 0 and standard deviation $\sigma$.

If we consider a common application of the analysis of variance, where the $X_{ij}$ represent crop yields of plots under various treatments, each plot yield, by hypothesis, would be the sum of the overall mean yield, the effect due to the particular treatment, and the unexplainable effects caused by random factors, or

Plot Yield = Overall Mean + Treatment Effect + Error.

The model, as given by (17-28), automatically implies that we assume the effect, if any, of each of the various treatments to be such that a certain fixed amount is added to the overall mean, or that the treatments have additive effects. If, on the other hand, the data clearly indicate that the effects are in fact not additive, the analysis of variance procedure, as outlined in this chapter, must be modified. When the effects are multiplicative the difficulty can easily be overcome by considering the logarithms of the $X_{ij}$ instead of the $X_{ij}$ themselves; clearly, under the hypothesis of multiplicative effects in the $X_{ij}$ there will be additive effects in the log $X_{ij}$, and the analysis of variance can be applied to the latter. In most nonadditive cases, however, other than the multiplicative one, the assumption of additive effects serves as an excellent approximation to the actual case. Indeed, whenever the largest sample mean is less than 50% greater than the smallest, the assumption of additivity can safely be made.

The reader will recall that the use of the $F$-test in the analysis of variance also requires that all samples be taken from the same normal population or, which is equivalent, that all samples belong to normal populations, all of which have identical standard deviations. A procedure for testing the homogeneity of two variances was given in Chapter 16; procedures for testing the homogeneity of more than two variances are also available, but are not discussed in this text. One of the more frequently used tests of this type is *Bartlett's test of homogeneity of variances*. If a large number of variates is available, the normality of the samples can be tested by the procedure shown in Section 13.5. Study has shown, however, that for cases showing only minor departures from the assumptions of equal variances and normal distributions the analysis of variance procedure still gives quite adequate results.

It should be noted carefully that the model, as given by (17-28), does not allow for any effects such as those present in the case of pairing of two samples or, more generally, effects which are common to specific variates of all samples. In such cases a second criterion of classification is present. This occurs, for example, in field trials where the yields of a crop under different conditions are to be tested. In that case, land is usually laid out in blocks, each block being subdivided into as many plots as there are treatments to be studied. In such an arrangement, called a *randomized complete-block experiment*, since each treatment has to appear in every block, all samples must be of equal size. Clearly, in the randomized complete-block experiment the chance that certain treatments are given only to low-yielding soils, while others are given only to high-yielding soils, is considerably smaller than for a completely randomized arrangement as discussed in this chapter.

Though the term randomized complete-block is obviously named after its most frequent application, the field trial, it is always applied whenever a set of variates is classified according to two criteria of classification, even though one criterion is not a "block" in the literal sense of the word. Thus, a feeding experiment to determine the effects of various diets is frequently performed by giving to a certain number of groups of animals each of the diets to be studied since the animals in each group can be kept under more uniform conditions than could the large number of animals under study in all the groups. Here each group is considered a "block."

In a study of comparison of prices in various types of stores (supermarkets, chain stores, small independent stores, and so on), an economist undoubtedly would select in various towns one of each of these types of stores. The "treatments" would be the types of store, the "blocks" the various towns.

The analysis of a randomized complete-block experiment is quite similar to the procedure discussed in this chapter for a design with one criterion of classification. The only modification necessary is to take account of the variation between block means. This is necessary both in the partitioning of the sum of squares and in the analysis of variance table, but a discussion will not be given.

## 17.9.  Transformations

Assumptions made in the use of the analysis of variance have already been discussed. Valid tests of significance require that the treatment and environmental effects be additive and that the experimental errors be independent, have equal variance, and be normally distributed. Departure from any of these assumptions results in actual probabilities different from those found by means of the $F$-distribution. Fortunately, the measurements in much experimental work conform sufficiently well to these assumptions that the resulting analysis of variance leads to valid conclusions. It is not unusual, however, to encounter samples from populations in which one or more of the assumptions is violated. In such cases, the experimenter can resort to non-parametric methods, or he may change the scale of measurement by means of a transformation. Transformations are also used to convert to a more workable scale data which are not recorded in a form very suitable for statistical analysis. An example of this was encountered in Chapter 12 where, in order to apply a test of significance involving a well-known distribution, the coefficient of correlation, $r$, was transformed into

$$Z = \tfrac{1}{2} \log_e \frac{1 + r}{1 - r},$$

which had an approximately normal distribution and a variance dependent only on the sample size.

Since nonnormality, nonadditivity, and heterogeneity of variance frequently occur together, often a single transformation which corrects one of these will, at the same time, result in improvements in the others. Sometimes it is found that a definite relationship exists between the treatment means and the corresponding treatment variances. In such cases, it is often possible to make a simple transformation of the data which will make the variance homogeneous and independent of the means and will result in more normally distributed data for each of the treatments. It should be pointed out, however, that, after a test or comparison has been made on the basis of transformed data, retransformation to the original units is often necessary for interpretable information.

The more common transformations are the square root, logarithmic, reciprocal, and angular or inverse sine transformations.

## 17.9.1. The Square Root Transformation, $\sqrt{X}$.

If data consist of small whole numbers, for which the treatment mean and variance are proportional (or possibly even equal, as in a Poisson distribution), each of the original observations should be replaced by its square root before proceeding with the analysis of variance. Bacterial colonies in a plate count or the number of plants or insects in a given area lead to data of this kind. If some of the counts are small (under 10) and especially when zeros are present, $\sqrt{X + 0.5}$ is the appropriate transformation. The square root transformation may also be used for data expressed as proportions or percentages where the range is from 0 to 20 or 80 to 100 but not both. Percentages between 80 and 100 should be subtracted from 100 before applying the transformation.

*Example 17-6.* Table 17.8 shows weed counts for five treatments on five plots each to control weed infestation. Compare the means and variances for each treatment with counts in the original form and after applying the square root transformation.

**TABLE 17-8.** Comparison of Weed Counts as Observed and After Applying the Square Root Transformation.

| | Original Data | | | | | Transformed Data | | | | |
|---|---|---|---|---|---|---|---|---|---|---|
| | Treatment | | | | | Treatment | | | | |
| | A | B | C | D | E | A | B | C | D | E |
| | 28 | 7 | 6 | 177 | 184 | 5.3 | 2.6 | 2.4 | 13.3 | 13.6 |
| | 22 | 11 | 9 | 151 | 146 | 4.7 | 3.3 | 3.0 | 12.3 | 12.1 |
| | 54 | 30 | 26 | 110 | 131 | 7.3 | 5.5 | 5.1 | 10.5 | 11.4 |
| | 19 | 6 | 7 | 117 | 110 | 4.4 | 2.4 | 2.6 | 10.8 | 10.5 |
| | 32 | 11 | 7 | 135 | 134 | 5.7 | 3.3 | 2.6 | 11.6 | 11.6 |
| Mean | 31 | 13 | 11 | 138 | 141 | 5.48 | 3.42 | 3.14 | 11.70 | 11.84 |
| Variance | 152.8 | 76.4 | 57.2 | 584.8 | 596.8 | 1.03 | 1.21 | 1.00 | 1.04 | 1.04 |

*Solution.* From the data in their original form it is apparent that the rank order of the means and variances is identical, indicating that the two are correlated. Consequently, we apply the square root transformation and note that there no longer is a correlation between the means and variances of the treatments.

If the error mean square were calculated for the data in its original form, it would be, on the average, too small for comparing treatments $D$ and $E$, and too large for comparing $A$, $B$, and $C$. This difficulty is eliminated by the transformation. The analysis of variance can now be applied to the transformed data. By stabilizing the variance, we have eliminated the correlation between the means and the variances, and hence, the mean squares between treatments and within treatments will be independent.

## 17.9.2. The Logarithmic Transformation, Log X.

If variances are proportional to the squares of the treatment means, the logarithmic transformation equalizes the variances. It is also used if effects are known to be proportional instead of additive. Proportional effects are common in economic data and in certain biological populations. When zero values are present, the transformation $\log (X + 1)$ is appropriate.

*Example 17-7.*  Calculate the means and variances of each of the four treatments of five variates each shown in Table 17-9. Apply the logarithmic transformation and compare the variances.

TABLE 17-9.  Original Data and Logarithmic Transformed Data for Four Groups of Five Values Each.

| | Original Data | | | | Transformed Data | | | |
|---|---|---|---|---|---|---|---|---|
| | Treatment | | | | | Treatment | | |
| | A | B | C | D | A | B | C | D |
| | 5 | 3 | 15 | 10 | 0.6990 | 0.4771 | 1.1761 | 1.0000 |
| | 11 | 6 | 8 | 6 | 1.0414 | 0.7782 | 0.9031 | 0.7782 |
| | 7 | 3 | 10 | 6 | 0.8451 | 0.4771 | 1.0000 | 0.7782 |
| | 7 | 5 | 6 | 12 | 0.8451 | 0.6990 | 0.7782 | 1.0792 |
| | 5 | 3 | 13 | 6 | 0.6990 | 0.4771 | 1.1139 | 0.7782 |
| Mean | 7.0 | 4.0 | 10.4 | 8.0 | 0.82592 | 0.58170 | 0.99426 | 0.88276 |
| Variance | 4.8 | 1.6 | 10.6 | 6.4 | 0.01588 | 0.01704 | 0.02048 | 0.01703 |

*Solution.*  The variances of the original data are considerably different in value and are proportional to the squares of the means. The transformation has resulted in nearly identical variances for all groups. The analysis of variance can now be applied to the transformed data.

## 17.9.3.  The Reciprocal Transformation, 1/X.

If the standard deviations are proportional to the square of the treatment means, the reciprocal transformation may be used. It is sometimes useful in psychological experiments involving word association or reaction time or in studies where one of the variables recorded is time of reaction or time to completion.

## 17.9.4.  The Angular or Inverse Sine Transformation, Arcsin $\sqrt{X}$ or $\sin^{-1} \sqrt{X}$.

Frequently in experimental work and research studies, as well as in economic and social data, the variable being studied is expressed as a probability, a proportion, or a percentage. In such cases the distribution tends to be binomial in form and the inverse sine (or arc sine) transformation is appropriate. This is an important transformation and is especially recommended when the percentages cover a wide range of values. It weights more heavily the small percentages which have small variance. Appendix Table VIII gives, for various percentages, the corresponding angles expressed in degrees corresponding to arcsin $\sqrt{\text{percentage}}$. If all percentages are less than 20 or more than 80, the square root transformation may be used: For percentages which are all in the range 30 to 70, it is doubtful if any transformation is needed.

*Example 17-8.* The percents of bunt infection determined from five sample collections of each of four varieties of wheat, together with the data transformed by use of the inverse sine transformation, are shown in Table 17-10. Apply the analysis of variance to the original and transformed data and compare the results.

**TABLE 17-10.** Percentage Bunt Infection in Four Varieties of Wheat Sampled Five Times.

|  | Original Data | | | | Transformed Data | | | |
|  | Variety | | | | Variety | | | |
|  | A | B | C | D | A | B | C | D |
|---|---|---|---|---|---|---|---|---|
|  | 0.8 | 4.0 | 9.8 | 6.0 | 5.13 | 11.54 | 18.24 | 14.18 |
|  | 3.8 | 1.9 | 56.2 | 79.8 | 11.24 | 7.92 | 48.56 | 63.29 |
|  | 0.0 | 0.7 | 66.0 | 7.0 | 0.0 | 4.80 | 54.33 | 15.34 |
|  | 6.0 | 3.5 | 10.3 | 84.6 | 14.18 | 10.78 | 18.72 | 66.89 |
|  | 1.7 | 3.2 | 9.2 | 2.8 | 7.49 | 10.31 | 17.66 | 9.63 |
| Total | 12.3 | 13.3 | 151.5 | 180.2 | 38.04 | 45.35 | 157.51 | 169.33 |
| Mean | 2.46 | 2.66 | 30.30 | 36.04 | 7.61 | 9.07 | 31.50 | 33.87 |

*Solution.* The results of the calculations are shown in Table 17-11.

**TABLE 17-11.** Analysis of Variance Tables for Both Sets of Data of Table 17-10.

| Original Data | | | | | Transformed Data | | | | | |
|---|---|---|---|---|---|---|---|---|---|---|
| Source of Variation | S.S. | d.f. | Mean Square | F | Source of Variation | S.S. | d.f. | Mean Square | F | $F_{.95}$ |
| Total | 15,133 | 19 | | | Total | 7,751 | 19 | | | |
| Between means (or treatments) | 4,798 | 3 | 1,599 | 2.48 | Between means (or treatments) | 2,983 | 3 | 994 | 3.34 | 3.24 |
| Within samples (or error) | 10,335 | 16 | 646 | | Within samples (or error) | 4,768 | 16 | 298 | | |

The F-value 2.48 for the original data is less than $F_{.95} = 3.24$, and, therefore, no significant differences between the mean bunt infections for the varieties are indicated. The F-value for the transformed data exceeds the tabular value and indicates significant differences. The transformation has, therefore, increased the sensitivity of the analysis.

For the transformed data,

$$L.S.D. = t_{.05} \sqrt{\frac{2s^2}{k}} = 2.12 \sqrt{\frac{2(298)}{5}} = 23.15.$$

The mean infection in variety $D$ is, therefore, significantly greater than those in varieties $A$ and $B$ and that in variety $C$ is significantly greater than that in $A$.

The means of the bunt infections in terms of the transformed data are expressed in degrees and, to have meaning, must be transformed back to percentages. Using Appendix Table VIII, these percentages are 1.8, 2.5, 27.3, and 31.1, which are different from the means of the original percentages.

## Exercises

1. A test is to be made on four given samples to determine whether they can all be assumed to have been taken from populations with identical means. An experimenter, unfamiliar with the analysis of variance, tests all possible pairs of these sample means separately by means of Student's $t$-test. If he uses the 10% level of significance, what is the probability that
   (a) he will draw all wrong conclusions;
   (b) he will draw exactly one wrong conclusion;
   (c) he will draw at least one wrong conclusion;
   (d) he will draw at least two correct conclusions?

2. Three samples are to be tested for significant differences between their means. An experimenter, unfamiliar with the fact that he should use the F-distribution to make this test, tests all possible pairs of these samples separately for significant differences between means by use of the Student $t$-test at the 5% level of significance. If the populations from which the samples are taken actually all have the same means, what is the probability that
   (a) he will draw at least one wrong conclusion;
   (b) he will draw at least two wrong conclusions;
   (c) he will draw all wrong conclusions?

3. Consider the following four samples:

| A | B | C | D |
|---|---|---|---|
| 11 | 18 | 10 | 13 |
| 9 | 12 | 9 | 8 |
| 7 | 15 | 11 | 9 |
| 12 | 13 | 10 | 12 |
| 14 | 16 | 7 | 11 |
| 13 | 16 | 10 | 10 |

Calculate by use of their definitions
(a) the total sum of squares;
(b) the between-means sum of squares;
(c) the within-samples sum of squares.
(d) Calculate the above three quantities by use of their computing forms.

4. Carry out the calculations required in exercise 3 for the following set of five samples.

| A | B | C | D | E |
|---|---|---|---|---|
| 12 | 14 | 16 | 14 | 11 |
| 10 | 13 | 14 | 15 | 9 |
| 15 | 12 | 11 | 11 | 8 |
| 13 | 9 | 14 | 12 | 12 |
| 12 | 11 | 15 | 9 | 9 |

5. Carry out the calculations required in exercise 3 for the following set of three samples.

| A | B | C |
|---|---|---|
| 16 | 10 | 14 |
| 10 | 11 | 17 |
| 12 | 9 | 13 |
| 13 | 6 | 15 |
| 11 | 7 | 12 |
| 13 | | 14 |
| | | 13 |

6. Prove formulae (17-13), (17-14), and (17-15).

7. (a) Are there significant differences between the means of the four samples in exercise 3 on the basis of the 5% level of significance?
   (b) If there are significant differences, use the L.S.D. to find which pairs of samples have significantly different means.

8. Answer the questions of exercise 7 for the five samples of exercise 4.

9. (a) Are there significantly different means among the three samples of exercise 5 at the 5% level of significance?

   (b) If so, find the pairs of samples having significantly different means.

10. Can the five samples below be considered as having been taken from populations with identical means on the basis of the 5% level of significance?

| A | B | C | D | E |
|---|---|---|---|---|
| 10 | 12 | 9 | 10 | 10 |
| 4 | 10 | 4 | 6 | 6 |
| 6 | 13 | 4 | 9 | 8 |
| 4 | 7 | 5 | 11 | 4 |

11. Solve Example 10-4 by means of the analysis of variance, and check that the $F$-value obtained equals the square of the $t$-value obtained in Example 10-4.

12. Prove that for two samples of unequal size the value of $F$ obtained in the analysis of variance equals the square of the $t$-value used in Student's $t$-test to determine whether the two sample means differ significantly.

13. The following experiment was designed to determine the relative merits of four different feeds in regard to the gain in weight of pigs. Twenty pigs are divided at random into four lots with five pigs in each. Each lot is given a different feed. The gain in weight (in pounds) of each of the pigs for a fixed length of time is given below. Make a complete analysis of the data, and state your conclusions.

| A | B | C | D |
|---|---|---|---|
| 133 | 163 | 210 | 195 |
| 144 | 148 | 233 | 184 |
| 135 | 152 | 220 | 199 |
| 149 | 146 | 226 | 187 |
| 143 | 157 | 229 | 193 |

14. An experimenter wishes to combine the results of similar experiments performed by different people. He needs from each of these experiments the sum of squares for error. In one of these experiments the error variance was not reported, and only the least significant difference was given; it was equal to 4.12 at the 5% level. If in this experiment there were four treatments each of which was replicated seven times, what was the sum of squares for error for this particular experiment?

15. From a certain population four samples of six variates are taken and the $F$-value is calculated. This process (i.e., taking four samples of six variates each from that population) is repeated many times and each time the $F$-value is calculated. Answer the following questions (give approximate answers where accurate answers are not possible).
   (a) What per cent of the time would you expect to obtain an $F$-value less than 1?
   (b) What per cent of the time would you expect to obtain an $F$-value less than 0.10?

16 Four methods of performing a certain operation have been tried, and we have 10 observations for each method. The mean productivities under each method are 60, 66, 70, and 72, respectively. Not having the original data from which to calculate the sum of squares we assume that the coefficient of variation (the pooled estimate of $\sigma$ divided by the average of all observations) is 0.10.
   (a) On this assumption, are there significant differences between these methods (5% level)?
   (b) If so, find which methods give significantly different mean productivities.

17. Complete the analysis and prepare an analysis of variance table for both the original and transformed data of Example 17-6. If significant differences between means are found, compare the means by calculating the L.S.D.

18. Complete the analysis and prepare an analysis of variance table for both the original and transformed data of Example 17-7. If significant differences are found, compare the means by calculating the L.S.D.

19. The severity of dry rot in potatoes after inoculation into five different types of wounds are shown below:

| $A$ | $B$ | $C$ | $D$ | $E$ |
|-----|-----|-----|-----|-----|
| 73 | 46 | 36 | 40 | 14 |
| 61 | 50 | 32 | 22 | 23 |
| 69 | 44 | 46 | 44 | 31 |
| 60 | 40 | 47 | 34 | 28 |

   (a) Perform an analysis of variance on the original data and on the data transformed by use of the inverse sine transformation to determine whether the inoculation has significantly different effects on the five types of wounds (5% level).
   (b) If there are significantly different effects, determine for which types of wounds they are significantly different.

# APPENDIX

Selected Readings

Answers to Odd-numbered Exercises

# Selected Readings

Books on probability and statistics fall into two basic categories: those which use the notation and methods of the calculus, and those which do not. In each category we have listed, for further study, typical reference and textbooks. The list does not begin to include all the statistics works available, but it does represent several types of books, each of which stresses certain phases of statistical procedures.

## A.1. Books Not Using the Calculus

### A.1.1. Analysis of Variance

After having completed a study of the material in this book, most readers will find analysis of variance the topic ranking next in order of importance and logical development. In Chapter 10, Student's $t$-distribution was used to determine whether the means of two samples were significantly different. If it is desired to determine whether the means of a set of more than two samples are significantly different, the appropriate procedure to employ is the analysis of variance, which makes use of the $F$-distribution. The following two books give brief introductions to the analysis of variance and the analysis of covariance.

Dixon, Wilfred J., and Massey, Frank J., Jr., *Introduction to Statistical Analysis*, 2d ed., McGraw-Hill Book Co., New York, 1957.

Edwards, Allen L., *Experimental Design in Psychological Research*, Rinehart and Co., Inc., New York, 1950.

A considerably more extensive treatment of the analysis of variance is presented in

Ostle, Bernard, *Statistics in Research*. Iowa State College Press, Ames, Iowa, 1954.

### A.1.2. Experimental Designs

Since many of the experimental designs in common use involve the analysis of variance, most books on experimental design also include an introduction to the analysis of variance.

Cochran, William G., Cox, Gertrude M., *Experimental Designs*, 2d ed., John Wiley and Sons, Inc., New York, 1957.

Goulden, Cyril H., *Methods of Statistical Analysis*, 2d ed., John Wiley and Sons, Inc., New York, 1952.

Snedecor, George W., *Statistical Methods*, 5th ed., Iowa State College Press, Ames, Iowa, 1956.

Steel, Robert G., Torrie, James H., *Principles and Procedures of Statistics*, McGraw-Hill Book Co., Inc., New York, 1960.

### A.1.3. Regression, Correlation (including rank correlation)

Chapter 12 presents an introduction to regression and correlation analysis with the main emphasis on linear regression. The reader desiring a more detailed treatment of linear regression as well as an introduction to nonlinear regression and multiple and partial correlation is referred to

Guilford, Joy P., *Fundamental Statistics in Psychology and Education*, 3d ed., McGraw-Hill Book Co., Inc., New York, 1956.

In many problems, it is very difficult, or impossible, to obtain measurements of a variable; but it may be possible to order a set of such measurements according to magnitude (i.e., obtain their ranks). Rank correlation is the name given to correlation between the ranks of two variables, a topic which is discussed extensively in

Kendall, Maurice G., *Rank Correlation Methods*, 2d ed., Charles Griffin and Co., Ltd., London, 1955.

### A.1.4. Index Numbers and Time Series

A very detailed study of index numbers is contained in

Mudgett, Bruce D., *Index Numbers*, John Wiley and Sons, Inc., New York, 1952.

Time series are treated thoroughly in

Davis, Harold T., *The Analysis of Economic Time Series*, The Principia Press, Inc., Bloomington, Indiana, 1941.

## A.2. Books Using the Calculus

### A.2.1. Fundamental Concepts

The reader—in particular, the prospective statistician or mathematician—who wishes to gain a thorough understanding of the foundations of probability and statistics without pursuing a great many topics is referred to

Neyman, Jerzy, *First Course in Probability and Statistics*, Henry Holt and Company, Inc., New York, 1950.

### A.2.2. General Statistics

The following three books use the calculus in treating most of the topics covered in this text.

Hoel, Paul G., *Introduction to Mathematical Statistics*, 2d ed., John Wiley and Sons, Inc., New York, 1954.

Kendall, Maurice G., *The Advanced Theory of Statistics*, Vol. I, new ed., 1958, and Vol. II, 3d ed., 1951. Charles Griffin and Co., Ltd., London.

Mood, Alexander M., *Introduction to the Theory of Statistics*, McGraw-Hill Book Co., Inc., New York, 1950.

## A.2.3. Analysis of Variance and Experimental Designs

The analysis of variance is introduced in some of the books listed immediately above. A very careful and rigorous treatment of this topic, in addition to many experimental designs and a number of other topics frequently encountered in statistics, is found in the following four books.

Anderson, Richard L., Bancroft, Theodore A., *Statistical Theory in Research*, McGraw-Hill Book Co., Inc., New York, 1952.

Federer, Walter T., *Experimental Design*, The Macmillan Co., New York, 1955.

Fisher, Ronald A., *The Design of Experiments*, 6th ed., Oliver and Boyd, Ltd., Edinburgh and London, 1951.

Kempthorne, Oscar, *The Design and Analysis of Experiments*, John Wiley and Sons, Inc., New York, 1952.

## A.2.4. Industrial Statistics

Statistical methods are employed extensively in engineering and industry, especially in the field of quality control. The following two works treat this topic.

Burr, Irving W., *Engineering Statistics and Quality Control*, McGraw-Hill Book Co., Inc., New York, 1953.

Cowden, Dudley J., *Statistical Methods in Quality Control*, Prentice-Hall, Inc., New Jersey, 1957.

TABLE I

## Areas Under the Normal Probability Curve

A denotes the area between the line of symmetry (i.e., $z = 0$) and the given z-value.

| z | A | z | A | z | A | z | A |
|---|---|---|---|---|---|---|---|
| 0.00 | 0.0000 | 0.30 | 0.1179 | 0.60 | 0.2258 | 0.90 | 0.3159 |
| .01 | .0040 | .31 | .1217 | .61 | .2291 | .91 | .3186 |
| .02 | .0080 | .32 | .1255 | .62 | .2324 | .92 | .3212 |
| .03 | .0120 | .33 | .1293 | .63 | .2357 | .93 | .3238 |
| .04 | .0160 | .34 | .1331 | .64 | .2389 | .94 | .3264 |
| .05 | .0199 | .35 | .1368 | .65 | .2422 | .95 | .3289 |
| .06 | .0239 | .36 | .1406 | .66 | .2454 | .96 | .3315 |
| .07 | .0279 | .37 | .1443 | .67 | .2486 | .97 | .3340 |
| .08 | .0319 | .38 | .1480 | .68 | .2518 | .98 | .3365 |
| .09 | .0359 | .39 | .1517 | .69 | .2549 | .99 | .3389 |
| .10 | .0398 | .40 | .1554 | .70 | .2580 | 1.00 | .3413 |
| .11 | .0438 | .41 | .1591 | .71 | .2612 | 1.01 | .3438 |
| .12 | .0478 | .42 | .1628 | .72 | .2642 | 1.02 | .3461 |
| .13 | .0517 | .43 | .1664 | .73 | .2673 | 1.03 | .3485 |
| .14 | .0557 | .44 | .1700 | .74 | .2704 | 1.04 | .3508 |
| .15 | .0596 | .45 | .1736 | .75 | .2734 | 1.05 | .3531 |
| .16 | .0636 | .46 | .1772 | .76 | .2764 | 1.06 | .3554 |
| .17 | .0675 | .47 | .1808 | .77 | .2794 | 1.07 | .3577 |
| .18 | .0714 | .48 | .1844 | .78 | .2823 | 1.08 | .3599 |
| .19 | .0754 | .49 | .1879 | .79 | .2852 | 1.09 | .3621 |
| .20 | .0793 | .50 | .1915 | .80 | .2881 | 1.10 | .3643 |
| .21 | .0832 | .51 | .1950 | .81 | .2910 | 1.11 | .3665 |
| .22 | .0871 | .52 | .1985 | .82 | .2939 | 1.12 | .3686 |
| .23 | .0910 | .53 | .2019 | .83 | .2967 | 1.13 | .3708 |
| .24 | .0948 | .54 | .2054 | .84 | .2996 | 1.14 | .3729 |
| .25 | .0987 | .55 | .2088 | .85 | .3023 | 1.15 | .3749 |
| .26 | .1026 | .56 | .2123 | .86 | .3051 | 1.16 | .3770 |
| .27 | .1064 | .57 | .2157 | .87 | .3079 | 1.17 | .3790 |
| .28 | .1103 | .58 | .2190 | .88 | .3106 | 1.18 | .3810 |
| .29 | .1141 | .59 | .2224 | .89 | .3133 | 1.19 | .3830 |

Table I

293

**TABLE I.** **Areas Under the Normal Probability Curve**
(continued)

| z | A | z | A | z | A | z | A |
|------|--------|------|--------|------|--------|------|--------|
| 1.20 | 0.3849 | 1.55 | 0.4394 | 1.90 | 0.4713 | 2.25 | 0.4878 |
| 1.21 | .3869 | 1.56 | .4406 | 1.91 | .4719 | 2.26 | .4881 |
| 1.22 | .3888 | 1.57 | .4418 | 1.92 | .4726 | 2.27 | .4884 |
| 1.23 | .3907 | 1.58 | .4430 | 1.93 | .4732 | 2.28 | .4887 |
| 1.24 | .3925 | 1.59 | .4441 | 1.94 | .4738 | 2.29 | .4890 |
| 1.25 | .3944 | 1.60 | .4452 | 1.95 | .4744 | 2.30 | .4893 |
| 1.26 | .3962 | 1.61 | .4463 | 1.96 | .4750 | 2.31 | .4896 |
| 1.27 | .3980 | 1.62 | .4474 | 1.97 | .4756 | 2.32 | .4898 |
| 1.28 | .3997 | 1.63 | .4485 | 1.98 | .4762 | 2.33 | .4901 |
| 1.29 | .4015 | 1.64 | .4495 | 1.99 | .4767 | 2.34 | .4904 |
| 1.30 | .4032 | 1.65 | .4505 | 2.00 | .4773 | 2.35 | .4906 |
| 1.31 | .4049 | 1.66 | .4515 | 2.01 | .4778 | 2.36 | .4909 |
| 1.32 | .4066 | 1.67 | .4525 | 2.02 | .4783 | 2.37 | .4911 |
| 1.33 | .4082 | 1.68 | .4535 | 2.03 | .4788 | 2.38 | .4913 |
| 1.34 | .4099 | 1.69 | .4545 | 2.04 | .4793 | 2.39 | .4916 |
| 1.35 | .4115 | 1.70 | .4554 | 2.05 | .4798 | 2.40 | .4918 |
| 1.36 | .4131 | 1.71 | .4564 | 2.06 | .4803 | 2.41 | .4920 |
| 1.37 | .4147 | 1.72 | .4573 | 2.07 | .4808 | 2.42 | .4922 |
| 1.38 | .4162 | 1.73 | .4582 | 2.08 | .4812 | 2.43 | .4925 |
| 1.39 | .4177 | 1.74 | .4591 | 2.09 | .4817 | 2.44 | .4927 |
| 1.40 | .4192 | 1.75 | .4599 | 2.10 | .4821 | 2.45 | .4929 |
| 1.41 | .4207 | 1.76 | .4608 | 2.11 | .4826 | 2.46 | .4931 |
| 1.42 | .4222 | 1.77 | .4616 | 2.12 | .4830 | 2.47 | .4932 |
| 1.43 | .4236 | 1.78 | .4625 | 2.13 | .4834 | 2.48 | .4934 |
| 1.44 | .4251 | 1.79 | .4633 | 2.14 | .4838 | 2.49 | .4936 |
| 1.45 | .4265 | 1.80 | .4641 | 2.15 | .4842 | 2.50 | .4938 |
| 1.46 | .4279 | 1.81 | .4649 | 2.16 | .4846 | 2.51 | .4940 |
| 1.47 | .4292 | 1.82 | .4656 | 2.17 | .4850 | 2.52 | .4941 |
| 1.48 | .4306 | 1.83 | .4664 | 2.18 | .4854 | 2.53 | .4943 |
| 1.49 | .4319 | 1.84 | .4671 | 2.19 | .4857 | 2.54 | .4945 |
| 1.50 | .4332 | 1.85 | .4678 | 2.20 | .4861 | 2.55 | .4946 |
| 1.51 | .4345 | 1.86 | .4686 | 2.21 | .4865 | 2.56 | .4948 |
| 1.52 | .4357 | 1.87 | .4693 | 2.22 | .4868 | 2.57 | .4949 |
| 1.53 | .4370 | 1.88 | .4700 | 2.23 | .4871 | 2.58 | .4951 |
| 1.54 | .4382 | 1.89 | .4706 | 2.24 | .4875 | 2.59 | .4952 |

**TABLE I.** Areas Under the Normal Probability Curve

(continued)

| z | A | z | A | z | A | z | A |
|---|---|---|---|---|---|---|---|
| 2.60 | 0.4953 | 2.95 | 0.4984 | 3.30 | 0.4995 | 3.65 | 0.4999 |
| 2.61 | .4955 | 2.96 | .4985 | 3.31 | .4995 | 3.66 | .4999 |
| 2.62 | .4956 | 2.97 | .4985 | 3.32 | .4996 | 3.67 | .4999 |
| 2.63 | .4957 | 2.98 | .4986 | 3.33 | .4996 | 3.68 | .4999 |
| 2.64 | .4959 | 2.99 | .4986 | 3.34 | .4996 | 3.69 | .4999 |
| 2.65 | .4960 | 3.00 | .4987 | 3.35 | .4996 | 3.70 | .4999 |
| 2.66 | .4961 | 3.01 | .4987 | 3.36 | .4996 | 3.71 | .4999 |
| 2.67 | .4962 | 3.02 | .4987 | 3.37 | .4996 | 3.72 | .4999 |
| 2.68 | .4963 | 3.03 | .4988 | 3.38 | .4996 | 3.73 | .4999 |
| 2.69 | .4964 | 3.04 | .4988 | 3.39 | .4997 | 3.74 | .4999 |
| 2.70 | .4965 | 3.05 | .4989 | 3.40 | .4997 | 3.75 | .4999 |
| 2.71 | .4966 | 3.06 | .4989 | 3.41 | .4997 | 3.76 | .4999 |
| 2.72 | .4967 | 3.07 | .4989 | 3.42 | .4997 | 3.77 | .4999 |
| 2.73 | .4968 | 3.08 | .4990 | 3.43 | .4997 | 3.78 | .4999 |
| 2.74 | .4969 | 3.09 | .4990 | 3.44 | .4997 | 3.79 | .4999 |
| 2.75 | .4970 | 3.10 | .4990 | 3.45 | .4997 | 3.80 | .4999 |
| 2.76 | .4971 | 3.11 | .4991 | 3.46 | .4997 | 3.81 | .4999 |
| 2.77 | .4972 | 3.12 | .4991 | 3.47 | .4997 | 3.82 | .4999 |
| 2.78 | .4973 | 3.13 | .4991 | 3.48 | .4998 | 3.83 | .4999 |
| 2.79 | .4974 | 3.14 | .4992 | 3.49 | .4998 | 3.84 | .4999 |
| 2.80 | .4974 | 3.15 | .4992 | 3.50 | .4998 | 3.85 | .4999 |
| 2.81 | .4975 | 3.16 | .4992 | 3.51 | .4998 | 3.86 | .4999 |
| 2.82 | .4976 | 3.17 | .4992 | 3.52 | .4998 | 3.87 | .5000 |
| 2.83 | .4977 | 3.18 | .4993 | 3.53 | .4998 | 3.88 | .5000 |
| 2.84 | .4977 | 3.19 | .4993 | 3.54 | .4998 | 3.89 | .5000 |
| 2.85 | .4978 | 3.20 | .4993 | 3.55 | .4998 | | |
| 2.86 | .4979 | 3.21 | .4993 | 3.56 | .4998 | | |
| 2.87 | .4980 | 3.22 | .4994 | 3.57 | .4998 | | |
| 2.88 | .4980 | 3.23 | .4994 | 3.58 | .4998 | | |
| 2.89 | .4981 | 3.24 | .4994 | 3.59 | .4998 | | |
| 2.90 | .4981 | 3.25 | .4994 | 3.60 | .4998 | | |
| 2.91 | .4982 | 3.26 | .4994 | 3.61 | .4999 | | |
| 2.92 | .4983 | 3.27 | .4995 | 3.62 | .4999 | | |
| 2.93 | .4983 | 3.28 | .4995 | 3.63 | .4999 | | |
| 2.94 | .4984 | 3.29 | .4995 | 3.64 | .4999 | | |

# TABLE Ia

## Ordinates (y-Values) for the Normal Probability Curve

y denotes the ordinate for the given z-value.

| z | y | z | y | z | y | z | y |
|---|---|---|---|---|---|---|---|
| 0.00 | 0.3989 | 0.30 | 0.3814 | 0.60 | 0.3332 | 0.90 | 0.2661 |
| .01 | .3989 | .31 | .3802 | .61 | .3312 | .91 | .2637 |
| .02 | .3989 | .32 | .3790 | .62 | .3292 | .92 | .2613 |
| .03 | .3988 | .33 | .3778 | .63 | .3271 | .93 | .2589 |
| .04 | .3986 | .34 | .3765 | .64 | .3251 | .94 | .2565 |
| .05 | .3984 | .35 | .3752 | .65 | .3230 | .95 | .2541 |
| .06 | .3982 | .36 | .3739 | .66 | .3209 | .96 | .2516 |
| .07 | .3980 | .37 | .3725 | .67 | .3187 | .97 | .2492 |
| .08 | .3977 | .38 | .3711 | .68 | .3166 | .98 | .2468 |
| .09 | .3973 | .39 | .3697 | .69 | .3144 | .99 | .2444 |
| .10 | .3969 | .40 | .3683 | .70 | .3122 | 1.00 | .2420 |
| .11 | .3965 | .41 | .3668 | .71 | .3101 | 1.01 | .2395 |
| .12 | .3961 | .42 | .3653 | .72 | .3078 | 1.02 | .2371 |
| .13 | .3956 | .43 | .3637 | .73 | .3056 | 1.03 | .2347 |
| .14 | .3950 | .44 | .3621 | .74 | .3034 | 1.04 | .2323 |
| .15 | .3945 | .45 | .3605 | .75 | .3011 | 1.05 | .2299 |
| .16 | .3939 | .46 | .3589 | .76 | .2989 | 1.06 | .2275 |
| .17 | .3932 | .47 | .3572 | .77 | .2966 | 1.07 | .2251 |
| .18 | .3925 | .48 | .3555 | .78 | .2943 | 1.08 | .2226 |
| .19 | .3918 | .49 | .3538 | .79 | .2920 | 1.09 | .2202 |
| .20 | .3910 | .50 | .3521 | .80 | .2897 | 1.10 | .2178 |
| .21 | .3902 | .51 | .3503 | .81 | .2874 | 1.11 | .2155 |
| .22 | .3894 | .52 | .3485 | .82 | .2850 | 1.12 | .2131 |
| .23 | .3885 | .53 | .3467 | .83 | .2827 | 1.13 | .2107 |
| .24 | .3876 | .54 | .3448 | .84 | .2803 | 1.14 | .2083 |
| .25 | .3867 | .55 | .3429 | .85 | .2780 | 1.15 | .2059 |
| .26 | .3857 | .56 | .3410 | .86 | .2756 | 1.16 | .2036 |
| .27 | .3847 | .57 | .3391 | .87 | .2732 | 1.17 | .2012 |
| .28 | .3836 | .58 | .3372 | .88 | .2709 | 1.18 | .1989 |
| .29 | .3825 | .59 | .3352 | .89 | .2685 | 1.19 | .1965 |

**TABLE Ia.** **Ordinates (y-Values) for the Normal Probability Curve**
(continued)

| z | y | z | y | z | y | z | y |
|---|---|---|---|---|---|---|---|
| 1.20 | 0.1942 | 1.55 | 0.1200 | 1.90 | 0.0656 | 2.25 | 0.0317 |
| 1.21 | .1919 | 1.56 | .1182 | 1.91 | .0644 | 2.26 | .0310 |
| 1.22 | .1895 | 1.57 | .1163 | 1.92 | .0632 | 2.27 | .0303 |
| 1.23 | .1872 | 1.53 | .1145 | 1.93 | .0619 | 2.28 | .0296 |
| 1.24 | .1849 | 1.59 | .1127 | 1.94 | .0608 | 2.29 | .0290 |
| 1.25 | .1826 | 1.60 | .1109 | 1.95 | .0596 | 2.30 | .0283 |
| 1.26 | .1804 | 1.61 | .1091 | 1.96 | .0584 | 2.31 | .0277 |
| 1.27 | .1781 | 1.62 | .1074 | 1.97 | .0573 | 2.32 | .0270 |
| 1.28 | .1758 | 1.63 | .1057 | 1.98 | .0562 | 2.33 | .0264 |
| 1.29 | .1736 | 1.64 | .1040 | 1.99 | .0551 | 2.34 | .2258 |
| 1.30 | .1714 | 1.65 | .1023 | 2.00 | .0540 | 2.35 | .0252 |
| 1.31 | .1691 | 1.66 | .1006 | 2.01 | .0529 | 2.36 | .0246 |
| 1.32 | .1669 | 1.67 | .0989 | 2.02 | .0519 | 2.37 | .0241 |
| 1.33 | .1647 | 1.68 | .0973 | 2.03 | .0508 | 2.38 | .0235 |
| 1.34 | .1626 | 1.69 | .0957 | 2.04 | .0498 | 2.39 | .0229 |
| 1.35 | .1604 | 1.70 | .0940 | 2.05 | .0488 | 2.40 | .0224 |
| 1.36 | .1582 | 1.71 | .0925 | 2.06 | .0478 | 2.41 | .0219 |
| 1.37 | .1561 | 1.72 | .0909 | 2.07 | .0468 | 2.42 | .0213 |
| 1.38 | .1539 | 1.73 | .0893 | 2.08 | .0459 | 2.43 | .0208 |
| 1.39 | .1518 | 1.74 | .0878 | 2.09 | .0449 | 2.44 | .0203 |
| 1.40 | .1497 | 1.75 | .0863 | 2.10 | .0440 | 2.45 | .0198 |
| 1.41 | .1476 | 1.76 | .0848 | 2.11 | .0431 | 2.46 | .0194 |
| 1.42 | .1456 | 1.77 | .0833 | 2.12 | .0422 | 2.47 | .0189 |
| 1.43 | .1435 | 1.78 | .0818 | 2.13 | .0413 | 2.48 | .0184 |
| 1.44 | .1415 | 1.79 | .0804 | 2.14 | .0404 | 2.49 | .0180 |
| 1.45 | .1394 | 1.80 | .0789 | 2.15 | .0395 | 2.50 | .0175 |
| 1.46 | .1374 | 1.81 | .0775 | 2.16 | .0387 | 2.51 | .0171 |
| 1.47 | .1354 | 1.82 | .0761 | 2.17 | .0379 | 2.52 | .0167 |
| 1.48 | .1334 | 1.83 | .0748 | 2.18 | .0371 | 2.53 | .0162 |
| 1.49 | .1315 | 1.84 | .0734 | 2.19 | .0363 | 2.54 | .0158 |
| 1.50 | .1295 | 1.85 | .0721 | 2.20 | .0355 | 2.55 | .0154 |
| 1.51 | .1276 | 1.86 | .0707 | 2.21 | .0347 | 2.56 | .0151 |
| 1.52 | .1257 | 1.87 | .0694 | 2.22 | .0339 | 2.57 | .0147 |
| 1.53 | .1238 | 1.88 | .0681 | 2.23 | .0332 | 2.58 | .0143 |
| 1.54 | .1219 | 1.89 | .0669 | 2.24 | .0325 | 2.59 | .0139 |

**TABLE Ia.  Ordinates (y-Values) for the Normal Probability Curve**
(*continued*)

| z | y | z | y | z | y | z | y |
|------|--------|------|--------|------|--------|------|--------|
| 2.60 | 0.0136 | 2.95 | 0.0051 | 3.30 | 0.0017 | 3.65 | 0.0005 |
| 2.61 | .0132 | 2.96 | .0050 | 3.31 | .0017 | 3.66 | .0005 |
| 2.62 | .0129 | 2.97 | .0048 | 3.32 | .0016 | 3.67 | .0005 |
| 2.63 | .0126 | 2.98 | .0047 | 3.33 | .0016 | 3.68 | .0005 |
| 2.64 | .0122 | 2.99 | .0046 | 3.34 | .0015 | 3.69 | .0004 |
| 2.65 | .0119 | 3.00 | .0044 | 3.35 | .0015 | 3.70 | .0004 |
| 2.66 | .0116 | 3.01 | .0043 | 3.36 | .0014 | 3.71 | .0004 |
| 2.67 | .0113 | 3.02 | .0042 | 3.37 | .0014 | 3.72 | .0004 |
| 2.68 | .0110 | 3.03 | .0040 | 3.38 | .0013 | 3.73 | .0004 |
| 2.69 | .0107 | 3.04 | .0039 | 3.39 | .0013 | 3.74 | .0004 |
| 2.70 | .0104 | 3.05 | .0038 | 3.40 | .0012 | 3.75 | .0003 |
| 2.71 | .0101 | 3.06 | .0037 | 3.41 | .0012 | 3.76 | .0003 |
| 2.72 | .0099 | 3.07 | .0036 | 3.42 | .0011 | 3.77 | .0003 |
| 2.73 | .0096 | 3.08 | .0035 | 3.43 | .0011 | 3.78 | .0003 |
| 2.74 | .0093 | 3.09 | .0034 | 3.44 | .0011 | 3.79 | .0003 |
| 2.75 | .0091 | 3.10 | .0033 | 3.45 | .0010 | 3.80 | .0003 |
| 2.76 | .0088 | 3.11 | .0032 | 3.46 | .0010 | 3.81 | .0003 |
| 2.77 | .0086 | 3.12 | .0031 | 3.47 | .0010 | 3.82 | .0003 |
| 2.78 | .0084 | 3.13 | .0030 | 3.48 | .0009 | 3.83 | .0003 |
| 2.79 | .0081 | 3.14 | .0029 | 3.49 | .0009 | 3.84 | .0002 |
| 2.80 | .0079 | 3.15 | .0028 | 3.50 | .0009 | 3.85 | .0002 |
| 2.81 | .0077 | 3.16 | .0027 | 3.51 | .0008 | 3.86 | .0002 |
| 2.82 | .0075 | 3.17 | .0026 | 3.52 | .0008 | 3.87 | .0002 |
| 2.83 | .0073 | 3.18 | .0025 | 3.53 | .0008 | 3.88 | .0002 |
| 2.84 | .0071 | 3.19 | .0025 | 3.54 | .0008 | 3.89 | .0002 |
| 2.85 | .0069 | 3.20 | .0024 | 3.55 | .0007 | 3.90 | .0002 |
| 2.86 | .0067 | 3.21 | .0023 | 3.56 | .0007 | 3.91 | .0002 |
| 2.87 | .0065 | 3.22 | .0022 | 3.57 | .0007 | 3.92 | .0002 |
| 2.88 | .0063 | 3.23 | .0022 | 3.58 | .0007 | 3.93 | .0002 |
| 2.89 | .0061 | 3.24 | .0021 | 3.59 | .0006 | 3.94 | .0002 |
| 2.90 | .0059 | 3.25 | .0020 | 3.60 | .0006 | 3.95 | .0002 |
| 2.91 | .0058 | 3.26 | .0020 | 3.61 | .0006 | 3.96 | .0002 |
| 2.92 | .0056 | 3.27 | .0019 | 3.62 | .0006 | 3.97 | .0001 |
| 2.93 | .0054 | 3.28 | .0018 | 3.63 | .0005 | 3.98 | .0001 |
| 2.94 | .0053 | 3.29 | .0018 | 3.64 | .0005 | 3.99 | .0001 |

TABLE II

# Student's *t*-Distribution

A denotes the sum of the two tail areas for the values of t given below. $\nu$ denotes the number of degrees of freedom (df).

$t=0$    $t$

| $\nu$ or df | A = 0.1 | A = 0.05 | A = 0.02 | A = 0.01 | A = 0.001 |
|---|---|---|---|---|---|
| 1 | 6.314 | 12.706 | 31.821 | 63.657 | 636.619 |
| 2 | 2.920 | 4.303 | 6.965 | 9.925 | 31.598 |
| 3 | 2.353 | 3.182 | 4.541 | 5.841 | 12.941 |
| 4 | 2.132 | 2.776 | 3.747 | 4.604 | 8.610 |
| 5 | 2.015 | 2.571 | 3.365 | 4.032 | 6.859 |
| 6 | 1.943 | 2.447 | 3.143 | 3.707 | 5.959 |
| 7 | 1.895 | 2.365 | 2.998 | 3.499 | 5.405 |
| 8 | 1.860 | 2.306 | 2.896 | 3.355 | 5.041 |
| 9 | 1.833 | 2.262 | 2.821 | 3.250 | 4.781 |
| 10 | 1.812 | 2.228 | 2.764 | 3.169 | 4.587 |
| 11 | 1.796 | 2.201 | 2.718 | 3.106 | 4.437 |
| 12 | 1.782 | 2.179 | 2.681 | 3.055 | 4.318 |
| 13 | 1.771 | 2.160 | 2.650 | 3.012 | 4.221 |
| 14 | 1.761 | 2.145 | 2.624 | 2.977 | 4.140 |
| 15 | 1.753 | 2.131 | 2.602 | 2.947 | 4.073 |
| 16 | 1.746 | 2.120 | 2.583 | 2.921 | 4.015 |
| 17 | 1.740 | 2.110 | 2.567 | 2.898 | 3.965 |
| 18 | 1.734 | 2.101 | 2.552 | 2.878 | 3.922 |
| 19 | 1.729 | 2.093 | 2.539 | 2.861 | 3.883 |
| 20 | 1.725 | 2.086 | 2.528 | 2.845 | 3.850 |
| 21 | 1.721 | 2.080 | 2.518 | 2.831 | 3.819 |
| 22 | 1.717 | 2.074 | 2.508 | 2.819 | 3.792 |
| 23 | 1.714 | 2.069 | 2.500 | 2.807 | 3.767 |
| 24 | 1.711 | 2.064 | 2.492 | 2.797 | 3.745 |
| 25 | 1.708 | 2.060 | 2.485 | 2.787 | 3.725 |
| 26 | 1.706 | 2.056 | 2.479 | 2.779 | 3.707 |
| 27 | 1.703 | 2.052 | 2.473 | 2.771 | 3.690 |
| 28 | 1.701 | 2.048 | 2.467 | 2.763 | 3.674 |
| 29 | 1.699 | 2.045 | 2.462 | 2.756 | 3.659 |
| 30 | 1.697 | 2.042 | 2.457 | 2.750 | 3.646 |
| 40 | 1.684 | 2.021 | 2.423 | 2.704 | 3.551 |
| 60 | 1.671 | 2.000 | 2.390 | 2.660 | 3.460 |
| 120 | 1.658 | 1.980 | 2.358 | 2.617 | 3.373 |
| $\infty$ | 1.645 | 1.960 | 2.326 | 2.576 | 3.291 |

Table II is abridged from Table III of Fisher and Yates: *Statistical Tables for Biological, Agricultural, and Medical Research*, published by Oliver and Boyd Limited, Edinburgh, by permission of the authors and publishers.

# TABLE III

## Transformation of $r$ to $Z$ $\left(\text{i.e., } Z = \frac{1}{2} \log_e \frac{1+r}{1-r}\right)$

| $r$ | $Z$ | $r$ | $Z$ | $r$ | $Z$ |
|-----|-----|-----|-----|-----|-----|
| .00 | .000 |     |     |     |     |
| .01 | .010 | .36 | .377 | .71 | .887 |
| .02 | .020 | .37 | .388 | .72 | .908 |
| .03 | .030 | .38 | .400 | .73 | .929 |
| .04 | .040 | .39 | .412 | .74 | .950 |
| .05 | .050 | .40 | .424 | .75 | 973 |
|     |     |     |     |     |     |
| .06 | .060 | .41 | .436 | .76 | .996 |
| .07 | .070 | .42 | .448 | .77 | 1.020 |
| .08 | .080 | .43 | .460 | .78 | 1.045 |
| .09 | .090 | .44 | .472 | .79 | 1.071 |
| .10 | .100 | .45 | .485 | .80 | 1.099 |
|     |     |     |     |     |     |
| .11 | .110 | .46 | .497 | .81 | 1.127 |
| .12 | .121 | .47 | .510 | .82 | 1.157 |
| .13 | .131 | .48 | .523 | .83 | 1.188 |
| .14 | .141 | .49 | .536 | .84 | 1.221 |
| .15 | .151 | .50 | .549 | .85 | 1.256 |
|     |     |     |     |     |     |
| .16 | .161 | .51 | .563 | .86 | 1.293 |
| .17 | .172 | .52 | .576 | .87 | 1.333 |
| .18 | .182 | .53 | .590 | .88 | 1.376 |
| .19 | .192 | .54 | .604 | .89 | 1.422 |
| .20 | .203 | .55 | .618 | .90 | 1.472 |
|     |     |     |     |     |     |
| .21 | .213 | .56 | .633 | .91 | 1.528 |
| .22 | .224 | .57 | .648 | .92 | 1.589 |
| .23 | .234 | .58 | .662 | .93 | 1.658 |
| .24 | .245 | .59 | .678 | .94 | 1.738 |
| .25 | .255 | .60 | .693 | .95 | 1.832 |
|     |     |     |     |     |     |
| .26 | .266 | .61 | .709 | .96 | 1.946 |
| .27 | .277 | .62 | .725 | .97 | 2.092 |
| .28 | .288 | .63 | .741 | .98 | 2.298 |
| .29 | .299 | .64 | .758 | .99 | 2.647 |
| .30 | .310 | .65 | .775 |     |     |
|     |     |     |     |     |     |
| .31 | .321 | .66 | .793 |     |     |
| .32 | .332 | .67 | .811 |     |     |
| .33 | .343 | .68 | .829 |     |     |
| .34 | .354 | .69 | .848 |     |     |
| .35 | .365 | .70 | .867 |     |     |

Table III is abridged from Table VII of Fisher and Yates: *Statistical Tables for Biological, Agricultural, and Medical Research*, published by Oliver and Boyd Limited, Edinburgh, by permission of the authors and publishers.

TABLE IV

# Chi-Square Distribution

A denotes the right tail area for the values of $\chi^2$ given below. $\nu$ denotes the number of degrees of freedom (df).

$\nu = 1 \& 2$     Other $\nu$

| $\nu$ or df | A = 0.99 | A = 0.98 | A = 0.95 | A = 0.90 | A = 0.80 | A = 0.70 | A = 0.50 |
|---|---|---|---|---|---|---|---|
| 1 | .00016 | .00063 | .0039 | .016 | .064 | .15 | .46 |
| 2 | .02 | .04 | .10 | .21 | .45 | .71 | 1.39 |
| 3 | .12 | .18 | .35 | .58 | 1.00 | 1.42 | 2.37 |
| 4 | .30 | .43 | .71 | 1.06 | 1.65 | 2.20 | 3.36 |
| 5 | .55 | .75 | 1.14 | 1.61 | 2.34 | 3.00 | 4.35 |
| 6 | .87 | 1.13 | 1.64 | 2.20 | 3.07 | 3.83 | 5.35 |
| 7 | 1.24 | 1.56 | 2.17 | 2.83 | 3.82 | 4.67 | 6.35 |
| 8 | 1.65 | 2.03 | 2.73 | 3.49 | 4.59 | 5.53 | 7.34 |
| 9 | 2.09 | 2.53 | 3.32 | 4.17 | 5.38 | 6.39 | 8.34 |
| 10 | 2.56 | 3.06 | 3.94 | 4.86 | 6.18 | 7.27 | 9.34 |
| 11 | 3.05 | 3.61 | 4.58 | 5.58 | 6.99 | 8.15 | 10.34 |
| 12 | 3.57 | 4.18 | 5.23 | 6.30 | 7.81 | 9.03 | 11.34 |
| 13 | 4.11 | 4.76 | 5.89 | 7.04 | 8.63 | 9.93 | 12.34 |
| 14 | 4.66 | 5.37 | 6.57 | 7.79 | 9.47 | 10.82 | 13.34 |
| 15 | 5.23 | 5.98 | 7.26 | 8.55 | 10.31 | 11.72 | 14.34 |
| 16 | 5.81 | 6.61 | 7.96 | 9.31 | 11.15 | 12.62 | 15.34 |
| 17 | 6.41 | 7.26 | 8.67 | 10.08 | 12.00 | 13.53 | 16.34 |
| 18 | 7.02 | 7.91 | 9.39 | 10.86 | 12.86 | 14.44 | 17.34 |
| 19 | 7.63 | 8.57 | 10.12 | 11.65 | 13.72 | 15.35 | 18.34 |
| 20 | 8.26 | 9.24 | 10.85 | 12.44 | 14.58 | 16.27 | 19.34 |
| 21 | 8.90 | 9.92 | 11.59 | 13.24 | 15.44 | 17.18 | 20.34 |
| 22 | 9.54 | 10.60 | 12.34 | 14.04 | 16.31 | 18.10 | 21.34 |
| 23 | 10.20 | 11.29 | 13.09 | 14.85 | 17.19 | 19.02 | 22.34 |
| 24 | 10.86 | 11.99 | 13.85 | 15.66 | 18.06 | 19.94 | 23.34 |
| 25 | 11.52 | 12.70 | 14.61 | 16.47 | 18.94 | 20.87 | 24.34 |
| 26 | 12.20 | 13.41 | 15.38 | 17.29 | 19.82 | 21.79 | 25.34 |
| 27 | 12.88 | 14.12 | 16.15 | 18.11 | 20.70 | 22.72 | 26.34 |
| 28 | 13.56 | 14.85 | 16.93 | 18.94 | 21.59 | 23.65 | 27.34 |
| 29 | 14.26 | 15.57 | 17.71 | 19.77 | 22.48 | 24.58 | 28.34 |
| 30 | 14.95 | 16.31 | 18.49 | 20.60 | 23.36 | 25.51 | 29.34 |

Table IV                                                                                              301

**TABLE IV.  Chi-Square Distribution**

(continued)

| $\nu$ or df | A = 0.30 | A = 0.20 | A = 0.10 | A = 0.05 | A = 0.02 | A = 0.01 | A = 0.001 |
|---|---|---|---|---|---|---|---|
| 1 | 1.07 | 1.64 | 2.71 | 3.84 | 5.41 | 6.64 | 10.83 |
| 2 | 2.41 | 3.22 | 4.60 | 5.99 | 7.82 | 9.21 | 13.82 |
| 3 | 3.66 | 4.64 | 6.25 | 7.82 | 9.84 | 11.34 | 16.27 |
| 4 | 4.88 | 5.99 | 7.78 | 9.49 | 11.67 | 13.28 | 18.46 |
| 5 | 6.06 | 7.29 | 9.24 | 11.07 | 13.39 | 15.09 | 20.52 |
| 6 | 7.23 | 8.56 | 10.64 | 12.59 | 15.03 | 16.81 | 22.46 |
| 7 | 8.38 | 9.80 | 12.02 | 14.07 | 16.62 | 18.48 | 24.32 |
| 8 | 9.52 | 11.03 | 13.36 | 15.51 | 18.17 | 20.09 | 26.12 |
| 9 | 10.66 | 12.24 | 14.68 | 16.92 | 19.68 | 21.67 | 27.88 |
| 10 | 11.78 | 13.44 | 15.99 | 18.31 | 21.16 | 23.21 | 29.59 |
| 11 | 12.90 | 14.63 | 17.28 | 19.68 | 22.62 | 24.72 | 31.26 |
| 12 | 14.01 | 15.81 | 18.55 | 21.03 | 24.05 | 26.22 | 32.91 |
| 13 | 15.12 | 16.98 | 19.81 | 22.36 | 25.47 | 27.69 | 34.53 |
| 14 | 16.22 | 18.15 | 21.06 | 23.68 | 26.87 | 29.14 | 36.12 |
| 15 | 17.32 | 19.31 | 22.31 | 25.00 | 28.26 | 30.58 | 37.70 |
| 16 | 18.42 | 20.46 | 23.54 | 26.30 | 29.63 | 32.00 | 39.25 |
| 17 | 19.51 | 21.62 | 24.77 | 27.59 | 31.00 | 33.41 | 40.79 |
| 18 | 20.60 | 22.76 | 25.99 | 28.87 | 32.35 | 34.80 | 42.31 |
| 19 | 21.69 | 23.90 | 27.20 | 30.14 | 33.69 | 36.19 | 43.82 |
| 20 | 22.78 | 25.04 | 28.41 | 31.41 | 35.02 | 37.57 | 45.32 |
| 21 | 23.86 | 26.17 | 29.62 | 32.67 | 36.34 | 38.93 | 46.80 |
| 22 | 24.94 | 27.30 | 30.81 | 33.92 | 37.66 | 30.29 | 48.27 |
| 23 | 26.02 | 28.43 | 32.01 | 35.17 | 38.97 | 41.64 | 49.73 |
| 24 | 27.10 | 29.55 | 33.20 | 36.42 | 40.27 | 42.98 | 51.18 |
| 25 | 28.17 | 30.68 | 34.38 | 37.65 | 41.57 | 44.31 | 52.62 |
| 26 | 29.25 | 31.80 | 35.56 | 38.88 | 42.86 | 45.64 | 54.05 |
| 27 | 30.32 | 32.91 | 36.74 | 40.11 | 44.14 | 46.96 | 55.48 |
| 28 | 31.39 | 34.03 | 37.92 | 41.34 | 45.42 | 48.28 | 56.89 |
| 29 | 32.46 | 35.14 | 39.09 | 42.56 | 46.69 | 49.59 | 58.30 |
| 30 | 33.53 | 36.25 | 40.26 | 43.77 | 47.96 | 50.89 | 59.70 |

Table IV is abridged from Table IV of Fisher and Yates: *Statistical Tables for Biological, Agricultural, and Medical Research*, published by Oliver and Boyd Limited, Edinburgh, by permission of the authors and publishers.

## TABLE Va

# F-Distribution ($F_{.95}$)

The numbers given in this table are the values of F for which the area to the left equals 0.95 for Table Va, 0.975 for Table Vb, and 0.99 for Table Vc for the indicated numerator and denominator degrees of freedom.

$F=1$  $F_{.95}$

| | | \multicolumn{10}{c}{Degrees of freedom for numerator} |
|---|---|---|---|---|---|---|---|---|---|---|---|
| | | 1 | 2 | 3 | 4 | 5 | 6 | 7 | 8 | 9 | 10 |
| | 1 | 161 | 200 | 216 | 225 | 230 | 234 | 237 | 239 | 241 | 242 |
| | 2 | 18.5 | 19.0 | 19.2 | 19.2 | 19.3 | 19.3 | 19.4 | 19.4 | 19.4 | 19.4 |
| | 3 | 10.1 | 9.55 | 9.28 | 9.12 | 9.01 | 8.94 | 8.89 | 8.85 | 8.81 | 8.79 |
| | 4 | 7.71 | 6.94 | 6.59 | 6.39 | 6.26 | 6.16 | 6.09 | 6.04 | 6.00 | 5.96 |
| | 5 | 6.61 | 5.79 | 5.41 | 5.19 | 5.05 | 4.95 | 4.88 | 4.82 | 4.77 | 4.74 |
| | 6 | 5.99 | 5.14 | 4.76 | 4.53 | 4.39 | 4.28 | 4.21 | 4.15 | 4.10 | 4.06 |
| | 7 | 5.59 | 4.74 | 4.35 | 4.12 | 3.97 | 3.87 | 3.79 | 3.73 | 3.68 | 3.64 |
| | 8 | 5.32 | 4.46 | 4.07 | 3.84 | 3.69 | 3.58 | 3.50 | 3.44 | 3.39 | 3.35 |
| | 9 | 5.12 | 4.26 | 3.86 | 3.63 | 3.48 | 3.37 | 3.29 | 3.23 | 3.18 | 3.14 |
| | 10 | 4.96 | 4.10 | 3.71 | 3.48 | 3.33 | 3.22 | 3.14 | 3.07 | 3.02 | 2.98 |
| Degrees of freedom for denominator | 11 | 4.84 | 3.98 | 3.59 | 3.36 | 3.20 | 3.09 | 3.01 | 2.95 | 2.90 | 2.85 |
| | 12 | 4.75 | 3.89 | 3.49 | 3.26 | 3.11 | 3.00 | 2.91 | 2.85 | 2.80 | 2.75 |
| | 13 | 4.67 | 3.81 | 3.41 | 3.18 | 3.03 | 2.92 | 2.83 | 2.77 | 2.71 | 2.67 |
| | 14 | 4.60 | 3.74 | 3.34 | 3.11 | 2.96 | 2.85 | 2.76 | 2.70 | 2.65 | 2.60 |
| | 15 | 4.54 | 3.68 | 3.29 | 3.06 | 2.90 | 2.79 | 2.71 | 2.64 | 2.59 | 2.54 |
| | 16 | 4.49 | 3.63 | 3.24 | 3.01 | 2.85 | 2.74 | 2.66 | 2.59 | 2.54 | 2.49 |
| | 17 | 4.45 | 3.59 | 3.20 | 2.96 | 2.81 | 2.70 | 2.61 | 2.55 | 2.49 | 2.45 |
| | 18 | 4.41 | 3.55 | 3.16 | 2.93 | 2.77 | 2.66 | 2.58 | 2.51 | 2.46 | 2.41 |
| | 19 | 4.38 | 3.52 | 3.13 | 2.90 | 2.74 | 2.63 | 2.54 | 2.48 | 2.42 | 2.38 |
| | 20 | 4.35 | 3.49 | 3.10 | 2.87 | 2.71 | 2.60 | 2.51 | 2.45 | 2.39 | 2.35 |
| | 21 | 4.32 | 3.47 | 3.07 | 2.84 | 2.68 | 2.57 | 2.49 | 2.42 | 2.37 | 2.32 |
| | 22 | 4.30 | 3.44 | 3.05 | 2.82 | 2.66 | 2.55 | 2.46 | 2.40 | 2.34 | 2.30 |
| | 23 | 4.28 | 3.42 | 3.03 | 2.80 | 2.64 | 2.53 | 2.44 | 2.37 | 2.32 | 2.27 |
| | 24 | 4.26 | 3.40 | 3.01 | 2.78 | 2.62 | 2.51 | 2.42 | 2.36 | 2.30 | 2.25 |
| | 25 | 4.24 | 3.39 | 2.99 | 2.76 | 2.60 | 2.49 | 2.40 | 2.34 | 2.28 | 2.24 |
| | 30 | 4.17 | 3.32 | 2.92 | 2.69 | 2.53 | 2.42 | 2.33 | 2.27 | 2.21 | 2.16 |
| | 40 | 4.08 | 3.23 | 2.84 | 2.61 | 2.45 | 2.34 | 2.25 | 2.18 | 2.12 | 2.08 |
| | 60 | 4.00 | 3.15 | 2.76 | 2.53 | 2.37 | 2.25 | 2.17 | 2.10 | 2.04 | 1.99 |
| | 120 | 3.92 | 3.07 | 2.68 | 2.45 | 2.29 | 2.18 | 2.09 | 2.02 | 1.96 | 1.91 |
| | ∞ | 3.84 | 3.00 | 2.60 | 2.37 | 2.21 | 2.10 | 2.01 | 1.94 | 1.88 | 1.83 |

**TABLE Va.**  **F-Distribution** ($F_{.95}$)
(continued)

|  |  | Degrees of freedom for numerator | | | | | | | | |
|---|---|---|---|---|---|---|---|---|---|---|
|  |  | 12 | 15 | 20 | 24 | 30 | 40 | 60 | 120 | ∞ |
|  | 1 | 244 | 246 | 248 | 249 | 250 | 251 | 252 | 253 | 254 |
|  | 2 | 19.4 | 19.4 | 19.4 | 19.5 | 19.5 | 19.5 | 19.5 | 19.5 | 19.5 |
|  | 3 | 8.74 | 8.70 | 8.66 | 8.64 | 8.62 | 8.59 | 8.57 | 8.55 | 8.53 |
|  | 4 | 5.91 | 5.86 | 5.80 | 5.77 | 5.75 | 5.72 | 5.69 | 5.66 | 5.63 |
|  | 5 | 4.68 | 4.62 | 4.56 | 4.53 | 4.50 | 4.46 | 4.43 | 4.40 | 4.37 |
|  | 6 | 4.00 | 3.94 | 3.87 | 3.84 | 3.81 | 3.77 | 3.74 | 3.70 | 3.67 |
|  | 7 | 3.57 | 3.51 | 3.44 | 3.41 | 3.38 | 3.34 | 3.30 | 3.27 | 3.23 |
|  | 8 | 3.28 | 3.22 | 3.15 | 3.12 | 3.08 | 3.04 | 3.01 | 2.97 | 2.93 |
|  | 9 | 3.07 | 3.01 | 2.94 | 2.90 | 2.86 | 2.83 | 2.79 | 2.75 | 2.71 |
|  | 10 | 2.91 | 2.85 | 2.77 | 2.74 | 2.70 | 2.66 | 2.62 | 2.58 | 2.54 |
| Degrees of freedom for denominator | 11 | 2.79 | 2.72 | 2.65 | 2.61 | 2.57 | 2.53 | 2.49 | 2.45 | 2.40 |
|  | 12 | 2.69 | 2.62 | 2.54 | 2.51 | 2.47 | 2.43 | 2.38 | 2.34 | 2.30 |
|  | 13 | 2.60 | 2.53 | 2.46 | 2.42 | 2.38 | 2.34 | 2.30 | 2.25 | 2.21 |
|  | 14 | 2.53 | 2.46 | 2.39 | 2.35 | 2.31 | 2.27 | 2.22 | 2.18 | 2.13 |
|  | 15 | 2.48 | 2.40 | 2.33 | 2.29 | 2.25 | 2.20 | 2.16 | 2.11 | 2.07 |
|  | 16 | 2.42 | 2.35 | 2.28 | 2.24 | 2.19 | 2.15 | 2.11 | 2.06 | 2.01 |
|  | 17 | 2.38 | 2.31 | 2.23 | 2.19 | 2.15 | 2.10 | 2.06 | 2.01 | 1.96 |
|  | 18 | 2.34 | 2.27 | 2.19 | 2.15 | 2.11 | 2.06 | 2.02 | 1.97 | 1.92 |
|  | 19 | 2.31 | 2.23 | 2.16 | 2.11 | 2.07 | 2.03 | 1.98 | 1.93 | 1.88 |
|  | 20 | 2.28 | 2.20 | 2.12 | 2.08 | 2.04 | 1.99 | 1.95 | 1.90 | 1.84 |
|  | 21 | 2.25 | 2.18 | 2.10 | 2.05 | 2.01 | 1.96 | 1.92 | 1.87 | 1.81 |
|  | 22 | 2.23 | 2.15 | 2.07 | 2.03 | 1.98 | 1.94 | 1.89 | 1.84 | 1.78 |
|  | 23 | 2.20 | 2.13 | 2.05 | 2.01 | 1.96 | 1.91 | 1.86 | 1.81 | 1.76 |
|  | 24 | 2.18 | 2.11 | 2.03 | 1.98 | 1.94 | 1.89 | 1.84 | 1.79 | 1.73 |
|  | 25 | 2.16 | 2.09 | 2.01 | 1.96 | 1.92 | 1.87 | 1.82 | 1.77 | 1.71 |
|  | 30 | 2.09 | 2.01 | 1.93 | 1.89 | 1.84 | 1.79 | 1.74 | 1.68 | 1.62 |
|  | 40 | 2.00 | 1.92 | 1.84 | 1.79 | 1.74 | 1.69 | 1.64 | 1.58 | 1.51 |
|  | 60 | 1.92 | 1.84 | 1.75 | 1.70 | 1.65 | 1.59 | 1.53 | 1.47 | 1.39 |
|  | 120 | 1.83 | 1.75 | 1.66 | 1.61 | 1.55 | 1.50 | 1.43 | 1.35 | 1.25 |
|  | ∞ | 1.75 | 1.67 | 1.57 | 1.52 | 1.46 | 1.39 | 1.32 | 1.22 | 1.00 |

TABLE Vb.

# F-Distribution ($F_{.975}$)

| | | Degrees of freedom for numerator | | | | | | | | | |
|---|---|---|---|---|---|---|---|---|---|---|---|
| | | 1 | 2 | 3 | 4 | 5 | 6 | 7 | 8 | 9 | 10 |
| Degrees of freedom for denominator | 1 | 648 | 800 | 864 | 900 | 922 | 937 | 948 | 957 | 963 | 969 |
| | 2 | 38.5 | 39.0 | 39.2 | 39.2 | 39.3 | 39.3 | 39.4 | 39.4 | 39.4 | 39.4 |
| | 3 | 17.4 | 16.0 | 15.4 | 15.1 | 14.9 | 14.7 | 14.6 | 14.5 | 14.5 | 14.4 |
| | 4 | 12.2 | 10.6 | 9.98 | 9.60 | 9.36 | 9.20 | 9.07 | 8.98 | 8.90 | 8.84 |
| | 5 | 10.0 | 8.43 | 7.76 | 7.39 | 7.15 | 6.98 | 6.85 | 6.76 | 6.68 | 6.62 |
| | 6 | 8.81 | 7.26 | 6.60 | 6.23 | 5.99 | 5.82 | 5.70 | 5.60 | 5.52 | 5.46 |
| | 7 | 8.07 | 6.54 | 5.89 | 5.52 | 5.29 | 5.12 | 4.99 | 4.90 | 4.82 | 4.76 |
| | 8 | 7.57 | 6.06 | 5.42 | 5.05 | 4.82 | 4.65 | 4.53 | 4.43 | 4.36 | 4.30 |
| | 9 | 7.21 | 5.71 | 5.08 | 4.72 | 4.48 | 4.32 | 4.20 | 4.10 | 4.03 | 3.96 |
| | 10 | 6.94 | 5.46 | 4.83 | 4.47 | 4.24 | 4.07 | 3.95 | 3.85 | 3.78 | 3.72 |
| | 11 | 6.72 | 5.26 | 4.63 | 4.28 | 4.04 | 3.88 | 3.76 | 3.66 | 3.59 | 3.53 |
| | 12 | 6.55 | 5.10 | 4.47 | 4.12 | 3.89 | 3.73 | 3.61 | 3.51 | 3.44 | 3.37 |
| | 13 | 6.41 | 4.97 | 4.35 | 4.00 | 3.77 | 3.60 | 3.48 | 3.39 | 3.31 | 3.25 |
| | 14 | 6.30 | 4.86 | 4.24 | 3.89 | 3.66 | 3.50 | 3.38 | 3.28 | 3.21 | 3.15 |
| | 15 | 6.20 | 4.77 | 4.15 | 3.80 | 3.58 | 3.41 | 3.29 | 3.20 | 3.12 | 3.06 |
| | 16 | 6.12 | 4.69 | 4.08 | 3.73 | 3.50 | 3.34 | 3.22 | 3.12 | 3.05 | 2.99 |
| | 17 | 6.04 | 4.62 | 4.01 | 3.66 | 3.44 | 3.28 | 3.16 | 3.06 | 2.98 | 2.92 |
| | 18 | 5.98 | 4.56 | 3.95 | 3.61 | 3.38 | 3.22 | 3.10 | 3.01 | 2.93 | 2.87 |
| | 19 | 5.92 | 4.51 | 3.90 | 3.56 | 3.33 | 3.17 | 3.05 | 2.96 | 2.88 | 2.82 |
| | 20 | 5.87 | 4.46 | 3.86 | 3.51 | 3.29 | 3.13 | 3.01 | 2.91 | 2.84 | 2.77 |
| | 21 | 5.83 | 4.42 | 3.82 | 3.48 | 3.25 | 3.09 | 2.97 | 2.87 | 2.80 | 2.73 |
| | 22 | 5.79 | 4.38 | 3.78 | 3.44 | 3.22 | 3.05 | 2.93 | 2.84 | 2.76 | 2.70 |
| | 23 | 5.75 | 4.35 | 3.75 | 3.41 | 3.18 | 3.02 | 2.90 | 2.81 | 2.73 | 2.67 |
| | 24 | 5.72 | 4.32 | 3.72 | 3.38 | 3.15 | 2.99 | 2.87 | 2.78 | 2.70 | 2.64 |
| | 25 | 5.69 | 4.29 | 3.69 | 3.35 | 3.13 | 2.97 | 2.85 | 2.75 | 2.68 | 2.61 |
| | 30 | 5.57 | 4.18 | 3.59 | 3.25 | 3.03 | 2.87 | 2.75 | 2.65 | 2.57 | 2.51 |
| | 40 | 5.42 | 4.05 | 3.46 | 3.13 | 2.90 | 2.74 | 2.62 | 2.53 | 2.45 | 2.39 |
| | 60 | 5.29 | 3.93 | 3.34 | 3.01 | 2.79 | 2.63 | 2.51 | 2.41 | 2.33 | 2.27 |
| | 120 | 5.15 | 3.80 | 3.23 | 2.89 | 2.67 | 2.52 | 2.39 | 2.30 | 2.22 | 2.16 |
| | ∞ | 5.02 | 3.69 | 3.12 | 2.79 | 2.57 | 2.41 | 2.29 | 2.19 | 2.11 | 2.05 |

**F-Distribution**  ($F_{.975}$)

(continued)

|  |  | Degrees of freedom for numerator | | | | | | | | |
|---|---|---|---|---|---|---|---|---|---|---|
|  |  | 12 | 15 | 20 | 24 | 30 | 40 | 60 | 120 | ∞ |
|  | 1 | 977 | 985 | 993 | 997 | 1,001 | 1,006 | 1,010 | 1,014 | 1,018 |
|  | 2 | 39.4 | 39.4 | 39.4 | 39.5 | 39.5 | 39.5 | 39.5 | 39.5 | 39.5 |
|  | 3 | 14.3 | 14.3 | 14.2 | 14.1 | 14.1 | 14.0 | 14.0 | 13.9 | 13.9 |
|  | 4 | 8.75 | 8.66 | 8.56 | 8.51 | 8.46 | 8.41 | 8.36 | 8.31 | 8.26 |
|  | 5 | 6.52 | 6.43 | 6.33 | 6.28 | 6.23 | 6.18 | 6.12 | 6.07 | 6.02 |
|  | 6 | 5.37 | 5.27 | 5.17 | 5.12 | 5.07 | 5.01 | 4.96 | 4.90 | 4.85 |
|  | 7 | 4.67 | 4.57 | 4.47 | 4.42 | 4.36 | 4.31 | 4.25 | 4.20 | 4.14 |
|  | 8 | 4.20 | 4.10 | 4.00 | 3.95 | 3.89 | 3.84 | 3.78 | 3.73 | 3.67 |
|  | 9 | 3.87 | 3.77 | 3.67 | 3.61 | 3.56 | 3.51 | 3.45 | 3.39 | 3.33 |
|  | 10 | 3.62 | 3.52 | 3.42 | 3.37 | 3.31 | 3.26 | 3.20 | 3.14 | 3.08 |
|  | 11 | 3.43 | 3.33 | 3.23 | 3.17 | 3.12 | 3.06 | 3.00 | 2.94 | 2.88 |
| Degrees of freedom for denominator | 12 | 3.28 | 3.18 | 3.07 | 3.02 | 2.96 | 2.91 | 2.85 | 2.79 | 2.72 |
|  | 13 | 3.15 | 3.05 | 2.95 | 2.89 | 2.84 | 2.78 | 2.72 | 2.66 | 2.60 |
|  | 14 | 3.05 | 2.95 | 2.84 | 2.79 | 2.73 | 2.67 | 2.61 | 2.55 | 2.49 |
|  | 15 | 2.96 | 2.86 | 2.76 | 2.70 | 2.64 | 2.59 | 2.52 | 2.46 | 2.40 |
|  | 16 | 2.89 | 2.79 | 2.68 | 2.63 | 2.57 | 2.51 | 2.45 | 2.38 | 2.32 |
|  | 17 | 2.82 | 2.72 | 2.62 | 2.56 | 2.50 | 2.44 | 2.38 | 2.32 | 2.25 |
|  | 18 | 2.77 | 2.67 | 2.56 | 2.50 | 2.44 | 2.38 | 2.32 | 2.26 | 2.19 |
|  | 19 | 2.72 | 2.62 | 2.51 | 2.45 | 2.39 | 2.33 | 2.27 | 2.20 | 2.13 |
|  | 20 | 2.68 | 2.57 | 2.46 | 2.41 | 2.35 | 2.29 | 2.22 | 2.16 | 2.09 |
|  | 21 | 2.64 | 2.53 | 2.42 | 2.37 | 2.31 | 2.25 | 2.18 | 2.11 | 2.04 |
|  | 22 | 2.60 | 2.50 | 2.39 | 2.33 | 2.27 | 2.21 | 2.14 | 2.08 | 2.00 |
|  | 23 | 2.57 | 2.47 | 2.36 | 2.30 | 2.24 | 2.18 | 2.11 | 2.04 | 1.97 |
|  | 24 | 2.54 | 2.44 | 2.33 | 2.27 | 2.21 | 2.15 | 2.08 | 2.01 | 1.94 |
|  | 25 | 2.51 | 2.41 | 2.30 | 2.24 | 2.18 | 2.12 | 2.05 | 1.98 | 1.91 |
|  | 30 | 2.41 | 2.31 | 2.20 | 2.14 | 2.07 | 2.01 | 1.94 | 1.87 | 1.79 |
|  | 40 | 2.29 | 2.18 | 2.07 | 2.01 | 1.94 | 1.88 | 1.80 | 1.72 | 1.64 |
|  | 60 | 2.17 | 2.06 | 1.94 | 1.88 | 1.82 | 1.74 | 1.67 | 1.58 | 1.48 |
|  | 120 | 2.05 | 1.95 | 1.82 | 1.76 | 1.69 | 1.61 | 1.53 | 1.43 | 1.31 |
|  | ∞ | 1.94 | 1.83 | 1.71 | 1.64 | 1.57 | 1.48 | 1.39 | 1.27 | 1.00 |

TABLE Vc.

# F-Distribution ($F_{.99}$)

| | | 1 | 2 | 3 | 4 | 5 | 6 | 7 | 8 | 9 | 10 |
|---|---|---|---|---|---|---|---|---|---|---|---|
| | | | | | | Degrees of freedom for numerator | | | | | |
| | 1 | 4,052 | 5,000 | 5,403 | 5,625 | 5,764 | 5,859 | 5,928 | 5,982 | 6,023 | 6,056 |
| | 2 | 98.5 | 99.0 | 99.2 | 99.2 | 99.3 | 99.3 | 99.4 | 99.4 | 99.4 | 99.4 |
| | 3 | 34.1 | 30.8 | 29.5 | 28.7 | 28.2 | 27.9 | 27.7 | 27.5 | 27.3 | 27.2 |
| | 4 | 21.2 | 18.0 | 16.7 | 16.0 | 15.5 | 15.2 | 15.0 | 14.8 | 14.7 | 14.5 |
| | 5 | 16.3 | 13.3 | 12.1 | 11.4 | 11.0 | 10.7 | 10.5 | 10.3 | 10.2 | 10.1 |
| | 6 | 13.7 | 10.9 | 9.78 | 9.15 | 8.75 | 8.47 | 8.26 | 8.10 | 7.98 | 7.87 |
| | 7 | 12.2 | 9.55 | 8.45 | 7.85 | 7.46 | 7.19 | 6.99 | 6.84 | 6.72 | 6.62 |
| | 8 | 11.3 | 8.65 | 7.59 | 7.01 | 6.63 | 6.37 | 6.18 | 6.03 | 5.91 | 5.81 |
| | 9 | 10.6 | 8.02 | 6.99 | 6.42 | 6.06 | 5.80 | 5.61 | 5.47 | 5.35 | 5.26 |
| | 10 | 10.0 | 7.56 | 6.55 | 5.99 | 5.64 | 5.39 | 5.20 | 5.06 | 4.94 | 4.85 |
| | 11 | 9.65 | 7.21 | 6.22 | 5.67 | 5.32 | 5.07 | 4.89 | 4.74 | 4.63 | 4.54 |
| | 12 | 9.33 | 6.93 | 5.95 | 5.41 | 5.06 | 4.82 | 4.64 | 4.50 | 4.39 | 4.30 |
| | 13 | 9.07 | 6.70 | 5.74 | 5.21 | 4.86 | 4.62 | 4.44 | 4.30 | 4.19 | 4.10 |
| | 14 | 8.86 | 6.51 | 5.56 | 5.04 | 4.70 | 4.46 | 4.28 | 4.14 | 4.03 | 3.94 |
| | 15 | 8.68 | 6.36 | 5.42 | 4.89 | 4.56 | 4.32 | 4.14 | 4.00 | 3.89 | 3.80 |
| | 16 | 8.53 | 6.23 | 5.29 | 4.77 | 4.44 | 4.20 | 4.03 | 3.89 | 3.78 | 3.69 |
| | 17 | 8.40 | 6.11 | 5.19 | 4.67 | 4.34 | 4.10 | 3.93 | 3.79 | 3.68 | 3.59 |
| | 18 | 8.29 | 6.01 | 5.09 | 4.58 | 4.25 | 4.01 | 3.84 | 3.71 | 3.60 | 3.51 |
| | 19 | 8.19 | 5.93 | 5.01 | 4.50 | 4.17 | 3.94 | 3.77 | 3.63 | 3.52 | 3.43 |
| | 20 | 8.10 | 5.85 | 4.94 | 4.43 | 4.10 | 3.87 | 3.70 | 3.56 | 3.46 | 3.37 |
| | 21 | 8.02 | 5.78 | 4.87 | 4.37 | 4.04 | 3.81 | 3.64 | 3.51 | 3.40 | 3.31 |
| | 22 | 7.95 | 5.72 | 4.82 | 4.31 | 3.99 | 3.76 | 3.59 | 3.45 | 3.35 | 3.26 |
| | 23 | 7.88 | 5.66 | 4.76 | 4.26 | 3.94 | 3.71 | 3.54 | 3.41 | 3.30 | 3.21 |
| | 24 | 7.82 | 5.61 | 4.72 | 4.22 | 3.90 | 3.67 | 3.50 | 3.36 | 3.26 | 3.17 |
| | 25 | 7.77 | 5.57 | 4.68 | 4.18 | 3.86 | 3.63 | 3.46 | 3.32 | 3.22 | 3.13 |
| | 30 | 7.56 | 5.39 | 4.51 | 4.02 | 3.70 | 3.47 | 3.30 | 3.17 | 3.07 | 2.98 |
| | 40 | 7.31 | 5.18 | 4.31 | 3.83 | 3.51 | 3.29 | 3.12 | 2.99 | 2.89 | 2.80 |
| | 60 | 7.08 | 4.98 | 4.13 | 3.65 | 3.34 | 3.12 | 2.95 | 2.82 | 2.72 | 2.63 |
| | 120 | 6.85 | 4.79 | 3.95 | 3.48 | 3.17 | 2.96 | 2.79 | 2.66 | 2.56 | 2.47 |
| | ∞ | 6.63 | 4.61 | 3.78 | 3.32 | 3.02 | 2.80 | 2.64 | 2.51 | 2.41 | 2.32 |

Degrees of freedom for denominator

Table Vc                                                    307

**TABLE Vc.** **F-Distribution ($F_{.99}$)**
(continued)

| | | 12 | 15 | 20 | 24 | 30 | 40 | 60 | 120 | ∞ |
|---|---|---|---|---|---|---|---|---|---|---|
| | | | | | Degrees of freedom for numerator | | | | | |
| | 1 | 6,106 | 6,157 | 6,209 | 6,235 | 6,261 | 6,287 | 6,313 | 6,339 | 6,366 |
| | 2 | 99.4 | 99.4 | 99.4 | 99.5 | 99.5 | 99.5 | 99.5 | 99.5 | 99.5 |
| | 3 | 27.1 | 26.9 | 26.7 | 26.6 | 26.5 | 26.4 | 26.3 | 26.2 | 26.1 |
| | 4 | 14.4 | 14.2 | 14.0 | 13.9 | 13.8 | 13.7 | 13.7 | 13.6 | 13.5 |
| | 5 | 9.89 | 9.72 | 9.55 | 9.47 | 9.38 | 9.29 | 9.20 | 9.11 | 9.02 |
| | 6 | 7.72 | 7.56 | 7.40 | 7.31 | 7.23 | 7.14 | 7.06 | 6.97 | 6.88 |
| | 7 | 6.47 | 6.31 | 6.16 | 6.07 | 5.99 | 5.91 | 5.82 | 5.74 | 5.65 |
| | 8 | 5.67 | 5.52 | 5.36 | 5.28 | 5.20 | 5.12 | 5.03 | 4.95 | 4.86 |
| | 9 | 5.11 | 4.96 | 4.81 | 4.73 | 4.65 | 4.57 | 4.48 | 4.40 | 4.31 |
| | 10 | 4.71 | 4.56 | 4.41 | 4.33 | 4.25 | 4.17 | 4.08 | 4.00 | 3.91 |
| Degrees of freedom for denominator | 11 | 4.40 | 4.25 | 4.10 | 4.02 | 3.94 | 3.86 | 3.78 | 3.69 | 3.60 |
| | 12 | 4.16 | 4.01 | 3.86 | 3.78 | 3.70 | 3.62 | 3.54 | 3.45 | 3.36 |
| | 13 | 3.96 | 3.82 | 3.66 | 3.59 | 3.51 | 3.43 | 3.34 | 3.25 | 3.17 |
| | 14 | 3.80 | 3.66 | 3.51 | 3.43 | 3.35 | 3.27 | 3.18 | 3.09 | 3.00 |
| | 15 | 3.67 | 3.52 | 3.37 | 3.29 | 3.21 | 3.13 | 3.05 | 2.96 | 2.87 |
| | 16 | 3.55 | 3.41 | 3.26 | 3.18 | 3.10 | 3.02 | 2.93 | 2.84 | 2.75 |
| | 17 | 3.46 | 3.31 | 3.16 | 3.08 | 3.00 | 2.92 | 2.83 | 2.75 | 2.65 |
| | 18 | 3.37 | 3.23 | 3.08 | 3.00 | 2.92 | 2.84 | 2.75 | 2.66 | 2.57 |
| | 19 | 3.30 | 3.15 | 3.00 | 2.92 | 2.84 | 2.76 | 2.67 | 2.58 | 2.49 |
| | 20 | 3.23 | 3.09 | 2.94 | 2.86 | 2.78 | 2.69 | 2.61 | 2.52 | 2.42 |
| | 21 | 3.17 | 3.03 | 2.88 | 2.80 | 2.72 | 2.64 | 2.55 | 2.46 | 2.36 |
| | 22 | 3.12 | 2.98 | 2.83 | 2.75 | 2.67 | 2.58 | 2.50 | 2.40 | 2.31 |
| | 23 | 3.07 | 2.93 | 2.78 | 2.70 | 2.62 | 2.54 | 2.45 | 2.35 | 2.26 |
| | 24 | 3.03 | 2.89 | 2.74 | 2.66 | 2.58 | 2.49 | 2.40 | 2.31 | 2.21 |
| | 25 | 2.99 | 2.85 | 2.70 | 2.62 | 2.53 | 2.45 | 2.36 | 2.27 | 2.17 |
| | 30 | 2.84 | 2.70 | 2.55 | 2.47 | 2.39 | 2.30 | 2.21 | 2.11 | 2.01 |
| | 40 | 2.66 | 2.52 | 2.37 | 2.29 | 2.20 | 2.11 | 2.02 | 1.92 | 1.80 |
| | 60 | 2.50 | 2.35 | 2.20 | 2.12 | 2.03 | 1.94 | 1.84 | 1.73 | 1.60 |
| | 120 | 2.34 | 2.19 | 2.03 | 1.95 | 1.86 | 1.76 | 1.66 | 1.53 | 1.38 |
| | ∞ | 2.18 | 2.04 | 1.88 | 1.79 | 1.70 | 1.59 | 1.47 | 1.32 | 1.00 |

Table V is reproduced with the permission of Professor E. S. Pearson from M. Merrington, C. M. Thompson, "Tables of percentage points of the inverted beta (F) distribution," *Biometrika*, Vol. 33 (1943), p. 73.

# TABLE VI

## Wilcoxon Distribution (with no pairing)

The numbers given in this table are the number of cases for which the sum of the ranks of the sample of size $n_1$ is less than or equal to $W_1$.

Values of $U$, where $U = W_1 - \frac{1}{2}n_1(n_1 + 1)$

| $n_1$ | $n_2$ | $C_{n,n_1}$ | 0 | 1 | 2 | 3 | 4 | 5 | 6 | 7 | 8 | 9 | 10 | 11 | 12 | 13 | 14 | 15 | 16 | 17 | 18 | 19 | 20 |
|---|---|---|---|---|---|---|---|---|---|---|---|---|---|---|---|---|---|---|---|---|---|---|---|
| 3 | 3 | 20 | 1 | 2 | 4 | 7 | 10 | 13 | 16 | 18 | 19 | 20 | | | | | | | | | | | |
| 3 | 4 | 35 | 1 | 2 | 4 | 7 | 11 | 15 | 20 | 24 | 28 | 31 | 33 | 34 | 35 | | | | | | | | |
| 4 | 4 | 70 | 1 | 2 | 4 | 7 | 12 | 17 | 24 | 31 | 39 | 46 | 53 | 58 | 63 | 66 | 68 | 69 | 70 | | | | |
| 3 | 5 | 56 | 1 | 2 | 4 | 7 | 11 | 16 | 22 | 28 | 34 | 40 | 45 | 49 | 52 | 54 | 55 | 56 | | | | | |
| 4 | 5 | 126 | 1 | 2 | 4 | 7 | 12 | 18 | 26 | 35 | 46 | 57 | 69 | 80 | 91 | 100 | 108 | 114 | 119 | 122 | 124 | 125 | 126 |
| 5 | 5 | 252 | 1 | 2 | 4 | 7 | 12 | 19 | 28 | 39 | 53 | 69 | 87 | 106 | 126 | 146 | 165 | 183 | 199 | 213 | 224 | 233 | 240 |
| 3 | 6 | 84 | 1 | 2 | 4 | 7 | 11 | 16 | 23 | 30 | 38 | 46 | 54 | 61 | 68 | 73 | 77 | 80 | 82 | 83 | 84 | | |
| 4 | 6 | 210 | 1 | 2 | 4 | 7 | 12 | 18 | 27 | 37 | 50 | 64 | 80 | 96 | 114 | 130 | 146 | 160 | 173 | 183 | 192 | 198 | 203 |
| 5 | 6 | 462 | 1 | 2 | 4 | 7 | 12 | 19 | 29 | 41 | 57 | 76 | 99 | 124 | 153 | 183 | 215 | 247 | 279 | 309 | 338 | 363 | 386 |
| 6 | 6 | 924 | 1 | 2 | 4 | 7 | 12 | 19 | 30 | 43 | 61 | 83 | 111 | 143 | 182 | 224 | 272 | 323 | 378 | 433 | 491 | 546 | 601 |
| 3 | 7 | 120 | 1 | 2 | 4 | 7 | 11 | 16 | 23 | 31 | 40 | 50 | 60 | 70 | 80 | 89 | 97 | 104 | 109 | 113 | 116 | 118 | 119 |
| 4 | 7 | 330 | 1 | 2 | 4 | 7 | 12 | 18 | 27 | 38 | 52 | 68 | 87 | 107 | 130 | 153 | 177 | 200 | 223 | 243 | 262 | 278 | 292 |
| 5 | 7 | 792 | 1 | 2 | 4 | 7 | 12 | 19 | 29 | 42 | 59 | 80 | 106 | 136 | 171 | 210 | 253 | 299 | 347 | 396 | 445 | 493 | 539 |
| 6 | 7 | 1716 | 1 | 2 | 4 | 7 | 12 | 19 | 30 | 44 | 63 | 87 | 118 | 155 | 201 | 253 | 314 | 382 | 458 | 539 | 627 | 717 | 811 |
| 7 | 7 | 3432 | 1 | 2 | 4 | 7 | 12 | 19 | 30 | 45 | 65 | 91 | 125 | 167 | 220 | 283 | 358 | 445 | 545 | 657 | 782 | 918 | 1064 |
| 3 | 8 | 165 | 1 | 2 | 4 | 7 | 11 | 16 | 23 | 31 | 41 | 52 | 64 | 76 | 89 | 101 | 113 | 124 | 134 | 142 | 149 | 154 | 158 |
| 4 | 8 | 495 | 1 | 2 | 4 | 7 | 12 | 18 | 27 | 38 | 53 | 70 | 91 | 114 | 141 | 169 | 200 | 231 | 264 | 295 | 326 | 354 | 381 |
| 5 | 8 | 1287 | 1 | 2 | 4 | 7 | 12 | 19 | 29 | 42 | 60 | 82 | 110 | 143 | 183 | 228 | 280 | 337 | 400 | 466 | 536 | 607 | 680 |
| 6 | 8 | 3003 | 1 | 2 | 4 | 7 | 12 | 19 | 30 | 44 | 64 | 89 | 122 | 162 | 213 | 272 | 343 | 424 | 518 | 621 | 737 | 860 | 994 |
| 7 | 8 | 6435 | 1 | 2 | 4 | 7 | 12 | 19 | 30 | 45 | 66 | 93 | 129 | 174 | 232 | 302 | 388 | 489 | 609 | 746 | 904 | 1080 | 1277 |
| 8 | 8 | 12870 | 1 | 2 | 4 | 7 | 12 | 19 | 30 | 45 | 67 | 95 | 133 | 181 | 244 | 321 | 418 | 534 | 675 | 839 | 1033 | 1254 | 1509 |

Table VI is reproduced from Table H of Hodges and Lehmann: Basic Concepts of Probability and Statistics, published by Holden-Day, San Francisco, by permission of the authors and publisher.

TABLE VII

## Wilcoxon Distribution (with pairing)

The numbers given in these tables are the number of cases for which the sum of the ranks is less than or equal to $W_1$.

**TABLE VIIa.** **The case where $W_1 \leq n$.**

| $W_1$ | | $W_1$ | | $W_1$ | | $W_1$ | |
|---|---|---|---|---|---|---|---|
| 0 | 1 | 6 | 14 | 11 | 55 | 16 | 169 |
| 1 | 2 | 7 | 19 | 12 | 70 | 17 | 207 |
| 2 | 3 | 8 | 25 | 13 | 88 | 18 | 253 |
| 3 | 5 | 9 | 33 | 14 | 110 | 19 | 307 |
| 4 | 7 | 10 | 43 | 15 | 137 | 20 | 371 |
| 5 | 10 | | | | | | |

**TABLE VIIb.  The case where $W_1 > n$.**

|  | | | | | | | | | $n$ | | | | | | | | | |
| $W_1 - n$ | 3 | 4 | 5 | 6 | 7 | 8 | 9 | 10 | 11 | 12 | 13 | 14 | 15 | 16 | 17 | 18 | 19 | 20 |
|---|---|---|---|---|---|---|---|---|---|---|---|---|---|---|---|---|---|---|
| 1 | 6 | 9 | 13 | 18 | 24 | 32 | 42 | 54 | 69 | 87 | 109 | 136 | 168 | 206 | 252 | 306 | 370 | 446 |
| 2 | 7 | 11 | 16 | 22 | 30 | 40 | 52 | 67 | 85 | 107 | 134 | 166 | 204 | 250 | 304 | 368 | 444 | 533 |
| 3 | 8 | 13 | 19 | 27 | 37 | 49 | 64 | 82 | 104 | 131 | 163 | 201 | 247 | 301 | 365 | 441 | 530 | 634 |
| 4 | | 14 | 22 | 32 | 44 | 59 | 77 | 99 | 126 | 158 | 196 | 242 | 296 | 360 | 436 | 525 | 629 | 751 |
| 5 | | 15 | 25 | 37 | 52 | 70 | 92 | 119 | 151 | 189 | 235 | 289 | 353 | 429 | 518 | 622 | 744 | 886 |
| 6 | | 16 | 27 | 42 | 60 | 82 | 109 | 141 | 179 | 225 | 279 | 343 | 419 | 508 | 612 | 734 | 876 | 1,041 |
| 7 | | | 29 | 46 | 68 | 95 | 127 | 165 | 211 | 265 | 329 | 405 | 494 | 598 | 720 | 862 | 1,027 | 1,219 |
| 8 | | | 30 | 50 | 76 | 108 | 146 | 192 | 246 | 310 | 386 | 475 | 579 | 701 | 843 | 1,008 | 1,200 | 1,422 |
| 9 | | | 31 | 54 | 84 | 121 | 167 | 221 | 285 | 361 | 450 | 554 | 676 | 818 | 983 | 1,175 | 1,397 | 1,653 |
| 10 | | | 32 | 57 | 91 | 135 | 188 | 252 | 328 | 417 | 521 | 643 | 785 | 950 | 1,142 | 1,364 | 1,620 | 1,916 |
| 11 | | | | 59 | 98 | 148 | 210 | 285 | 374 | 478 | 600 | 742 | 907 | 1,099 | 1,321 | 1,577 | 1,873 | 2,213 |
| 12 | | | | 61 | 104 | 161 | 253 | 320 | 423 | 545 | 687 | 852 | 1,044 | 1,266 | 1,522 | 1,818 | 2,158 | 2,548 |
| 13 | | | | 62 | 109 | 174 | 256 | 356 | 476 | 617 | 782 | 974 | 1,196 | 1,452 | 1,748 | 2,088 | 2,478 | 2,926 |
| 14 | | | | 63 | 114 | 186 | 279 | 394 | 532 | 695 | 886 | 1,108 | 1,364 | 1,660 | 2,000 | 2,390 | 2,838 | 3,350 |
| 15 | | | | 64 | 118 | 197 | 302 | 433 | 591 | 779 | 999 | 1,254 | 1,550 | 1,890 | 2,280 | 2,728 | 3,240 | 3,825 |
| 16 | | | | | 121 | 207 | 324 | 472 | 653 | 868 | 1,120 | 1,414 | 1,753 | 2,143 | 2,591 | 3,103 | 3,688 | 4,356 |
| 17 | | | | | 123 | 216 | 345 | 512 | 717 | 962 | 1,251 | 1,587 | 1,975 | 2,422 | 2,934 | 3,519 | 4,187 | 4,947 |
| 18 | | | | | 125 | 224 | 366 | 552 | 783 | 1,062 | 1,391 | 1,774 | 2,218 | 2,728 | 3,312 | 3,980 | 4,740 | 5,604 |
| 19 | | | | | 126 | 231 | 385 | 591 | 851 | 1,166 | 1,539 | 1,976 | 2,481 | 3,062 | 3,728 | 4,487 | 5,351 | 6,333 |
| 20 | | | | | 127 | 237 | 403 | 630 | 920 | 1,274 | 1,697 | 2,192 | 2,766 | 3,427 | 4,183 | 5,045 | 6,026 | 7,139 |
| 21 | | | | | 128 | 242 | 420 | 668 | 989 | 1,387 | 1,863 | 2,423 | 3,074 | 3,823 | 4,680 | 5,658 | 6,769 | 8,028 |
| 22 | | | | | | 246 | 435 | 704 | 1,059 | 1,502 | 2,037 | 2,669 | 3,404 | 4,251 | 5,222 | 6,328 | 7,584 | 9,008 |
| 23 | | | | | | 249 | 448 | 739 | 1,128 | 1,620 | 2,219 | 2,929 | 3,757 | 4,714 | 5,810 | 7,059 | 8,478 | 10,084 |
| 24 | | | | | | 251 | 460 | 772 | 1,197 | 1,741 | 2,408 | 3,203 | 4,135 | 5,212 | 6,447 | 7,856 | 9,455 | 11,264 |
| 25 | | | | | | 253 | 470 | 803 | 1,265 | 1,863 | 2,603 | 3,492 | 4,536 | 5,746 | 7,136 | 8,721 | 10,520 | 12,557 |
| 26 | | | | | | 254 | 479 | 832 | 1,331 | 1,986 | 2,805 | 3,794 | 4,961 | 6,318 | 7,878 | 9,658 | 11,681 | 13,968 |
| 27 | | | | | | 255 | 487 | 859 | 1,395 | 2,110 | 3,012 | 4,109 | 5,411 | 6,928 | 8,675 | 10,673 | 12,941 | 15,506 |
| 28 | | | | | | 256 | 493 | 883 | 1,457 | 2,233 | 3,223 | 4,437 | 5,884 | 7,576 | 9,531 | 11,766 | 14,306 | 17,180 |
| 29 | | | | | | | 498 | 905 | 1,516 | 2,355 | 3,438 | 4,776 | 6,380 | 8,265 | 10,445 | 12,942 | 15,783 | 18,997 |
| 30 | | | | | | | 502 | 925 | 1,572 | 2,476 | 3,656 | 5,126 | 6,901 | 8,993 | 11,420 | 14,206 | 17,377 | 20,966 |

Table VII is reproduced from Tables J and K of Hodges and Lehmann: *Basic Concepts of Probability and Statistics*, published by Holden-Day, Inc., San Francisco, by permission of the authors and publisher.

## TABLE VIII

# Transformation of Percentage to Arcsin $\sqrt{\text{Percentage}}$

The numbers in this table are the angles (in degrees) corresponding to given percentages under the transformation arcsin $\sqrt{\text{percentage}}$.

| %   | 0     | 1     | 2     | 3     | 4     | 5     | 6     | 7     | 8     | 9     |
|-----|-------|-------|-------|-------|-------|-------|-------|-------|-------|-------|
| 0.0 | 0     | 0.57  | 0.81  | 0.99  | 1.15  | 1.28  | 1.40  | 1.52  | 1.62  | 1.72  |
| 0.1 | 1.81  | 1.90  | 1.99  | 2.07  | 2.14  | 2.22  | 2.29  | 2.36  | 2.43  | 2.50  |
| 0.2 | 2.56  | 2.63  | 2.69  | 2.75  | 2.81  | 2.87  | 2.92  | 2.98  | 3.03  | 3.09  |
| 0.3 | 3.14  | 3.19  | 3.24  | 3.29  | 3.34  | 3.39  | 3.44  | 3.49  | 3.53  | 3.58  |
| 0.4 | 3.63  | 3.67  | 3.72  | 3.76  | 3.80  | 3.85  | 3.89  | 3.93  | 3.97  | 4.01  |
| 0.5 | 4.05  | 4.09  | 4.13  | 4.17  | 4.21  | 4.25  | 4.29  | 4.33  | 4.37  | 4.40  |
| 0.6 | 4.44  | 4.48  | 4.52  | 4.55  | 4.59  | 4.62  | 4.66  | 4.69  | 4.73  | 4.76  |
| 0.7 | 4.80  | 4.83  | 4.87  | 4.90  | 4.93  | 4.97  | 5.00  | 5.03  | 5.07  | 5.10  |
| 0.8 | 5.13  | 5.16  | 5.20  | 5.23  | 5.26  | 5.29  | 5.32  | 5.35  | 5.38  | 5.41  |
| 0.9 | 5.44  | 5.47  | 5.50  | 5.53  | 5.56  | 5.59  | 5.62  | 5.65  | 5.68  | 5.71  |
| 1   | 5.74  | 6.02  | 6.29  | 6.55  | 6.80  | 7.04  | 7.27  | 7.49  | 7.71  | 7.92  |
| 2   | 8.13  | 8.33  | 8.53  | 8.72  | 8.91  | 9.10  | 9.28  | 9.46  | 9.63  | 9.81  |
| 3   | 9.98  | 10.14 | 10.31 | 10.47 | 10.63 | 10.78 | 10.94 | 11.09 | 11.24 | 11.39 |
| 4   | 11.54 | 11.68 | 11.83 | 11.97 | 12.11 | 12.25 | 12.39 | 12.52 | 12.66 | 12.79 |
| 5   | 12.92 | 13.05 | 13.18 | 13.31 | 13.44 | 13.56 | 13.69 | 13.81 | 13.94 | 14.06 |
| 6   | 14.18 | 14.30 | 14.42 | 14.54 | 14.65 | 14.77 | 14.89 | 15.00 | 15.12 | 15.23 |
| 7   | 15.34 | 15.45 | 15.56 | 15.68 | 15.79 | 15.89 | 16.00 | 16.11 | 16.22 | 16.32 |
| 8   | 16.43 | 16.54 | 16.64 | 16.74 | 16.85 | 16.95 | 17.05 | 17.16 | 17.26 | 17.36 |
| 9   | 17.46 | 17.56 | 17.66 | 17.76 | 17.85 | 17.95 | 18.05 | 18.15 | 18.24 | 18.34 |
| 10  | 18.44 | 18.53 | 18.63 | 18.72 | 18.81 | 18.91 | 19.00 | 19.09 | 19.19 | 19.28 |
| 11  | 19.37 | 19.46 | 19.55 | 19.64 | 19.73 | 19.82 | 19.91 | 20.00 | 20.09 | 20.18 |
| 12  | 20.27 | 20.36 | 20.44 | 20.53 | 20.62 | 20.70 | 20.79 | 20.88 | 20.96 | 21.05 |
| 13  | 21.13 | 21.22 | 21.30 | 21.39 | 21.47 | 21.56 | 21.64 | 21.72 | 21.81 | 21.89 |
| 14  | 21.97 | 22.06 | 22.14 | 22.22 | 22.30 | 22.38 | 22.46 | 22.55 | 22.63 | 22.71 |
| 15  | 22.79 | 22.87 | 22.95 | 23.03 | 23.11 | 23.19 | 23.26 | 23.34 | 23.42 | 23.50 |
| 16  | 23.58 | 23.66 | 23.73 | 23.81 | 23.89 | 23.97 | 24.04 | 24.12 | 24.20 | 24.27 |
| 17  | 24.35 | 24.43 | 24.50 | 24.58 | 24.65 | 24.73 | 24.80 | 24.88 | 24.95 | 25.03 |
| 18  | 25.10 | 25.18 | 25.25 | 25.33 | 25.40 | 25.48 | 25.55 | 25.62 | 25.70 | 25.77 |
| 19  | 25.84 | 25.92 | 25.99 | 26.06 | 26.13 | 26.21 | 26.28 | 26.35 | 26.42 | 26.49 |
| 20  | 26.56 | 26.64 | 26.71 | 26.78 | 26.85 | 26.92 | 26.99 | 27.06 | 27.13 | 27.20 |
| 21  | 27.28 | 27.35 | 27.42 | 27.49 | 27.56 | 27.63 | 27.69 | 27.76 | 27.83 | 27.90 |
| 22  | 27.97 | 28.04 | 28.11 | 28.18 | 28.25 | 28.32 | 28.38 | 28.45 | 28.52 | 28.59 |
| 23  | 28.66 | 28.73 | 28.79 | 28.86 | 28.93 | 29.00 | 29.06 | 29.13 | 29.20 | 29.27 |
| 24  | 29.33 | 29.40 | 29.47 | 29.53 | 29.60 | 29.67 | 29.73 | 29.80 | 29.87 | 29.93 |
| 25  | 30.00 | 30.07 | 30.13 | 30.20 | 30.26 | 30.33 | 30.40 | 30.46 | 30.53 | 30.59 |
| 26  | 30.66 | 30.72 | 30.79 | 30.85 | 30.92 | 30.98 | 31.05 | 31.11 | 31.18 | 31.24 |
| 27  | 31.31 | 31.37 | 31.44 | 31.50 | 31.56 | 31.63 | 31.69 | 31.76 | 31.82 | 31.88 |
| 28  | 31.95 | 32.01 | 32.08 | 32.14 | 32.20 | 32.27 | 32.33 | 32.39 | 32.46 | 32.52 |
| 29  | 32.58 | 32.65 | 32.71 | 32.77 | 32.83 | 32.90 | 32.96 | 33.02 | 33.09 | 33.15 |
| 30  | 33.21 | 33.27 | 33.34 | 33.40 | 33.46 | 33.52 | 33.58 | 33.65 | 33.71 | 33.77 |

TABLE VIII. **Transformation of Percentage to Arcsin $\sqrt{\text{Percentage}}$**
(continued)

| %  | 0     | 1     | 2     | 3     | 4     | 5     | 6     | 7     | 8     | 9     |
|----|-------|-------|-------|-------|-------|-------|-------|-------|-------|-------|
| 31 | 33.83 | 33.89 | 33.96 | 34.02 | 34.08 | 34.14 | 34.20 | 34.27 | 34.33 | 34.39 |
| 32 | 34.45 | 34.51 | 34.57 | 34.63 | 34.70 | 34.76 | 34.82 | 34.88 | 34.94 | 35.00 |
| 33 | 35.06 | 35.12 | 35.18 | 35.24 | 35.30 | 35.37 | 35.43 | 35.49 | 35.55 | 35.61 |
| 34 | 35.67 | 35.73 | 35.79 | 35.85 | 35.91 | 35.97 | 36.03 | 36.09 | 36.15 | 36.21 |
| 35 | 36.27 | 36.33 | 36.39 | 36.45 | 36.51 | 36.57 | 36.63 | 36.69 | 36.75 | 36.81 |
| 36 | 36.87 | 36.93 | 36.99 | 37.05 | 37.11 | 37.17 | 37.23 | 37.29 | 37.35 | 37.41 |
| 37 | 37.47 | 37.52 | 37.58 | 37.64 | 37.70 | 37.76 | 37.82 | 37.88 | 37.94 | 38.00 |
| 38 | 38.06 | 38.12 | 38.17 | 38.23 | 38.29 | 38.35 | 38.41 | 38.47 | 38.53 | 38.59 |
| 39 | 38.65 | 38.70 | 38.76 | 38.82 | 38.88 | 38.94 | 39.00 | 39.06 | 39.11 | 39.17 |
| 40 | 39.23 | 39.29 | 39.35 | 39.41 | 39.47 | 39.52 | 39.58 | 39.64 | 39.70 | 39.76 |
| 41 | 39.82 | 39.87 | 39.93 | 39.99 | 40.05 | 40.11 | 40.16 | 40.22 | 40.28 | 40.34 |
| 42 | 40.40 | 40.46 | 40.51 | 40.57 | 40.63 | 40.69 | 40.74 | 40.80 | 40.86 | 40.92 |
| 43 | 40.98 | 41.03 | 41.09 | 41.15 | 41.21 | 41.27 | 41.32 | 41.38 | 41.44 | 41.50 |
| 44 | 41.55 | 41.61 | 41.67 | 41.73 | 41.78 | 41.84 | 41.90 | 41.96 | 42.02 | 42.07 |
| 45 | 42.13 | 42.19 | 42.25 | 42.30 | 42.36 | 42.42 | 42.48 | 42.53 | 42.59 | 42.65 |
| 46 | 42.71 | 42.76 | 42.82 | 42.88 | 42.94 | 42.99 | 43.05 | 43.11 | 43.17 | 43.22 |
| 47 | 43.28 | 43.34 | 43.39 | 43.45 | 43.51 | 43.57 | 43.62 | 43.68 | 43.74 | 43.80 |
| 48 | 43.85 | 43.91 | 43.97 | 44.03 | 44.08 | 44.14 | 44.20 | 44.25 | 44.31 | 44.37 |
| 49 | 44.43 | 44.48 | 44.54 | 44.60 | 44.66 | 44.71 | 44.77 | 44.83 | 44.89 | 44.94 |
| 50 | 45.00 | 45.06 | 45.11 | 45.17 | 45.23 | 45.29 | 45.34 | 45.40 | 45.46 | 45.52 |
| 51 | 45.57 | 45.63 | 45.69 | 45.75 | 45.80 | 45.86 | 45.92 | 45.97 | 46.03 | 46.09 |
| 52 | 46.15 | 46.20 | 46.26 | 46.32 | 46.38 | 46.43 | 46.49 | 46.55 | 46.61 | 46.66 |
| 53 | 46.72 | 46.78 | 46.83 | 46.89 | 46.95 | 47.01 | 47.06 | 47.12 | 47.18 | 47.24 |
| 54 | 47.29 | 47.35 | 47.41 | 47.47 | 47.52 | 47.58 | 47.64 | 47.70 | 47.75 | 47.81 |
| 55 | 47.87 | 47.93 | 47.98 | 48.04 | 48.10 | 48.16 | 48.22 | 48.27 | 48.33 | 48.39 |
| 56 | 48.45 | 48.50 | 48.56 | 48.62 | 48.68 | 48.73 | 48.79 | 48.85 | 48.91 | 48.97 |
| 57 | 49.02 | 49.08 | 49.14 | 49.20 | 49.26 | 49.31 | 49.37 | 49.43 | 49.49 | 49.54 |
| 58 | 49.60 | 49.66 | 49.72 | 49.78 | 49.84 | 49.89 | 49.95 | 50.01 | 50.07 | 50.13 |
| 59 | 50.18 | 50.24 | 50.30 | 50.36 | 50.42 | 50.48 | 50.53 | 50.59 | 50.65 | 50.71 |
| 60 | 50.77 | 50.83 | 50.89 | 50.94 | 51.00 | 51.06 | 51.12 | 51.18 | 51.24 | 51.30 |
| 61 | 51.35 | 51.41 | 51.47 | 51.53 | 51.59 | 51.65 | 51.71 | 51.77 | 51.83 | 51.88 |
| 62 | 51.94 | 52.00 | 52.06 | 52.12 | 52.18 | 52.24 | 52.30 | 52.36 | 52.42 | 52.48 |
| 63 | 52.53 | 52.59 | 52.65 | 52.71 | 52.77 | 52.83 | 52.89 | 52.95 | 53.01 | 53.07 |
| 64 | 53.13 | 53.19 | 53.25 | 53.31 | 53.37 | 53.43 | 53.49 | 53.55 | 53.61 | 53.67 |
| 65 | 53.73 | 53.79 | 53.85 | 53.91 | 53.97 | 54.03 | 54.09 | 54.15 | 54.21 | 54.27 |
| 66 | 54.33 | 54.39 | 54.45 | 54.51 | 54.57 | 54.63 | 54.70 | 54.76 | 54.82 | 54.88 |
| 67 | 54.94 | 55.00 | 55.06 | 55.12 | 55.18 | 55.24 | 55.30 | 55.37 | 55.43 | 55.49 |
| 68 | 55.55 | 55.61 | 55.67 | 55.73 | 55.80 | 55.86 | 55.92 | 55.98 | 56.04 | 56.11 |
| 69 | 56.17 | 56.23 | 56.29 | 56.35 | 56.42 | 56.48 | 56.54 | 56.60 | 56.66 | 56.73 |
| 70 | 56.79 | 56.85 | 56.91 | 56.98 | 57.04 | 57.10 | 57.17 | 57.23 | 57.29 | 57.35 |
| 71 | 57.42 | 57.48 | 57.54 | 57.61 | 57.67 | 57.73 | 57.80 | 57.86 | 57.92 | 57.99 |
| 72 | 58.05 | 58.12 | 58.18 | 58.24 | 58.31 | 58.37 | 58.44 | 58.50 | 58.56 | 58.63 |
| 73 | 58.69 | 58.76 | 58.82 | 58.89 | 58.95 | 59.02 | 59.08 | 59.15 | 59.21 | 59.28 |
| 74 | 59.34 | 59.41 | 59.47 | 59.54 | 59.60 | 59.67 | 59.74 | 59.80 | 59.87 | 59.93 |
| 75 | 60.00 | 60.07 | 60.13 | 60.20 | 60.27 | 60.33 | 60.40 | 60.47 | 60.53 | 60.60 |

Table VIII                                                                    313

**TABLE VIII. Transformation of Percentage to Arcsin $\sqrt{\text{Percentage}}$**
(continued)

| | | | | | | | | | |
|---|---|---|---|---|---|---|---|---|---|
| 76 | 60.67 | 60.73 | 60.80 | 60.87 | 60.94 | 61.00 | 61.07 | 61.14 | 61.21 | 61.27 |
| 77 | 61.34 | 61.41 | 61.48 | 61.55 | 61.62 | 61.68 | 61.75 | 61.82 | 61.89 | 61.96 |
| 78 | 62.03 | 62.10 | 62.17 | 62.24 | 62.31 | 62.37 | 62.44 | 62.51 | 62.58 | 62.65 |
| 79 | 62.72 | 62.80 | 62.87 | 62.94 | 63.01 | 63.08 | 63.15 | 63.22 | 63.29 | 63.36 |
| 80 | 63.44 | 63.51 | 63.58 | 63.65 | 63.72 | 63.79 | 63.87 | 63.94 | 64.01 | 64.08 |
| 81 | 64.16 | 64.23 | 64.30 | 64.38 | 64.45 | 64.52 | 64.60 | 64.67 | 64.75 | 64.82 |
| 82 | 64.90 | 64.97 | 65.05 | 65.12 | 65.20 | 65.27 | 65.35 | 65.42 | 65.50 | 65.57 |
| 83 | 65.65 | 65.73 | 65.80 | 65.88 | 65.96 | 66.03 | 66.11 | 66.19 | 66.27 | 66.34 |
| 84 | 66.42 | 66.50 | 66.58 | 66.66 | 66.74 | 66.81 | 66.89 | 66.97 | 67.05 | 67.13 |
| 85 | 67.21 | 67.29 | 67.37 | 67.45 | 67.54 | 67.62 | 67.70 | 67.78 | 67.86 | 67.94 |
| 86 | 68.03 | 68.11 | 68.19 | 68.28 | 68.36 | 68.44 | 68.53 | 68.61 | 68.70 | 68.78 |
| 87 | 68.87 | 68.95 | 69.04 | 69.12 | 69.21 | 69.30 | 69.38 | 69.47 | 69.56 | 69.64 |
| 88 | 69.73 | 69.82 | 69.91 | 70.00 | 70.09 | 70.18 | 70.27 | 70.36 | 70.45 | 70.54 |
| 89 | 70.63 | 70.72 | 70.81 | 70.91 | 71.00 | 71.09 | 71.19 | 71.28 | 71.37 | 71.47 |
| 90 | 71.56 | 71.66 | 71.76 | 71.85 | 71.95 | 72.05 | 72.15 | 72.24 | 72.34 | 72.44 |
| 91 | 72.54 | 72.64 | 72.74 | 72.84 | 72.95 | 73.05 | 73.15 | 73.26 | 73.36 | 73.46 |
| 92 | 73.57 | 73.68 | 73.78 | 73.89 | 74.00 | 74.11 | 74.21 | 74.32 | 74.44 | 74.55 |
| 93 | 74.66 | 74.77 | 74.88 | 75.00 | 75.11 | 75.23 | 75.35 | 75.46 | 75.58 | 75.70 |
| 94 | 75.82 | 75.94 | 76.06 | 76.19 | 76.31 | 76.44 | 76.56 | 76.69 | 76.82 | 76.95 |
| 95 | 77.08 | 77.21 | 77.34 | 77.48 | 77.61 | 77.75 | 77.89 | 78.03 | 78.17 | 78.32 |
| 96 | 78.46 | 78.61 | 78.76 | 78.91 | 79.06 | 79.22 | 79.37 | 79.53 | 79.69 | 79.86 |
| 97 | 80.02 | 80.19 | 80.37 | 80.54 | 80.72 | 80.90 | 81.09 | 81.28 | 81.47 | 81.67 |
| 98 | 81.87 | 82.08 | 82.29 | 82.51 | 82.73 | 82.96 | 83.20 | 83.45 | 83.71 | 83.98 |
| 99.0 | 84.26 | 84.29 | 84.32 | 84.35 | 84.38 | 84.41 | 84.44 | 84.47 | 84.50 | 84.53 |
| 99.1 | 84.56 | 84.59 | 84.62 | 84.65 | 84.68 | 84.71 | 84.74 | 84.77 | 84.80 | 84.84 |
| 99.2 | 84.87 | 84.90 | 84.93 | 84.97 | 85.00 | 85.03 | 85.07 | 85.10 | 85.13 | 85.17 |
| 99.3 | 85.20 | 85.24 | 85.27 | 85.31 | 85.34 | 85.38 | 85.41 | 85.45 | 85.48 | 85.52 |
| 99.4 | 85.56 | 85.60 | 85.63 | 85.67 | 85.71 | 85.75 | 85.79 | 85.83 | 85.87 | 85.91 |
| 99.5 | 85.95 | 85.99 | 86.03 | 86.07 | 86.11 | 86.15 | 86.20 | 86.24 | 86.28 | 86.33 |
| 99.6 | 86.37 | 86.42 | 86.47 | 86.51 | 86.56 | 86.61 | 86.66 | 86.71 | 86.76 | 86.81 |
| 99.7 | 86.86 | 86.91 | 86.97 | 87.02 | 87.08 | 87.13 | 87.19 | 87.25 | 87.31 | 87.37 |
| 99.8 | 87.44 | 87.50 | 87.57 | 87.64 | 87.71 | 87.78 | 87.86 | 87.93 | 88.01 | 88.10 |
| 99.9 | 88.19 | 88.28 | 88.38 | 88.48 | 88.60 | 88.72 | 88.85 | 89.01 | 89.19 | 89.43 |
| 100.0 | 90.00 | — | — | — | — | — | — | — | — | — |

Table VIII appeared in *Plant Protection* (Leningrad), Vol. 12 (1937), p. 67, and is reproduced with permission of the author, C. I. Bliss.

TABLE IX

## Squares and Square Roots

| N | $N^2$ | $\sqrt{N}$ | $\sqrt{10N}$ | N | $N^2$ | $\sqrt{N}$ | $\sqrt{10N}$ |
|---|---|---|---|---|---|---|---|
| 1.00 | 1.0000 | 1.00000 | 3.16228 | 1.45 | 2.1025 | 1.20416 | 3.80789 |
| 1.01 | 1.0201 | 1.00499 | 3.17805 | 1.46 | 2.1316 | 1.20830 | 3.82099 |
| 1.02 | 1.0404 | 1.00995 | 3.19374 | 1.47 | 2.1609 | 1.21244 | 3.83406 |
| 1.03 | 1.0609 | 1.01489 | 3.20936 | 1.48 | 2.1904 | 1.21655 | 3.84708 |
| 1.04 | 1.0816 | 1.01980 | 3.22490 | 1.49 | 2.2201 | 1.22066 | 3.86005 |
| 1.05 | 1.1025 | 1.02470 | 3.24037 | 1.50 | 2.2500 | 1.22474 | 3.87298 |
| 1.06 | 1.1236 | 1.02956 | 3.25576 | 1.51 | 2.2801 | 1.22882 | 3.88587 |
| 1.07 | 1.1449 | 1.03441 | 3.27109 | 1.52 | 2.3104 | 1.23288 | 3.89872 |
| 1.08 | 1.1664 | 1.03923 | 3.28634 | 1.53 | 2.3409 | 1.23693 | 3.91152 |
| 1.09 | 1.1881 | 1.04403 | 3.30151 | 1.54 | 2.3716 | 1.24097 | 3.92428 |
| 1.10 | 1.2100 | 1.04881 | 3.31662 | 1.55 | 2.4025 | 1.24499 | 3.93700 |
| 1.11 | 1.2321 | 1.05357 | 3.33167 | 1.56 | 2.4336 | 1.24900 | 3.94968 |
| 1.12 | 1.2544 | 1.05830 | 3.34664 | 1.57 | 2.4649 | 1.25300 | 3.96232 |
| 1.13 | 1.2769 | 1.06301 | 3.36155 | 1.58 | 2.4964 | 1.25698 | 3.97492 |
| 1.14 | 1.2996 | 1.06771 | 3.37639 | 1.59 | 2.5281 | 1.26095 | 3.98748 |
| 1.15 | 1.3225 | 1.07238 | 3.39116 | 1.60 | 2.5600 | 1.26491 | 4.00000 |
| 1.16 | 1.3456 | 1.07703 | 3.40588 | 1.61 | 2.5921 | 1.26886 | 4.01248 |
| 1.17 | 1.3689 | 1.08167 | 3.42053 | 1.62 | 2.6244 | 1.27279 | 4.02492 |
| 1.18 | 1.3924 | 1.08628 | 3.43511 | 1.63 | 2.6569 | 1.27671 | 4.03733 |
| 1.19 | 1.4161 | 1.09087 | 3.44964 | 1.64 | 2.6896 | 1.28062 | 4.04969 |
| 1.20 | 1.4400 | 1.09545 | 3.46410 | 1.65 | 2.7225 | 1.28452 | 4.06202 |
| 1.21 | 1.4641 | 1.10000 | 3.47851 | 1.66 | 2.7556 | 1.28841 | 4.07431 |
| 1.22 | 1.4884 | 1.10454 | 3.49285 | 1.67 | 2.7889 | 1.29228 | 4.08656 |
| 1.23 | 1.5129 | 1.10905 | 3.50714 | 1.68 | 2.8224 | 1.29615 | 4.09878 |
| 1.24 | 1.5376 | 1.11355 | 3.52136 | 1.69 | 2.8561 | 1.30000 | 4.11096 |
| 1.25 | 1.5625 | 1.11803 | 3.53553 | 1.70 | 2.8900 | 1.30384 | 4.12311 |
| 1.26 | 1.5876 | 1.12250 | 3.54965 | 1.71 | 2.9241 | 1.30767 | 4.13521 |
| 1.27 | 1.6129 | 1.12694 | 3.56371 | 1.72 | 2.9584 | 1.31149 | 4.14729 |
| 1.28 | 1.6384 | 1.13137 | 3.57771 | 1.73 | 2.9929 | 1.31529 | 4.15933 |
| 1.29 | 1.6641 | 1.13578 | 3.59166 | 1.74 | 3.0276 | 1.31909 | 4.17133 |
| 1.30 | 1.6900 | 1.14018 | 3.60555 | 1.75 | 3.0625 | 1.32288 | 4.18330 |
| 1.31 | 1.7161 | 1.14455 | 3.61939 | 1.76 | 3.0976 | 1.32665 | 4.19524 |
| 1.32 | 1.7424 | 1.14891 | 3.63318 | 1.77 | 3.1329 | 1.33041 | 4.20714 |
| 1.33 | 1.7689 | 1.15326 | 3.64692 | 1.78 | 3.1684 | 1.33417 | 4.21900 |
| 1.34 | 1.7956 | 1.15758 | 3.66060 | 1.79 | 3.2041 | 1.33791 | 4.23084 |
| 1.35 | 1.8225 | 1.16190 | 3.67423 | 1.80 | 3.2400 | 1.34164 | 4.24264 |
| 1.36 | 1.8496 | 1.16619 | 3.68782 | 1.81 | 3.2761 | 1.34536 | 4.25441 |
| 1.37 | 1.8769 | 1.17047 | 3.70135 | 1.82 | 3.3124 | 1.34907 | 4.26615 |
| 1.38 | 1.9044 | 1.17473 | 3.71484 | 1.83 | 3.3489 | 1.35277 | 4.27785 |
| 1.39 | 1.9321 | 1.17898 | 3.72827 | 1.84 | 3.3856 | 1.35647 | 4.28952 |
| 1.40 | 1.9600 | 1.18322 | 3.74166 | 1.85 | 3.4225 | 1.36015 | 4.30116 |
| 1.41 | 1.9881 | 1.18743 | 3.75500 | 1.86 | 3.4596 | 1.36382 | 4.31277 |
| 1.42 | 2.0164 | 1.19164 | 3.76829 | 1.87 | 3.4969 | 1.36748 | 4.32435 |
| 1.43 | 2.0449 | 1.19583 | 3.78153 | 1.88 | 3.5344 | 1.37113 | 4.33590 |
| 1.44 | 2.0736 | 1.20000 | 3.79473 | 1.89 | 3.5721 | 1.37477 | 4.34741 |

Table IX                                                                                          315

**TABLE IX. Squares and Square Roots**

(continued)

| N | $N^2$ | $\sqrt{N}$ | $\sqrt{10N}$ | N | $N^2$ | $\sqrt{N}$ | $\sqrt{10N}$ |
|---|---|---|---|---|---|---|---|
| 1.90 | 3.6100 | 1.37840 | 4.35890 | 2.35 | 5.5225 | 1.53297 | 4.84768 |
| 1.91 | 3.6481 | 1.38203 | 4.37035 | 2.36 | 5.5696 | 1.53623 | 4.85798 |
| 1.92 | 3.6864 | 1.38564 | 4.38178 | 2.37 | 5.6169 | 1.53948 | 4.86826 |
| 1.93 | 3.7249 | 1.38924 | 4.39318 | 2.38 | 5.6644 | 1.54272 | 4.87852 |
| 1.94 | 3.7636 | 1.39284 | 4.40454 | 2.39 | 5.7121 | 1.54596 | 4.88876 |
| 1.95 | 3.8025 | 1.39642 | 4.41588 | 2.40 | 5.7600 | 1.54919 | 4.89898 |
| 1.96 | 3.8416 | 1.40000 | 4.42719 | 2.41 | 5.8081 | 1.55242 | 4.90918 |
| 1.97 | 3.8809 | 1.40357 | 4.43847 | 2.42 | 5.8564 | 1.55563 | 4.91935 |
| 1.98 | 3.9204 | 1.40712 | 4.44972 | 2.43 | 5.9049 | 1.55885 | 4.92950 |
| 1.99 | 3.9601 | 1.41067 | 4.46094 | 2.44 | 5.9536 | 1.56205 | 4.93964 |
| 2.00 | 4.0000 | 1.41421 | 4.47214 | 2.45 | 6.0025 | 1.56525 | 4.94975 |
| 2.01 | 4.0401 | 1.41774 | 4.48330 | 2.46 | 6.0516 | 1.56844 | 4.95984 |
| 2.02 | 4.0804 | 1.42127 | 4.49444 | 2.47 | 6.1009 | 1.57162 | 4.96991 |
| 2.03 | 4.1209 | 1.42478 | 4.50555 | 2.48 | 6.1504 | 1.57480 | 4.97996 |
| 2.04 | 4.1616 | 1.42829 | 4.51664 | 2.49 | 6.2001 | 1.57797 | 4.98999 |
| 2.05 | 4.2025 | 1.43178 | 4.52769 | 2.50 | 6.2500 | 1.58114 | 5.00000 |
| 2.06 | 4.2436 | 1.43527 | 4.53872 | 2.51 | 6.3001 | 1.58430 | 5.00999 |
| 2.07 | 4.2849 | 1.43875 | 4.54973 | 2.52 | 6.3504 | 1.58745 | 5.01996 |
| 2.08 | 4.3264 | 1.44222 | 4.56070 | 2.53 | 6.4009 | 1.59060 | 5.02991 |
| 2.09 | 4.3681 | 1.44568 | 4.57165 | 2.54 | 6.4516 | 1.59374 | 5.03984 |
| 2.10 | 4.4100 | 1.44914 | 4.58258 | 2.55 | 6.5025 | 1.59687 | 5.04975 |
| 2.11 | 4.4521 | 1.45258 | 4.59347 | 2.56 | 6.5536 | 1.60000 | 5.05964 |
| 2.12 | 4.4944 | 1.45602 | 4.60435 | 2.57 | 6.6049 | 1.60312 | 5.06952 |
| 2.13 | 4.5369 | 1.45945 | 4.61519 | 2.58 | 6.6564 | 1.60624 | 5.07937 |
| 2.14 | 4.5796 | 1.46287 | 4.62601 | 2.59 | 6.7081 | 1.60935 | 5.08920 |
| 2.15 | 4.6225 | 1.46629 | 4.63681 | 2.60 | 6.7600 | 1.61245 | 5.09902 |
| 2.16 | 4.6656 | 1.46969 | 4.64758 | 2.61 | 6.8121 | 1.61555 | 5.10882 |
| 2.17 | 4.7089 | 1.47309 | 4.65833 | 2.62 | 6.8644 | 1.61864 | 5.11859 |
| 2.18 | 4.7524 | 1.47648 | 4.66905 | 2.63 | 6.9169 | 1.62173 | 5.12835 |
| 2.19 | 4.7961 | 1.47986 | 4.67974 | 2.64 | 6.9696 | 1.62481 | 5.13809 |
| 2.20 | 4.8400 | 1.48324 | 4.69042 | 2.65 | 7.0225 | 1.62788 | 5.14782 |
| 2.21 | 4.8841 | 1.48661 | 4.70106 | 2.66 | 7.0756 | 1.63095 | 5.15752 |
| 2.22 | 4.9284 | 1.48997 | 4.71169 | 2.67 | 7.1289 | 1.63401 | 5.16720 |
| 2.23 | 4.9729 | 1.49332 | 4.72229 | 2.68 | 7.1824 | 1.63707 | 5.17687 |
| 2.24 | 5.0176 | 1.49666 | 4.73286 | 2.69 | 7.2361 | 1.64012 | 5.18652 |
| 2.25 | 5.0625 | 1.50000 | 4.74342 | 2.70 | 7.2900 | 1.64317 | 5.19615 |
| 2.26 | 5.1076 | 1.50333 | 4.75395 | 2.71 | 7.3441 | 1.64621 | 5.20577 |
| 2.27 | 5.1529 | 1.50665 | 4.76445 | 2.72 | 7.3984 | 1.64924 | 5.21536 |
| 2.28 | 5.1984 | 1.50997 | 4.77493 | 2.73 | 7.4529 | 1.65227 | 5.22494 |
| 2.29 | 5.2441 | 1.51327 | 4.78539 | 2.74 | 7.5076 | 1.65529 | 5.23450 |
| 2.30 | 5.2900 | 1.51658 | 4.79583 | 2.75 | 7.5625 | 1.65831 | 5.24404 |
| 2.31 | 5.3361 | 1.51987 | 4.80625 | 2.76 | 7.6176 | 1.66132 | 5.25357 |
| 2.32 | 5.3824 | 1.52315 | 4.81664 | 2.77 | 7.6729 | 1.66433 | 5.26308 |
| 2.33 | 5.4289 | 1.52643 | 4.82701 | 2.78 | 7.7284 | 1.66733 | 5.27257 |
| 2.34 | 5.4756 | 1.52971 | 4.83735 | 2.79 | 7.7841 | 1.67033 | 5.28205 |

**TABLE IX. Squares and Square Roots**

(continued)

| N | $N^2$ | $\sqrt{N}$ | $\sqrt{10N}$ | N | $N^2$ | $\sqrt{N}$ | $\sqrt{10N}$ |
|---|---|---|---|---|---|---|---|
| 2.80 | 7.8400 | 1.67332 | 5.29150 | 3.25 | 10.5625 | 1.80278 | 5.70088 |
| 2.81 | 7.8961 | 1.67631 | 5.30094 | 3.26 | 10.6276 | 1.80555 | 5.70964 |
| 2.82 | 7.9524 | 1.67929 | 5.31037 | 3.27 | 10.6929 | 1.80831 | 5.71839 |
| 2.83 | 8.0089 | 1.68226 | 5.31977 | 3.28 | 10.7584 | 1.81108 | 5.72713 |
| 2.84 | 8.0656 | 1.68523 | 5.32917 | 3.29 | 10.8241 | 1.81384 | 5.73585 |
| 2.85 | 8.1225 | 1.68819 | 5.33854 | 3.30 | 10.8900 | 1.81659 | 5.74456 |
| 2.86 | 8.1796 | 1.69115 | 5.34790 | 3.31 | 10.9561 | 1.81934 | 5.75326 |
| 2.87 | 8.2369 | 1.69411 | 5.35724 | 3.32 | 11.0224 | 1.82209 | 5.76194 |
| 2.88 | 8.2944 | 1.69706 | 5.36656 | 3.33 | 11.0889 | 1.82483 | 5.77062 |
| 2.89 | 8.3521 | 1.70000 | 5.37587 | 3.34 | 11.1556 | 1.82757 | 5.77927 |
| 2.90 | 8.4100 | 1.70294 | 5.38516 | 3.35 | 11.2225 | 1.83030 | 5.78792 |
| 2.91 | 8.4681 | 1.70587 | 5.39444 | 3.36 | 11.2896 | 1.83303 | 5.79655 |
| 2.92 | 8.5264 | 1.70880 | 5.40370 | 3.37 | 11.3569 | 1.83576 | 5.80517 |
| 2.93 | 8.5849 | 1.71172 | 5.41295 | 3.38 | 11.4244 | 1.83848 | 5.81378 |
| 2.94 | 8.6436 | 1.71464 | 5.42218 | 3.39 | 11.4921 | 1.84120 | 5.82237 |
| 2.95 | 8.7025 | 1.71756 | 5.43139 | 3.40 | 11.5600 | 1.84391 | 5.83095 |
| 2.96 | 8.7616 | 1.72047 | 5.44059 | 3.41 | 11.6281 | 1.84662 | 5.83952 |
| 2.97 | 8.8209 | 1.72337 | 5.44977 | 3.42 | 11.6964 | 1.84932 | 5.84808 |
| 2.98 | 8.8804 | 1.72627 | 5.45894 | 3.43 | 11.7649 | 1.85203 | 5.85662 |
| 2.99 | 8.9401 | 1.72916 | 5.46809 | 3.44 | 11.8336 | 1.85472 | 5.86515 |
| 3.00 | 9.0000 | 1.73205 | 5.47723 | 3.45 | 11.9025 | 1.85742 | 5.87367 |
| 3.01 | 9.0601 | 1.73494 | 5.48635 | 3.46 | 11.9716 | 1.86011 | 5.88218 |
| 3.02 | 9.1204 | 1.73781 | 5.49545 | 3.47 | 12.0409 | 1.86279 | 5.89067 |
| 3.03 | 9.1809 | 1.74069 | 5.50454 | 3.48 | 12.1104 | 1.86548 | 5.89915 |
| 3.04 | 9.2416 | 1.74356 | 5.51362 | 3.49 | 12.1801 | 1.86815 | 5.90762 |
| 3.05 | 9.3025 | 1.74642 | 5.52268 | 3.50 | 12.2500 | 1.87083 | 5.91608 |
| 3.06 | 9.3636 | 1.74929 | 5.53173 | 3.51 | 12.3201 | 1.87350 | 5.92453 |
| 3.07 | 9.4249 | 1.75214 | 5.54076 | 3.52 | 12.3904 | 1.87617 | 5.93296 |
| 3.08 | 9.4864 | 1.75499 | 5.54977 | 3.53 | 12.4609 | 1.87883 | 5.94138 |
| 3.09 | 9.5481 | 1.75784 | 5.55878 | 3.54 | 12.5316 | 1.88149 | 5.94979 |
| 3.10 | 9.6100 | 1.76068 | 5.56776 | 3.55 | 12.6025 | 1.88414 | 5.95819 |
| 3.11 | 9.6721 | 1.76352 | 5.57674 | 3.56 | 12.6736 | 1.88680 | 5.96657 |
| 3.12 | 9.7344 | 1.76635 | 5.58570 | 3.57 | 12.7449 | 1.88944 | 5.97495 |
| 3.13 | 9.7969 | 1.76918 | 5.59464 | 3.58 | 12.8164 | 1.89209 | 5.98331 |
| 3.14 | 9.8596 | 1.77200 | 5.60357 | 3.59 | 12.8881 | 1.89473 | 5.99166 |
| 3.15 | 9.9225 | 1.77482 | 5.61249 | 3.60 | 12.9600 | 1.89737 | 6.00000 |
| 3.16 | 9.9856 | 1.77764 | 5.62139 | 3.61 | 13.0321 | 1.90000 | 6.00833 |
| 3.17 | 10.0489 | 1.78045 | 5.63028 | 3.62 | 13.1044 | 1.90263 | 6.01664 |
| 3.18 | 10.1124 | 1.78326 | 5.63915 | 3.63 | 13.1769 | 1.90526 | 6.02495 |
| 3.19 | 10.1761 | 1.78606 | 5.64801 | 3.64 | 13.2496 | 1.90788 | 6.03324 |
| 3.20 | 10.2400 | 1.78885 | 5.65685 | 3.65 | 13.3225 | 1.91050 | 6.04152 |
| 3.21 | 10.3041 | 1.79165 | 5.66569 | 3.66 | 13.3956 | 1.91311 | 6.04979 |
| 3.22 | 10.3684 | 1.79444 | 5.67450 | 3.67 | 13.4689 | 1 91572 | 6.05805 |
| 3.23 | 10.4329 | 1.79722 | 5.68331 | 3.68 | 13.5424 | 1.91833 | 6.06630 |
| 3.24 | 10.4976 | 1.80000 | 5.69210 | 3.69 | 13.6161 | 1.92094 | 6.07454 |

Table IX 317

**TABLE IX.** Squares and Square Roots

(continued)

| N | $N^2$ | $\sqrt{N}$ | $\sqrt{10N}$ | N | $N^2$ | $\sqrt{N}$ | $\sqrt{10N}$ |
|---|---|---|---|---|---|---|---|
| 3.70 | 13.6900 | 1.92354 | 6.08276 | 4.15 | 17.2225 | 2.03715 | 6.44205 |
| 3.71 | 13.7641 | 1.92614 | 6.09098 | 4.16 | 17.3056 | 2.03961 | 6.44981 |
| 3.72 | 13.8384 | 1.92873 | 6.09918 | 4.17 | 17.3889 | 2.04206 | 6.45755 |
| 3.73 | 13.9129 | 1.93132 | 6.10737 | 4.18 | 17.4724 | 2.04450 | 6.46529 |
| 3.74 | 13.9876 | 1.93391 | 6.11555 | 4.19 | 17.5561 | 2.04695 | 6.47302 |
| 3.75 | 14.0625 | 1.93649 | 6.12372 | 4.20 | 17.6400 | 2.04939 | 6.48074 |
| 3.76 | 14.1376 | 1.93907 | 6.13188 | 4.21 | 17.7241 | 2.05183 | 6.48845 |
| 3.77 | 14.2129 | 1.94165 | 6.14003 | 4.22 | 17.8084 | 2.05426 | 6.49615 |
| 3.78 | 14.2884 | 1.94422 | 6.14817 | 4.23 | 17.8929 | 2.05670 | 6.50384 |
| 3.79 | 14.3641 | 1.94679 | 6.15630 | 4.24 | 17.9776 | 2.05913 | 6.51153 |
| 3.80 | 14.4400 | 1.94936 | 6.16441 | 4.25 | 18.0625 | 2.06155 | 6.51920 |
| 3.81 | 14.5161 | 1.95192 | 6.17252 | 4.26 | 18.1476 | 2.06398 | 6.52687 |
| 3.82 | 14.5924 | 1.95448 | 6.18061 | 4.27 | 18.2329 | 2.06640 | 6.53452 |
| 3.83 | 14.6689 | 1.95704 | 6.18870 | 4.28 | 18.3184 | 2.06882 | 6.54217 |
| 3.84 | 14.7456 | 1.95959 | 6.19677 | 4.29 | 18.4041 | 2.07123 | 6.54981 |
| 3.85 | 14.8225 | 1.96214 | 6.20484 | 4.30 | 18.4900 | 2.07364 | 6.55744 |
| 3.86 | 14.8996 | 1.96469 | 6.21289 | 4.31 | 18.5761 | 2.07605 | 6.56506 |
| 3.87 | 14.9769 | 1.96723 | 6.22093 | 4.32 | 18.6624 | 2.07846 | 6.57267 |
| 3.88 | 15.0544 | 1.96977 | 6.22896 | 4.33 | 18.7489 | 2.08087 | 6.58027 |
| 3.89 | 15.1321 | 1.97231 | 6.23699 | 4.34 | 18.8356 | 2.08327 | 6.58787 |
| 3.90 | 15.2100 | 1.97484 | 6.24500 | 4.35 | 18.9225 | 2.08567 | 6.59545 |
| 3.91 | 15.2881 | 1.97737 | 6.25300 | 4.36 | 19.0096 | 2.08806 | 6.60303 |
| 3.92 | 15.3664 | 1.97990 | 6.26099 | 4.37 | 19.0969 | 2.09045 | 6.61060 |
| 3.93 | 15.4449 | 1.98242 | 6.26897 | 4.38 | 19.1844 | 2.09284 | 6.61816 |
| 3.94 | 15.5236 | 1.98494 | 6.27694 | 4.39 | 19.2721 | 2.09523 | 6.62571 |
| 3.95 | 15.6025 | 1.98746 | 6.28490 | 4.40 | 19.3600 | 2.09762 | 6.63325 |
| 3.96 | 15.6816 | 1.98997 | 6.29285 | 4.41 | 19.4481 | 2.10000 | 6.64078 |
| 3.97 | 15.7609 | 1.99249 | 6.30079 | 4.42 | 19.5364 | 2.10238 | 6.64831 |
| 3.98 | 15.8404 | 1.99499 | 6.30872 | 4.43 | 19.6249 | 2.10476 | 6.65582 |
| 3.99 | 15.9201 | 1.99750 | 6.31664 | 4.44 | 19.7136 | 2.10713 | 6.66333 |
| 4.00 | 16.0000 | 2.00000 | 6.32456 | 4.45 | 19.8025 | 2.10950 | 6.67083 |
| 4.01 | 16.0801 | 2.00250 | 6.33246 | 4.46 | 19.8916 | 2.11187 | 6.67832 |
| 4.02 | 16.1604 | 2.00499 | 6.34035 | 4.47 | 19.9809 | 2.11424 | 6.68581 |
| 4.03 | 16.2409 | 2.00749 | 6.34823 | 4.48 | 20.0704 | 2.11660 | 6.69328 |
| 4.04 | 16.3216 | 2.00998 | 6.35610 | 4.49 | 20.1601 | 2.11896 | 6.70075 |
| 4.05 | 16.4025 | 2.01246 | 6.36396 | 4.50 | 20.2500 | 2.12132 | 6.70820 |
| 4.06 | 16.4836 | 2.01494 | 6.37181 | 4.51 | 20.3401 | 2.12368 | 6.71565 |
| 4.07 | 16.5649 | 2.01742 | 6.37966 | 4.52 | 20.4304 | 2.12603 | 6.72309 |
| 4.08 | 16.6464 | 2.01990 | 6.38749 | 4.53 | 20.5209 | 2.12838 | 6.73053 |
| 4.09 | 16.7281 | 2.02237 | 6.39531 | 4.54 | 20.6116 | 2.13073 | 6.73795 |
| 4.10 | 16.8100 | 2.02485 | 6.40312 | 4.55 | 20.7025 | 2.13307 | 6.74537 |
| 4.11 | 16.8921 | 2.02731 | 6.41093 | 4.56 | 20.7936 | 2.13542 | 6.75278 |
| 4.12 | 16.9744 | 2.02978 | 6.41872 | 4.57 | 20.8849 | 2.13776 | 6.76018 |
| 4.13 | 17.0569 | 2.03224 | 6.42651 | 4.58 | 20.9764 | 2.14009 | 6.76757 |
| 4.14 | 17.1396 | 2.03470 | 6.43428 | 4.59 | 21.0681 | 2.14243 | 6.77495 |

**TABLE IX. Squares and Square Roots**

(continued)

| N | N² | √N | √10N | N | N² | √N | √10N |
|---|---|---|---|---|---|---|---|
| 4.60 | 21.1600 | 2.14476 | 6.78233 | 5.05 | 25.5025 | 2.24722 | 7.10634 |
| 4.61 | 21.2521 | 2.14709 | 6.78970 | 5.06 | 25.6036 | 2.24944 | 7.11337 |
| 4.62 | 21.3444 | 2.14942 | 6.79706 | 5.07 | 25.7049 | 2.25167 | 7.12039 |
| 4.63 | 21.4369 | 2.15174 | 6.80441 | 5.08 | 25.8064 | 2.25389 | 7.12741 |
| 4.64 | 21.5296 | 2.15407 | 6.81175 | 5.09 | 25.9081 | 2.25610 | 7.13442 |
| 4.65 | 21.6225 | 2.15639 | 6.81909 | 5.10 | 26.0100 | 2.25832 | 7.14143 |
| 4.66 | 21.7156 | 2.15870 | 6.82642 | 5.11 | 26.1121 | 2.26053 | 7.14843 |
| 4.67 | 21.8089 | 2.16102 | 6.83374 | 5.12 | 26.2144 | 2.26274 | 7.15542 |
| 4.68 | 21.9024 | 2.16333 | 6.84105 | 5.13 | 26.3169 | 2.26495 | 7.16240 |
| 4.69 | 21.9961 | 2.16564 | 6.84836 | 5.14 | 26.4196 | 2.26716 | 7.16938 |
| 4.70 | 22.0900 | 2.16795 | 6.85565 | 5.15 | 26.5225 | 2.26936 | 7.17635 |
| 4.71 | 22.1841 | 2.17025 | 6.86294 | 5.16 | 26.6256 | 2.27156 | 7.18331 |
| 4.72 | 22.2784 | 2.17256 | 6.87023 | 5.17 | 26.7289 | 2.27376 | 7.19027 |
| 4.73 | 22.3729 | 2.17486 | 6.87750 | 5.18 | 26.8324 | 2.27596 | 7.19722 |
| 4.74 | 22.4676 | 2.17715 | 6.88477 | 5.19 | 26.9361 | 2.27816 | 7.20417 |
| 4.75 | 22.5625 | 2.17945 | 6.89202 | 5.20 | 27.0400 | 2.28035 | 7.21110 |
| 4.76 | 22.6576 | 2.18174 | 6.89928 | 5.21 | 27.1441 | 2.28254 | 7.21803 |
| 4.77 | 22.7529 | 2.18403 | 6.90652 | 5.22 | 27.2484 | 2.28473 | 7.22496 |
| 4.78 | 22.8484 | 2.18632 | 6.91375 | 5.23 | 27.3529 | 2.28692 | 7.23187 |
| 4.79 | 22.9441 | 2.18861 | 6.92098 | 5.24 | 27.4576 | 2.28910 | 7.23878 |
| 4.80 | 23.0400 | 2.19089 | 6.92820 | 5.25 | 27.5625 | 2.29129 | 7.24569 |
| 4.81 | 23.1361 | 2.19317 | 6.93542 | 5.26 | 27.6676 | 2.29347 | 7.25259 |
| 4.82 | 23.2324 | 2.19545 | 6.94262 | 5.27 | 27.7729 | 2.29565 | 7.25948 |
| 4.83 | 23.3289 | 2.19773 | 6.94982 | 5.28 | 27.8784 | 2.29783 | 7.26636 |
| 4.84 | 23.4256 | 2.20000 | 6.95701 | 5.29 | 27.9841 | 2.30000 | 7.27324 |
| 4.85 | 23.5225 | 2.20227 | 6.96419 | 5.30 | 28.0900 | 2.30217 | 7.28011 |
| 4.86 | 23.6196 | 2.20454 | 6.97137 | 5.31 | 28.1961 | 2.30434 | 7.28697 |
| 4.87 | 23.7169 | 2.20681 | 6.97854 | 5.32 | 28.3024 | 2.30651 | 7.29383 |
| 4.88 | 23.8144 | 2.20907 | 6.98570 | 5.33 | 28.4089 | 2.30868 | 7.30068 |
| 4.89 | 23.9121 | 2.21133 | 6.99285 | 5.34 | 28.5156 | 2.31084 | 7.30753 |
| 4.90 | 24.0100 | 2.21359 | 7.00000 | 5.35 | 28.6225 | 2.31301 | 7.31437 |
| 4.91 | 24.1081 | 2.21585 | 7.00714 | 5.36 | 28.7296 | 2.31517 | 7.32120 |
| 4.92 | 24.2064 | 2.21811 | 7.01427 | 5.37 | 28.8369 | 2.31733 | 7.32803 |
| 4.93 | 24.3049 | 2.22036 | 7.02140 | 5.38 | 28.9444 | 2.31948 | 7.33485 |
| 4.94 | 24.4036 | 2.22261 | 7.02851 | 5.39 | 29.0521 | 2.32164 | 7.34166 |
| 4.95 | 24.5025 | 2.22486 | 7.03562 | 5.40 | 29.1600 | 2.32379 | 7.34847 |
| 4.96 | 24.6016 | 2.22711 | 7.04273 | 5.41 | 29.2681 | 2.32594 | 7.35527 |
| 4.97 | 24.7009 | 2.22935 | 7.04982 | 5.42 | 29.3764 | 2.32809 | 7.36206 |
| 4.98 | 24.8004 | 2.23159 | 7.05691 | 5.43 | 29.4849 | 2.33024 | 7.36885 |
| 4.99 | 24.9001 | 2.23383 | 7.06399 | 5.44 | 29.5936 | 2.33238 | 7.37564 |
| 5.00 | 25.0000 | 2.23607 | 7.07107 | 5.45 | 29.7025 | 2.33452 | 7.38241 |
| 5.01 | 25.1001 | 2.23830 | 7.07814 | 5.46 | 29.8116 | 2.33666 | 7.38918 |
| 5.02 | 25.2004 | 2.24054 | 7.08520 | 5.47 | 29.9209 | 2.33880 | 7.39594 |
| 5.03 | 25.3009 | 2.24277 | 7.09225 | 5.48 | 30.0304 | 2.34094 | 7.40270 |
| 5.04 | 25.4016 | 2.24499 | 7.09930 | 5.49 | 30.1401 | 2.34307 | 7.40945 |

Table IX                                                                     319

TABLE IX.  **Squares and Square Roots**

     (continued)

| N | N² | √N | √10N | N | N² | √N | √10N |
|---|-----|------|------|---|-----|------|------|
| 5.50 | 30.2500 | 2.34521 | 7.41620 | 5.95 | 35.4025 | 2.43926 | 7.71362 |
| 5.51 | 30.3601 | 2.34734 | 7.42294 | 5.96 | 35.5216 | 2.44131 | 7.72010 |
| 5.52 | 30.4704 | 2.34947 | 7.42967 | 5.97 | 35.6409 | 2.44336 | 7.72658 |
| 5.53 | 30.5809 | 2.35160 | 7.43640 | 5.98 | 35.7604 | 2.44540 | 7.73305 |
| 5.54 | 30.6916 | 2.35372 | 7.44312 | 5.99 | 35.8801 | 2.44745 | 7.73951 |
| 5.55 | 30.8025 | 2.35584 | 7.44983 | 6.00 | 36.0000 | 2.44949 | 7.74597 |
| 5.56 | 30.9136 | 2.35797 | 7.45654 | 6.01 | 36.1201 | 2.45153 | 7.75242 |
| 5.57 | 31.0249 | 2.36008 | 7.46324 | 6.02 | 36.2404 | 2.45357 | 7.75887 |
| 5.58 | 31.1364 | 2.36220 | 7.46994 | 6.03 | 36.3609 | 2.45561 | 7.76531 |
| 5.59 | 31.2481 | 2.36432 | 7.47663 | 6.04 | 36.4816 | 2.45764 | 7.77174 |
| 5.60 | 31.3600 | 2.36643 | 7.48331 | 6.05 | 36.6025 | 2.45967 | 7.77817 |
| 5.61 | 31.4721 | 2.36854 | 7.48999 | 6.06 | 36.7236 | 2.46171 | 7.78460 |
| 5.62 | 31.5844 | 2.37065 | 7.49667 | 6.07 | 36.8449 | 2.46374 | 7.79102 |
| 5.63 | 31.6969 | 2.37276 | 7.50333 | 6.08 | 36.9664 | 2.46577 | 7.79744 |
| 5.64 | 31.8096 | 2.37487 | 7.50999 | 6.09 | 37.0881 | 2.46779 | 7.80385 |
| 5.65 | 31.9225 | 2.37697 | 7.51665 | 6.10 | 37.2100 | 2.46982 | 7.81025 |
| 5.66 | 32.0356 | 2.37908 | 7.52330 | 6.11 | 37.3321 | 2.47184 | 7.81665 |
| 5.67 | 32.1489 | 2.38118 | 7.52994 | 6.12 | 37.4544 | 2.47386 | 7.82304 |
| 5.68 | 32.2624 | 2.38328 | 7.53658 | 6.13 | 37.5769 | 2.47588 | 7.82943 |
| 5.69 | 32.3761 | 2.38537 | 7.54321 | 6.14 | 37.6996 | 2.47790 | 7.83582 |
| 5.70 | 32.4900 | 2.38747 | 7.54983 | 6.15 | 37.8225 | 2.47992 | 7.84219 |
| 5.71 | 32.6041 | 2.38956 | 7.55645 | 6.16 | 37.9456 | 2.48193 | 7.84857 |
| 5.72 | 32.7184 | 2.39165 | 7.56307 | 6.17 | 38.0689 | 2.48395 | 7.85493 |
| 5.73 | 32.8329 | 2.39374 | 7.56968 | 6.18 | 38.1924 | 2.48596 | 7.86130 |
| 5.74 | 32.9476 | 2.39583 | 7.57628 | 6.19 | 38.3161 | 2.48797 | 7.86766 |
| 5.75 | 33.0625 | 2.39792 | 7.58288 | 6.20 | 38.4400 | 2.48998 | 7.87401 |
| 5.76 | 33.1776 | 2.40000 | 7.58947 | 6.21 | 38.5641 | 2.49199 | 7.88036 |
| 5.77 | 33.2929 | 2.40208 | 7.59605 | 6.22 | 38.6884 | 2.49399 | 7.88670 |
| 5.78 | 33.4084 | 2.40416 | 7.60263 | 6.23 | 38.8129 | 2.49600 | 7.89303 |
| 5.79 | 33.5241 | 2.40624 | 7.60920 | 6.24 | 38.9376 | 2.49800 | 7.89937 |
| 5.80 | 33.6400 | 2.40832 | 7.61577 | 6.25 | 39.0625 | 2.50000 | 7.90569 |
| 5.81 | 33.7561 | 2.41039 | 7.62234 | 6.26 | 39.1876 | 2.50200 | 7.91202 |
| 5.82 | 33.8724 | 2.41247 | 7.62889 | 6.27 | 39.3129 | 2.50400 | 7.91833 |
| 5.83 | 33.9889 | 2.41454 | 7.63544 | 6.28 | 39.4384 | 2.50599 | 7.92465 |
| 5.84 | 34.1056 | 2.41661 | 7.64199 | 6.29 | 39.5641 | 2.50799 | 7.93095 |
| 5.85 | 34.2225 | 2.41868 | 7.64853 | 6.30 | 39.6900 | 2.50998 | 7.93725 |
| 5.86 | 34.3396 | 2.42074 | 7.65506 | 6.31 | 39.8161 | 2.51197 | 7.94355 |
| 5.87 | 34.4569 | 2.42281 | 7.66159 | 6.32 | 39.9424 | 2.51396 | 7.94984 |
| 5.88 | 34.5744 | 2.42487 | 7.66812 | 6.33 | 40.0689 | 2.51595 | 7.95613 |
| 5.89 | 34.6921 | 2.42693 | 7.67463 | 6.34 | 40.1956 | 2.51794 | 7.96241 |
| 5.90 | 34.8100 | 2.42899 | 7.68115 | 6.35 | 40.3225 | 2.51992 | 7.96869 |
| 5.91 | 34.9281 | 2.43105 | 7.68765 | 6.36 | 40.4496 | 2.52190 | 7.97496 |
| 5.92 | 35.0464 | 2.43311 | 7.69415 | 6.37 | 40.5769 | 2.52389 | 7.98123 |
| 5.93 | 35.1649 | 2.43516 | 7.70065 | 6.38 | 40.7044 | 2.52587 | 7.98749 |
| 5.94 | 35.2836 | 2.43721 | 7.70714 | 6.39 | 40.8321 | 2.52784 | 7.99375 |

**TABLE IX.  Squares and Square Roots**
  (continued)

| N | N² | √N | √10N | N | N² | √N | √10N |
|---|---|---|---|---|---|---|---|
| 6.40 | 40.9600 | 2.52982 | 8.00000 | 6.85 | 46.9225 | 2.61725 | 8.27647 |
| 6.41 | 41.0881 | 2.53180 | 8.00625 | 6.86 | 47.0596 | 2.61916 | 8.28251 |
| 6.42 | 41.2164 | 2.53377 | 8.01249 | 6.87 | 47.1969 | 2.62107 | 8.28855 |
| 6.43 | 41.3449 | 2.53574 | 8.01873 | 6.88 | 47.3344 | 2.62298 | 8.29458 |
| 6.44 | 41.4736 | 2.53772 | 8.02496 | 6.89 | 47.4721 | 2.62488 | 8.30060 |
| 6.45 | 41.6025 | 2.53969 | 8.03119 | 6.90 | 47.6100 | 2.62679 | 8.30662 |
| 6.46 | 41.7316 | 2.54165 | 8.03741 | 6.91 | 47.7481 | 2.62869 | 8.31264 |
| 6.47 | 41.8609 | 2.54362 | 8.04363 | 6.92 | 47.8864 | 2.63059 | 8.31865 |
| 6.48 | 41.9904 | 2.54558 | 8.04984 | 6.93 | 48.0249 | 2.63249 | 8.32466 |
| 6.49 | 42.1201 | 2.54755 | 8.05605 | 6.94 | 48.1636 | 2.63439 | 8.33067 |
| 6.50 | 42.2500 | 2.54951 | 8.06226 | 6.95 | 48.3025 | 2.63629 | 8.33667 |
| 6.51 | 42.3801 | 2.55147 | 8.06846 | 6.96 | 48.4416 | 2.63818 | 8.34266 |
| 6.52 | 42.5104 | 2.55343 | 8.07465 | 6.97 | 48.5809 | 2.64008 | 8.34865 |
| 6.53 | 42.6409 | 2.55539 | 8.08084 | 6.98 | 48.7204 | 2.64197 | 8.35464 |
| 6.54 | 42.7716 | 2.55734 | 8.08703 | 6.99 | 48.8601 | 2.64386 | 8.36062 |
| 6.55 | 42.9025 | 2.55930 | 8.09321 | 7.00 | 49.0000 | 2.64575 | 8.36660 |
| 6.56 | 43.0336 | 2.56125 | 8.09938 | 7.01 | 49.1401 | 2.64764 | 8.37257 |
| 6.57 | 43.1649 | 2.56320 | 8.10555 | 7.02 | 49.2804 | 2.64953 | 8.37854 |
| 6.58 | 43.2964 | 2.56515 | 8.11172 | 7.03 | 49.4209 | 2.65141 | 8.38451 |
| 6.59 | 43.4281 | 2.56710 | 8.11788 | 7.04 | 49.5616 | 2.65330 | 8.39047 |
| 6.60 | 43.5600 | 2.56905 | 8.12404 | 7.05 | 49.7025 | 2.65518 | 8.39643 |
| 6.61 | 43.6921 | 2.57099 | 8.13019 | 7.06 | 49.8436 | 2.65707 | 8.40238 |
| 6.62 | 43.8244 | 2.57294 | 8.13634 | 7.07 | 49.9849 | 2.65895 | 8.40833 |
| 6.63 | 43.9569 | 2.57488 | 8.14248 | 7.08 | 50.1264 | 2.66083 | 8.41427 |
| 6.64 | 44.0896 | 2.57682 | 8.14862 | 7.09 | 50.2681 | 2.66271 | 8.42021 |
| 6.65 | 44.2225 | 2.57876 | 8.15475 | 7.10 | 50.4100 | 2.66458 | 8.42615 |
| 6.66 | 44.3556 | 2.58070 | 8.16088 | 7.11 | 50.5521 | 2.66646 | 8.43208 |
| 6.67 | 44.4889 | 2.58263 | 8.16701 | 7.12 | 50.6944 | 2.66833 | 8.43801 |
| 6.68 | 44.6224 | 2.58457 | 8.17313 | 7.13 | 50.8369 | 2.67021 | 8.44393 |
| 6.69 | 44.7561 | 2.58650 | 8.17924 | 7.14 | 50.9796 | 2.67208 | 8.44985 |
| 6.70 | 44.8900 | 2.58844 | 8.18535 | 7.15 | 51.1225 | 2.67395 | 8.45577 |
| 6.71 | 45.0241 | 2.59037 | 8.19146 | 7.16 | 51.2656 | 2.67582 | 8.46168 |
| 6.72 | 45.1584 | 2.59230 | 8.19756 | 7.17 | 51.4089 | 2.67769 | 8.46759 |
| 6.73 | 45.2929 | 2.59422 | 8.20366 | 7.18 | 51.5524 | 2.67955 | 8.47349 |
| 6.74 | 45.4276 | 2.59615 | 8.20975 | 7.19 | 51.6961 | 2.68142 | 8.47939 |
| 6.75 | 45.5625 | 2.59808 | 8.21584 | 7.20 | 51.8400 | 2.68328 | 8.48528 |
| 6.76 | 45.6976 | 2.60000 | 8.22192 | 7.21 | 51.9841 | 2.68514 | 8.49117 |
| 6.77 | 45.8329 | 2.60192 | 8.22800 | 7.22 | 52.1284 | 2.68701 | 8.49706 |
| 6.78 | 45.9684 | 2.60384 | 8.23408 | 7.23 | 52.2729 | 2.68887 | 8.50294 |
| 6.79 | 46.1041 | 2.60576 | 8.24015 | 7.24 | 52.4176 | 2.69072 | 8.50882 |
| 6.80 | 46.2400 | 2.60768 | 8.24621 | 7.25 | 52.5625 | 2.69258 | 8.51469 |
| 6.81 | 46.3761 | 2.60960 | 8.25227 | 7.26 | 52.7076 | 2.69444 | 8.52056 |
| 6.82 | 46.5124 | 2.61151 | 8.25833 | 7.27 | 52.8529 | 2.69629 | 8.52643 |
| 6.83 | 46.6489 | 2.61343 | 8.26438 | 7.28 | 52.9984 | 2.69815 | 8.53229 |
| 6.84 | 46.7856 | 2.61534 | 8.27043 | 7.29 | 53.1441 | 2.70000 | 8.53815 |

Table IX 321

**TABLE IX. Squares and Square Roots**
(continued)

| N | N² | √N | √10N | N | N² | √N | √10N |
|------|---------|---------|---------|------|---------|---------|---------|
| 7.30 | 53.2900 | 2.70185 | 8.54400 | 7.75 | 60.0625 | 2.78388 | 8.80341 |
| 7.31 | 53.4361 | 2.70370 | 8.54985 | 7.76 | 60.2176 | 2.78568 | 8.80909 |
| 7.32 | 53.5824 | 2.70555 | 8.55570 | 7.77 | 60.3729 | 2.78747 | 8.81476 |
| 7.33 | 53.7289 | 2.70740 | 8.56154 | 7.78 | 60.5284 | 2.78927 | 8.82043 |
| 7.34 | 53.8756 | 2.70924 | 8.56738 | 7.79 | 60.6841 | 2.79106 | 8.82610 |
| 7.35 | 54.0225 | 2.71109 | 8.57321 | 7.80 | 60.8400 | 2.79285 | 8.83176 |
| 7.36 | 54.1696 | 2.71293 | 8.57904 | 7.81 | 60.9961 | 2.79464 | 8.83742 |
| 7.37 | 54.3169 | 2.71477 | 8.58487 | 7.82 | 61.1524 | 2.79643 | 8.84308 |
| 7.38 | 54.4644 | 2.71662 | 8.59069 | 7.83 | 61.3089 | 2.79821 | 8.84873 |
| 7.39 | 54.6121 | 2.71846 | 8.59651 | 7.84 | 61.4656 | 2.80000 | 8.85438 |
| 7.40 | 54.7600 | 2.72029 | 8.60233 | 7.85 | 61.6225 | 2.80179 | 8.86002 |
| 7.41 | 54.9081 | 2.72213 | 8.60814 | 7.86 | 61.7796 | 2.80357 | 8.86566 |
| 7.42 | 55.0564 | 2.72397 | 8.61394 | 7.87 | 61.9369 | 2.80535 | 8.87130 |
| 7.43 | 55.2049 | 2.72580 | 8.61974 | 7.88 | 62.0944 | 2.80713 | 8.87694 |
| 7.44 | 55.3536 | 2.72764 | 8.62554 | 7.89 | 62.2521 | 2.80891 | 8.88257 |
| 7.45 | 55.5025 | 2.72947 | 8.63134 | 7.90 | 62.4100 | 2.81069 | 8.88819 |
| 7.46 | 55.6516 | 2.73130 | 8.63713 | 7.91 | 62.5681 | 2.81247 | 8.89382 |
| 7.47 | 55.8009 | 2.73313 | 8.64292 | 7.92 | 62.7264 | 2.81425 | 8.89944 |
| 7.48 | 55.9504 | 2.73496 | 8.64870 | 7.93 | 62.8849 | 2.81603 | 8.90505 |
| 7.49 | 56.1001 | 2.73679 | 8.65448 | 7.94 | 63.0436 | 2.81780 | 8.91067 |
| 7.50 | 56.2500 | 2.73861 | 8.66025 | 7.95 | 63.2025 | 2.81957 | 8.91628 |
| 7.51 | 56.4001 | 2.74044 | 8.66603 | 7.96 | 63.3616 | 2.82135 | 8.92188 |
| 7.52 | 56.5504 | 2.74226 | 8.67179 | 7.97 | 63.5209 | 2.82312 | 8.92749 |
| 7.53 | 56.7009 | 2.74408 | 8.67756 | 7.98 | 63.6804 | 2.82489 | 8.93308 |
| 7.54 | 56.8516 | 2.74591 | 8.68332 | 7.99 | 63.8401 | 2.82666 | 8.93868 |
| 7.55 | 57.0025 | 2.74773 | 8.68907 | 8.00 | 64.0000 | 2.82843 | 8.94427 |
| 7.56 | 57.1536 | 2.74955 | 8.69483 | 8.01 | 64.1601 | 2.83019 | 8.94986 |
| 7.57 | 57.3049 | 2.75136 | 8.70057 | 8.02 | 64.3204 | 2.83196 | 8.95545 |
| 7.58 | 57.4564 | 2.75318 | 8.70632 | 8.03 | 64.4809 | 2.83373 | 8.96103 |
| 7.59 | 57.6081 | 2.75500 | 8.71206 | 8.04 | 64.6416 | 2.83549 | 8.96660 |
| 7.60 | 57.7600 | 2.75681 | 8.71780 | 8.05 | 64.8025 | 2.83725 | 8.97218 |
| 7.61 | 57.9121 | 2.75862 | 8.72353 | 8.06 | 64.9636 | 2.83901 | 8.97775 |
| 7.62 | 58.0644 | 2.76043 | 8.72926 | 8.07 | 65.1249 | 2.84077 | 8.98332 |
| 7.63 | 58.2169 | 2.76225 | 8.73499 | 8.08 | 65.2864 | 2.84253 | 8.98888 |
| 7.64 | 58.3696 | 2.76405 | 8.74071 | 8.09 | 65.4481 | 2.84429 | 8.99444 |
| 7.65 | 58.5225 | 2.76586 | 8.74643 | 8.10 | 65.6100 | 2.84605 | 9.00000 |
| 7.66 | 58.6756 | 2.76767 | 8.75214 | 8.11 | 65.7721 | 2.84781 | 9.00555 |
| 7.67 | 58.8289 | 2.76948 | 8.75785 | 8.12 | 65.9344 | 2.84956 | 9.01110 |
| 7.68 | 58.9824 | 2.77128 | 8.76356 | 8.13 | 66.0969 | 2.85132 | 9.01665 |
| 7.69 | 59.1361 | 2.77308 | 8.76926 | 8.14 | 66.2596 | 2.85307 | 9.02219 |
| 7.70 | 59.2900 | 2.77489 | 8.77496 | 8.15 | 66.4225 | 2.85482 | 9.02774 |
| 7.71 | 59.4441 | 2.77669 | 8.78066 | 8.16 | 66.5856 | 2.85657 | 9.03327 |
| 7.72 | 59.5984 | 2.77849 | 8.78635 | 8.17 | 66.7489 | 2.85832 | 9.03881 |
| 7.73 | 59.7529 | 2.78029 | 8.79204 | 8.18 | 66.9124 | 2.86007 | 9.04434 |
| 7.74 | 59.9076 | 2.78209 | 8.79773 | 8.19 | 67.0761 | 2.86182 | 9.04986 |

Table IX

**TABLE IX. Squares and Square Roots**
(continued)

| N | $N^2$ | $\sqrt{N}$ | $\sqrt{10N}$ | N | $N^2$ | $\sqrt{N}$ | $\sqrt{10N}$ |
|---|---|---|---|---|---|---|---|
| 8.20 | 67.2400 | 2.86356 | 9.05539 | 8.65 | 74.8225 | 2.94109 | 9.30054 |
| 8.21 | 67.4041 | 2.86531 | 9.06091 | 8.66 | 74.9956 | 2.94279 | 9.30591 |
| 8.22 | 67.5684 | 2.86705 | 9.06642 | 8.67 | 75.1689 | 2.94449 | 9.31128 |
| 8.23 | 67.7329 | 2.86880 | 9.07193 | 8.68 | 75.3424 | 2.94618 | 9.31665 |
| 8.24 | 67.8976 | 2.87054 | 9.07744 | 8.69 | 75.5161 | 2.94788 | 9.32202 |
| 8.25 | 68.0625 | 2.87228 | 9.08295 | 8.70 | 75.6900 | 2.94958 | 9.32738 |
| 8.26 | 68.2276 | 2.87402 | 9.08845 | 8.71 | 75.8641 | 2.95127 | 9.33274 |
| 8.27 | 68.3929 | 2.87576 | 9.09395 | 8.72 | 76.0384 | 2.95296 | 9.33809 |
| 8.28 | 68.5584 | 2.87750 | 9.09945 | 8.73 | 76.2129 | 2.95466 | 9.34345 |
| 8.29 | 68.7241 | 2.87924 | 9.10494 | 8.74 | 76.3876 | 2.95635 | 9.34880 |
| 8.30 | 68.8900 | 2.88097 | 9.11043 | 8.75 | 76.5625 | 2.95804 | 9.35414 |
| 8.31 | 69.0561 | 2.88271 | 9.11592 | 8.76 | 76.7376 | 2.95973 | 9.35949 |
| 8.32 | 69.2224 | 2.88444 | 9.12140 | 8.77 | 76.9129 | 2.96142 | 9.36483 |
| 8.33 | 69.3889 | 2.88617 | 9.12688 | 8.78 | 77.0884 | 2.96311 | 9.37017 |
| 8.34 | 69.5556 | 2.88791 | 9.13236 | 8.79 | 77.2641 | 2.96479 | 9.37550 |
| 8.35 | 69.7225 | 2.88964 | 9.13783 | 8.80 | 77.4400 | 2.96648 | 9.38083 |
| 8.36 | 69.8896 | 2.89137 | 9.14330 | 8.81 | 77.6161 | 2.96816 | 9.38616 |
| 8.37 | 70.0569 | 2.89310 | 9.14877 | 8.82 | 77.7924 | 2.96985 | 9.39149 |
| 8.38 | 70.2244 | 2.89482 | 9.15423 | 8.83 | 77.9689 | 2.97153 | 9.39681 |
| 8.39 | 70.3921 | 2.89655 | 9.15969 | 8.84 | 78.1456 | 2.97321 | 9.40213 |
| 8.40 | 70.5600 | 2.89828 | 9.16515 | 8.85 | 78.3225 | 2.97489 | 9.40744 |
| 8.41 | 70.7281 | 2.90000 | 9.17061 | 8.86 | 78.4996 | 2.97658 | 9.41276 |
| 8.42 | 70.8964 | 2.90172 | 9.17606 | 8.87 | 78.6769 | 2.97825 | 9.41807 |
| 8.43 | 71.0649 | 2.90345 | 9.18150 | 8.88 | 78.8544 | 2.97993 | 9.42338 |
| 8.44 | 71.2336 | 2.90517 | 9.18695 | 8.89 | 79.0321 | 2.98161 | 9.42868 |
| 8.45 | 71.4025 | 2.90689 | 9.19239 | 8.90 | 79.2100 | 2.98329 | 9.43398 |
| 8.46 | 71.5716 | 2.90861 | 9.19783 | 8.91 | 79.3881 | 2.98496 | 9.43928 |
| 8.47 | 71.7409 | 2.91033 | 9.20326 | 8.92 | 79.5664 | 2.98664 | 9.44458 |
| 8.48 | 71.9104 | 2.91204 | 9.20869 | 8.93 | 79.7449 | 2.98831 | 9.44987 |
| 8.49 | 72.0801 | 2.91376 | 9.21412 | 8.94 | 79.9236 | 2.98998 | 9.45516 |
| 8.50 | 72.2500 | 2.91548 | 9.21954 | 8.95 | 80.1025 | 2.99166 | 9.46044 |
| 8.51 | 72.4201 | 2.91719 | 9.22497 | 8.96 | 80.2816 | 2.99333 | 9.46573 |
| 8.52 | 72.5904 | 2.91890 | 9.23038 | 8.97 | 80.4609 | 2.99500 | 9.47101 |
| 8.53 | 72.7609 | 2.92062 | 9.23580 | 8.98 | 80.6404 | 2.99666 | 9.47629 |
| 8.54 | 72.9316 | 2.92233 | 9.24121 | 8.99 | 80.8201 | 2.99833 | 9.48156 |
| 8.55 | 73.1025 | 2.92404 | 9.24662 | 9.00 | 81.0000 | 3.00000 | 9.48683 |
| 8.56 | 73.2736 | 2.92575 | 9.25203 | 9.01 | 81.1801 | 3.00167 | 9.49210 |
| 8.57 | 73.4449 | 2.92746 | 9.25743 | 9.02 | 81.3604 | 3.00333 | 9.49737 |
| 8.58 | 73.6164 | 2.92916 | 9.26283 | 9.03 | 81.5409 | 3.00500 | 9.50263 |
| 8.59 | 73.7881 | 2.93087 | 9.26823 | 9.04 | 81.7216 | 3.00666 | 9.50789 |
| 8.60 | 73.9600 | 2.93258 | 9.27362 | 9.05 | 81.9025 | 3.00832 | 9.51315 |
| 8.61 | 74.1321 | 2.93428 | 9.27901 | 9.06 | 82.0836 | 3.00998 | 9.51840 |
| 8.62 | 74.3044 | 2.93598 | 9.28440 | 9.07 | 82.2649 | 3.01164 | 9.52365 |
| 8.63 | 74.4769 | 2.93769 | 9.28978 | 9.08 | 82.4464 | 3.01330 | 9.52890 |
| 8.64 | 74.6496 | 2.93939 | 9.29516 | 9.09 | 82.6281 | 3.01496 | 9.53415 |

Table IX 323

**TABLE IX. Squares and Square Roots**

(concluded)

| N | N² | √N | √10N | N | N² | √N | √10N |
|---|-----|------|------|---|-----|------|------|
| 9.10 | 82.8100 | 3.01662 | 9.53939 | 9.55 | 91.2025 | 3.09031 | 9.77241 |
| 9.11 | 82.9921 | 3.01828 | 9.54463 | 9.56 | 91.3936 | 3.09192 | 9.77753 |
| 9.12 | 83.1744 | 3.01993 | 9.54987 | 9.57 | 91.5849 | 3.09354 | 9.78264 |
| 9.13 | 83.3569 | 3.02159 | 9.55510 | 9.58 | 91.7764 | 3.09516 | 9.78775 |
| 9.14 | 83.5396 | 3.02324 | 9.56033 | 9.59 | 91.9681 | 3.09677 | 9.79285 |
| 9.15 | 83.7225 | 3.02490 | 9.56556 | 9.60 | 92.1600 | 3.09839 | 9.79796 |
| 9.16 | 83.9056 | 3.02655 | 9.57079 | 9.61 | 92.3521 | 3.10000 | 9.80306 |
| 9.17 | 84.0889 | 3.02820 | 9.57601 | 9.62 | 92.5444 | 3.10161 | 9.80816 |
| 9.18 | 84.2724 | 3.02985 | 9.58123 | 9.63 | 92.7369 | 3.10322 | 9.81326 |
| 9.19 | 84.4561 | 3.03150 | 9.58645 | 9.64 | 92.9296 | 3.10483 | 9.81835 |
| 9.20 | 84.6400 | 3.03315 | 9.59166 | 9.65 | 93.1225 | 3.10644 | 9.82344 |
| 9.21 | 84.8241 | 3.03480 | 9.59687 | 9.66 | 93.3156 | 3.10805 | 9.82853 |
| 9.22 | 85.0084 | 3.03645 | 9.60208 | 9.67 | 93.5089 | 3.10966 | 9.83362 |
| 9.23 | 85.1929 | 3.03809 | 9.60729 | 9.68 | 93.7024 | 3.11127 | 9.83870 |
| 9.24 | 85.3776 | 3.03974 | 9.61249 | 9.69 | 93.8961 | 3.11288 | 9.84378 |
| 9.25 | 85.5625 | 3.04138 | 9.61769 | 9.70 | 94.0900 | 3.11448 | 9.84886 |
| 9.26 | 85.7476 | 3.04302 | 9.62289 | 9.71 | 94.2841 | 3.11609 | 9.85393 |
| 9.27 | 85.9329 | 3.04467 | 9.62808 | 9.72 | 94.4784 | 3.11769 | 9.85901 |
| 9.28 | 86.1184 | 3.04631 | 9.63328 | 9.73 | 94.6729 | 3.11929 | 9.86408 |
| 9.29 | 86.3041 | 3.04795 | 9.63846 | 9.74 | 94.8676 | 3.12090 | 9.86914 |
| 9.30 | 86.4900 | 3.04959 | 9.64365 | 9.75 | 95.0625 | 3.12250 | 9.87421 |
| 9.31 | 86.6761 | 3.05123 | 9.64883 | 9.76 | 95.2576 | 3.12410 | 9.87927 |
| 9.32 | 86.8624 | 3.05287 | 9.65401 | 9.77 | 95.4529 | 3.12570 | 9.88433 |
| 9.33 | 87.0489 | 3.05450 | 9.65919 | 9.78 | 95.6484 | 3.12730 | 9.88939 |
| 9.34 | 87.2356 | 3.05614 | 9.66437 | 9.79 | 95.8441 | 3.12890 | 9.89444 |
| 9.35 | 87.4225 | 3.05778 | 9.66954 | 9.80 | 96.0400 | 3.13050 | 9.89949 |
| 9.36 | 87.6096 | 3.05941 | 9.67471 | 9.81 | 96.2361 | 3.13209 | 9.90454 |
| 9.37 | 87.7969 | 3.06105 | 9.67988 | 9.82 | 96.4324 | 3.13369 | 9.90959 |
| 9.38 | 87.9844 | 3.06268 | 9.68504 | 9.83 | 96.6289 | 3.13528 | 9.91464 |
| 9.39 | 88.1721 | 3.06431 | 9.69020 | 9.84 | 96.8256 | 3.13688 | 9.91968 |
| 9.40 | 88.3600 | 3.06594 | 9.69536 | 9.85 | 97.0225 | 3.13847 | 9.92472 |
| 9.41 | 88.5481 | 3.06757 | 9.70052 | 9.86 | 97.2196 | 3.14006 | 9.92975 |
| 9.42 | 88.7364 | 3.06920 | 9.70567 | 9.87 | 97.4169 | 3.14166 | 9.93479 |
| 9.43 | 88.9249 | 3.07083 | 9.71082 | 9.88 | 97.6144 | 3.14325 | 9.93982 |
| 9.44 | 89.1136 | 3.07246 | 9.71597 | 9.89 | 97.8121 | 3.14484 | 9.94485 |
| 9.45 | 89.3025 | 3.07409 | 9.72111 | 9.90 | 98.0100 | 3.14643 | 9.94987 |
| 9.46 | 89.4916 | 3.07571 | 9.72625 | 9.91 | 98.2081 | 3.14802 | 9.95490 |
| 9.47 | 89.6809 | 3.07734 | 9.73139 | 9.92 | 98.4064 | 3.14960 | 9.95992 |
| 9.48 | 89.8704 | 3.07896 | 9.73653 | 9.93 | 98.6049 | 3.15119 | 9.96494 |
| 9.49 | 90.0601 | 3.08058 | 9.74166 | 9.94 | 98.8036 | 3.15278 | 9.96995 |
| 9.50 | 90.2500 | 3.08221 | 9.74679 | 9.95 | 99.0025 | 3.15436 | 9.97497 |
| 9.51 | 90.4401 | 3.08383 | 9.75192 | 9.96 | 99.2016 | 3.15595 | 9.97998 |
| 9.52 | 90.6304 | 3.08545 | 9.75705 | 9.97 | 99.4009 | 3.15753 | 9.98499 |
| 9.53 | 90.8209 | 3.08707 | 9.76217 | 9.98 | 99.6004 | 3.15911 | 9.98999 |
| 9.54 | 91.0116 | 3.08869 | 9.76729 | 9.99 | 99.8001 | 3.16070 | 9.99500 |

# Answers to Odd-numbered Exercises

## CHAPTER 3

1a. $X_2 + X_3 + X_4 + X_5 + X_6$    1c. $(X_1 + X_2 + X_3 + X_4 + X_5 + X_6 + X_7)^2$

1e. $[(X_1 + 3) X_1 + (X_2 + 3) X_2 + (X_3 + 3) X_3 + (X_4 + 3) X_4]^2$

1g. $(Y_2 + 7) + (Y_3 + 7) + (Y_4 + 7) + (Y_5 + 7)$

1i. $f_1 X_1^2 + f_2 X_2^2 + f_3 X_3^2 + f_4 X_4^2$

| | | | |
|---|---|---|---|
| 3a. 140 | 3b. 104 | 5a. 81 | 5b. 80 |
| 7. 65 | 9a. 150 | 9b. 7 | 11a. $n$ |
| 11b. 18 | | | |

## CHAPTER 4

| | | | |
|---|---|---|---|
| 1a. 8.40 | 1b. 8.85 | 1c. 1.42 | 1d. 1.88 |
| 3a. 2.74 | 3b. 2.74 | 3c. 2.74 | |
| 3d. Class with boundaries 2.65 and 2.75 | | | 3e. 0.11 |
| 3f. 0.14 | 3g. 0.14 | 5a. 40.20 | 5b. 40.20 |
| 5c. Class with boundaries 35 and 45 | | 5d. 40.26 | |
| 5e. Class with boundaries 35 and 45 | | 5f. 7.87 | 5g. 10.86 |
| 7a. 8.90 | 7b. 8.90 | 7c. Class with boundaries 6.5 and 9.5 | |
| 7d. Class with boundaries 9.5 and 12.5 | | | 7e. 3.09 |
| 7f. 16.29 | 7g. 16.29 | 9a. 65.40 | 9b. 8.99 |
| 9c. 12.01 | 11. 70.29 | 13. 23 | 17. 74.04 |
| 19. 118.84 | 21. $5202.00 | 23. 53.44 mph | 27. 10     29. 20 |

## CHAPTER 5

| | | | |
|---|---|---|---|
| 1. $\frac{4}{13}$ | 3. $\frac{5}{18}$ | 5. $\frac{13}{18}$ | 7. $\frac{5}{8}$ |
| 9a. $\frac{1}{17}$ | 9b. $\frac{19}{34}$ | 9c. $\frac{15}{34}$ | 9d. $\frac{13}{34}$ |
| 11. $\frac{5}{288}$ | 13. $\frac{11}{425}$ | 15a. 0.0005 | 15b. 0.0590 |
| 15c. 0.9405 | 17. $1.38 | 19. 0.902 | 21. $\frac{25}{28}$ |
| 23a. $\frac{3}{8}$ | 23b. $\frac{3}{8}$ | 23c. $\frac{1}{4}$ | 25. $\frac{13}{3888}$ |
| 27. $72.90, $63.79, $55.81 | | 29. $\frac{3}{8}$ | 31a. $\frac{27}{80}$ |
| 31b. $R$ | 33. $\frac{7}{8}$ | 35a. $\frac{59}{125}$ | 35b. $\frac{4}{5}$ |

37. 360    39. 120    41a. 210    41b. 371

43a. 35    43b. 15    45. 5760    47a. 495

47b. 450    47c. 255    49. 8640    51. 115, 165, 670, 400

53a. $\frac{280}{2187}$    53b. $\frac{232}{243}$    55a. $\frac{216}{625}$    55b. $\frac{1053}{3125}$

57. $\frac{6,385,729}{6,400,000}$    59. $\frac{11}{64}$    61. $\frac{5}{16}$    63. $\frac{75}{154}$

65. $\frac{160}{729}$    67. $\frac{71}{132}$    69. Second arrangement, since $P = \frac{19}{26}$

71. $\frac{22}{25}$    73a. $\frac{1}{28}$    73b. $\frac{1}{28}$    73c. $\frac{1}{4}$

73d. $\frac{3}{4}$    75a. $\frac{17}{81}$    75b. $\frac{4}{243}$    77. $\frac{15}{256}$

79a. $\frac{125}{1296}$    79b. $\frac{25}{36}$    81. $\frac{11}{32}$    83. $\frac{5}{36}$

85. $\frac{8}{33}$    87. $\frac{3}{28}$    89. $300.00    91. $\frac{419}{420}$

93. $\frac{40}{63}$    95. $\frac{2}{7}$    97. $\frac{2}{7}, \frac{1}{7}$    99. $\frac{12}{23}, \frac{11}{23}$

101. $\frac{3}{5}$    103. $\frac{4}{9}$    105. $\frac{244}{495}$

## CHAPTER 6

3b. 2, 12, 30, 40, 30, 12, 2      5a. 3.50      5b. $\frac{7}{10}$

5c. 0.2187, 2.5515, 11.9070, 27.7830, 32.4135, 15.1263

## CHAPTER 7

1a. 0.0796    1b. 0.0287    3a. 17    3b. 17

5. 0.8925    7. 0.1251    9. 32.11    11. 68.26

13. 0.0305    15. 27    17a. 1151

17b. 66.12 in., 71.88 in.    19. 3.82 oz., 5.63 oz.

21. 38    23. 19.23    25a. 2.29 in.    25b. 1.54 in.

27. 20.0 mm.    29. 735    31. 237    33. 71.00, 18.18

35. 242

## CHAPTER 8

9. 0.2236    11. 0.1314    13. 0.6170    15. $n_2 = k^2 n_1$

17. 6    19. 0.0233    21. 18.69, 21.31    23. 5.42

25. 96    27. 42

## CHAPTER 9

1. No, since $P = 0.2714$ for a two-tailed test    3. Yes, since $P = 0.0073$

5. Yes, since $P = 0.0071$    7. Yes, since $P = 0.2628$

9. Yes, since $P = 0.0008$    11. Yes, since $P = 0.0055$ for a one-tailed test

13. Yes, since $z = 7.34$    15. No, since $P = 0.0950$

17a. 0.0606    19. $35 \pm 1.26$    21. $15 \pm 2.94$

23. 11    25. 6.37

## CHAPTER 10

1. $34.86 \pm 3.52$    3a. $16.90 \pm 2.56$    3b. $16.90 \pm 2.58$

5a. $12.15 \pm 0.25$    5b. Yes    7. 7.61

9. $24.00 \pm 3.01$      11. No, since $t = 0.79$      13. Yes, since $t = -3.00$
15. Yes, since $t = -3.08$    17. Yes, since $t = 3.26$     19. $6 \pm 12.92$
21. Yes, since $t = 3.06$     23. No, since $t = 1.67$     25. No, since $t = 1.19$
27. $5 \pm 7.43$

## CHAPTER 11

1. No significant difference, since $P = 0.0646$ for a two-tailed test.
3. No, since $P = 0.3524$          5. Yes, since $P = 0.0318$
7. No significant difference, since $P = 0.0512$
9. Same average scores, since $P = 0.2748$
11. Yes, since $P = 0.0032$       13. 7
15. 12                    17. No, since $P = 0.0644$
19. No, since $P = 0.0781$       21. No, since $P = 0.2188$

## CHAPTER 12

1a. $Y_e = 6.46 - 3.52X$     1c. $-7.62$                1d. $0.97$
1e. $-0.992$            3a. $S_e = 54.20 + 0.52T$    3b. $80.20$
3c. $0.28$               3d. $0.9998$           5a. $Y_e = 17.76 + 0.819X$
5b. $30.86$           5c. $X_e = 3.93 + 0.433Y$    5d. $0.595$
5e. $35.40$           7a. $13.6$               7b. $-0.96$
7c. $X_e = 43.3 - 0.66Y$    9. No, since $t = -2.57$     11. $\pm 0.73$
13. Reject hypothesis, since $z = 7.79$                15. $0.07, 0.52$
17a. $-0.52, 0.21$      17b. No significant correlation
19. 19                 21. $0.0375$            23. 31
25. 979              27. 25               29. 46

## CHAPTER 13

1. Can be considered honest die, since $\chi^2 = 4.51$
3. Yes, since $\chi^2 = 2.46$     5a. $0.178$           5b. $0.1706$
7a. $0.0749$             7b. $0.0799$           9. 64
11. Yes, since adj. $\chi^2 = 35.74$
13. Color blindness occurs more frequently in males, since adj. $\chi^2 = 25.62$
15. Significant difference in listening habits, since adj. $\chi^2 = 4.92$
17a. Yes, since adj. $\chi^2 = 5.36$                17b. $0.05$
23. No, since $\chi^2 = 0.38$     25. Yes, since $\chi^2 = 7.43$     27. Yes, since $\chi^2 = 4.80$

## CHAPTER 14

1a. 100, 118.7, 119.1, and so on     1b. 84.3, 100, 100.4, and so on
3. \$13,256         5a. 100.7, 103.6     5b. 102.3, 106.4     5c. 19.5

## CHAPTER 15

1a. $Y_e = 3.29 + 0.26\,x$    1c. 2.12, 2.38, 2.64, and so on

3. Specific seasonals for 1948: 112, 104, 103, and so on. Typical seasonals: 109 for Jan., 104 for Feb., 102 for Mar., and so on

5a. 59, 94, 174, 67, and so on    5b. 65, 83, 170, 83, and so on

5c. 1337, 1558, 1374, 1047, and so on

5d. $Y'_e = 1711.1 + 78.4\,x$, $Y'_e = 2{,}241.1 - 19.9\,x$

5e. 1368, 1388, 1407, 1427, and so on, where the trend values are calculated for the middle of the quarters.    5f. $-31$, 170, $-33$, $-380$, and so on

## CHAPTER 16

1a. 0.098    1b. 0.179    1c. 0.455    3. Yes, since $F = 1.95$

5. Not homogeneous, since $F = 19.03$    7. 5.58 and 18.31    9. $n_2 \geq 11$

## CHAPTER 17

1a. $\dfrac{1}{1,000,000}$    1b. $\dfrac{177,147}{500,000}$    1c. $\dfrac{468,559}{1,000,000}$    1d. $\dfrac{999,945}{1,000,000}$

3a. 190.00    3b. 105.00    3c. 85.00    5a. 142.00

5b. 87.30    5c. 54.70    7a. Yes, since $F = 8.24$.

7b. $AB$, $BC$, and $BD$.    9a. Yes, since $F = 11.96$.

9b. $AB$ and $BC$    11. $F = 1.85$

13. Highly significant difference between feeds, since $F = 135.92$; pairs with highly significantly different means are $AC$, $AD$, $BC$, $BD$, and $CD$

15a. 50    15b. 4.4

17. Significant difference for original data, since $F = 60.85$; significant difference for transformed data, since $F = 70.93$

19a. Significant difference for original data, since $F = 18.33$; significant difference for transformed data, since $F = 16.78$

19b. $AB$, $AC$, $AD$, $AE$, $BE$, $CE$, and $DE$ for both sets of data

# Index